THE APPLICATION OF CONTINUED FRACTIONS AND THEIR GENERALIZATIONS TO PROBLEMS IN APPROXIMATION THEORY

LIBRARY OF APPLIED ANALYSIS AND COMPUTATIONAL MATHEMATICS

THE APPLICATION OF CONTINUED FRACTIONS AND THEIR GENERALIZATIONS TO PROBLEMS IN APPROXIMATION THEORY

by

ALEXEY NIKOLAEVITCH KHOVANSKII

translated by

PETER WYNN

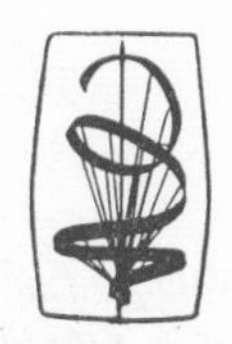

P. NOORDHOFF N.V. - GRONINGEN - THE NETHERLANDS

Printed in The Netherlands.

Library published under the general direction
of the chair of Computational Mathematics
of the Moscow State University

CONTENTS

Chapter I

Certain Problems in the Theory of Continued Fractions

Chapter II

Continued Fraction Expansions of Certain Functions

Chapter III

Further Methods for Obtaining Rational Function Approximations

Chapter IV

Generalized Continued Fractions

TRANSLATOR'S PREFACE

The decision to translate the following book was taken, firstly because it contains a considerable amount of new material relating to the numerical application of continued fractions which will be of interest to the Western reader, and secondly because it offers an introduction to the analytic theory of continued fractions which, in the reasoned and systematic form given, is not available in the English language.

Additional references to standard works on Analysis in the English language have been added, the notation has been slightly modified in places to conform to Western usage, and a number of corrections kindly communicated by the author have been inserted.

I have added an index and a short list of supplementary references (which, of course, contain further references for the interested reader). In the translation I have allowed myself a certain degree of freedom and must apologize to the reader in advance for any imperfections which have been introduced in this way. In the original Russian, at least, Dr. Khovanskii's book is a delight to read and a masterpiece of clarity.

Mathematisch Centrum, Amsterdam.
January, 1962.

PREFACE

In modern mathematics the approximate representation of functions is ordinarily sought for in the form of a polynomial in the independent variable. In cases in which such polynomials are difficult to find, other numerical methods are used.

For this purpose approximations by rational functions of the independent variable have seldom been used. A characteristic of rational function approximations is that they may often successfully represent the given function in a domain of variation of the argument where the power series expansion of the function diverges and where, in consequence, in a great number of cases a polynomial approximation is inapplicable.

Furthermore, with the help of rational function approximations, the determination of the zeros and poles of the given function is greatly facilitated, since it is required to solve an algebraic equation of lower degree than that which occurs when using an approximation in the form of a polynomial.

Finally, the use of a rational function approximation tends to remove the necessity of computing high powers of the argument.

Thus the application of rational function approximations brings about a great simplification in many of the computing formulae.

That approximation by means of a rational function should have gained so small a currency is explained by the fact that the direct derivation of this function necessitates lengthy calculations. Furthermore the transition from one rational function approximation to another involves, in general, the recomputation of all coefficients contained in the numerators and denominators of these approximations. However methods exist allowing the derivation of arbitrarily many rational function approximations to the given function, in a manner not demanding complicated calculations. The most widely known methods of this type are based on the use of continued fractions.

In the first chapter of the present work a short exposition of the analytic theory of continued fractions is given. Problems in the arithmetic theory of continued fractions are not considered in this book.

The second chapter is devoted to the continued fraction expansion (by the method of Lagrange) of some well known functions. All expansions given in this chapter are special cases of a general expansion derived at the beginning of the chapter.

In the third chapter there is a short consideration of further methods for deriving rational function approximations to functions, leading to a series of approximation formulae for computing certain well known functions.

In the fourth chapter are considered the generalized continued fractions proposed by Euler. Examples are quoted showing the possibility of further generalizations of continued fractions which permit the approximate solution of algebraic equations of arbitrary degree.

The author expresses deep thanks to L. A. Liusternik, Corresponding Member of the Academy of Sciences of the U.S.S.R.

The author is greatly indebted to A. F. Lapko, editor of the State publishing house of technical-theoretical literature, who very attentively read the manuscript of the book and introduced a number of essential corrections.

Institute of Education,
Ioshkar-Ola
September 1956

CHAPTER I

CERTAIN PROBLEMS IN THE THEORY OF CONTINUED FRACTIONS

§ 1. Convergents

1. The development

$$b_0 + \cfrac{a_1}{b_1 + \cfrac{a_2}{b_2 + \cfrac{\ddots}{\ddots + \cfrac{a_n}{b_n + \ddots}}}}$$

is called a *continued fraction*.

In view of the unwieldiness of this notation, various authors have proposed other ways of writing continued fractions, for example

$$\left.\begin{array}{ll} b_0 + \dfrac{a_1|}{|b_1} + \dfrac{a_2|}{|b_2} + \dots + \dfrac{a_n|}{|b_n} + \dots & \text{(Pringsheim [76][1]);} \\ b_0 + \dfrac{a_1}{b_1} \dotplus \dfrac{a_2}{b_2} \dotplus \dots \dotplus \dfrac{a_n}{b_n} \dotplus \dots & \text{(Müller [56]);} \\ b_0 + \dfrac{a_1}{b_1 +}\,\dfrac{a_2}{b_2 +} \cdots \dfrac{a_n}{+\, b_n +} \cdots & \text{(Rogers [81]).} \end{array}\right\} \quad (1.1)$$

[1] Numbers in square brackets refer to the list of References given at the end of the book.

We shall use the latter notation. Sometimes, for conciseness, we shall also use the following notation proposed by Pringsheim [76]: $\left[b_0; \frac{a_\nu}{b_\nu}\right]_1^\infty$. This notation fulfils a function in respect of notation (1.1) very much the same as that of the notation $\sum_{n=1}^{\infty} a_n$ with regard to $a_1 + a_2 + \dots$

Often it occurs that in the continued fraction (1.1), a_1 and b_1 are constructed according to a different law than that which obtains for the remaining a_n and b_n. In this case Pringsheim [76] used the notation $\left[b_0; \frac{a_1}{b_1}, \frac{a_\nu}{b_\nu}\right]_2^\infty$.

The fraction a_n/b_n is called the nth *partial quotient* of the continued fraction (1.1); a_n and b_n are the *coefficients* of the continued fraction; $a_1, a_2, a_3, \dots$ are called its *partial numerators;* $b_1, b_2, b_3, \dots$ — its *partial denominators.*

We shall assume that all coefficients of a continued fraction are finite. We shall assume that all partial denominators of a continued fraction are not equal to zero.

The terminating continued fraction

$$b_0 + \frac{a_1}{b_1} + \frac{a_2}{b_2} + \dots + \frac{a_n}{b_n} \equiv \frac{P_n}{Q_n}$$

is called the nth convergent (reduite) of the continued fraction (1.1).

2. We derive the relations connecting the numerators and denominators of three consecutive convergents. From the definition of a continued fraction we have

$$\frac{P_0}{Q_0} = \frac{b_0}{1}, \qquad \frac{P_1}{Q_1} = \frac{b_0 b_1 + a_1}{b_1},$$

$$\frac{P_2}{Q_2} = b_0 + \cfrac{a_1}{b_1 + \cfrac{a_2}{b_2}} = b_0 + \frac{a_1 b_2}{b_1 b_2 + a_2} =$$

$$= \frac{b_0 b_1 b_2 + b_0 a_2 + a_1 b_2}{b_1 b_2 + a_2} = \frac{b_2 P_1 + a_2 P_0}{b_2 Q_1 + a_2 Q_0}.$$

Assume that

$$\left.\begin{aligned} P_n &= b_n P_{n-1} + a_n P_{n-2}, \\ Q_n &= b_n Q_{n-1} + a_n Q_{n-2}. \end{aligned}\right\} \tag{1.2}$$

Then

$$\frac{P_n}{Q_n} = \frac{b_n P_{n-1} + a_n P_{n-2}}{b_n Q_{n-1} + a_n Q_{n-2}}$$

We prove that relations (1.2) are valid when n is replaced by $n + 1$. For this we note that in order to progress from P_n/Q_n to P_{n+1}/Q_{n+1} one must replace b_n by $b_n + (a_{n+1}/b_{n+1}.)$ Then

$$\frac{P_{n+1}}{Q_{n+1}} = \frac{b_n P_{n-1} + \dfrac{a_{n+1}}{b_{n+1}} P_{n-1} + a_n P_{n-2}}{b_n Q_{n-1} + \dfrac{a_{n+1}}{b_{n+1}} Q_{n-1} + a_n Q_{n-2}} = \frac{b_{n+1} P_n + a_{n+1} P_{n-1}}{b_{n+1} Q_n + a_{n+1} Q_{n-1}}.$$

Consequently equation (1.2) is valid for all integer $n \geqslant 2$.

Relationships (1.2) were first established by Wallis [104] and were considered in detail by Euler [14]. In this work Euler, for the first time, uses the expression "continued fraction" (fractio continua).

In order that relationships (1.2) should be valid for $n = 1$, we put, following Euler, $P_{-1} = 1$, $Q_{-1} = 0$.

3. We shall use the following scheme:

$$b_0 + \frac{a_1}{b_1} + \frac{a_2}{b_2} + \dots + \frac{a_n}{b_n} + \dots,$$

$$\frac{1}{0} \quad \frac{b_0}{1} \quad \frac{P_1}{Q_1} \quad \frac{P_2}{Q_2} \quad \dots \quad \frac{P_n}{Q_n} \quad \dots.$$

to indicate the computation of the successive convergents.

For example, for $\sqrt{2}$ we have the following expansion and convergents:

$$\sqrt{2} = 1 + (\sqrt{2} - 1) = 1 + \frac{1}{1 + \sqrt{2}}$$

$$= 1 + \frac{1}{2} + \frac{1}{2} + \frac{1}{2} + \frac{1}{2} + \frac{1}{2} + \frac{1}{2} + \dots$$

$$\frac{1}{1} \quad \frac{3}{2} \quad \frac{7}{5} \quad \frac{17}{12} \quad \frac{41}{29} \quad \frac{99}{70} \quad \frac{239}{169} \quad \dots$$

$$1{\cdot}0 \quad 1{\cdot}5 \quad 1{\cdot}4 \quad 1{\cdot}417 \quad 1{\cdot}4138 \quad 1{\cdot}41429 \quad 1{\cdot}41420 \quad \dots$$

4. In order to study the behaviour of the convergents we consider the difference between two successive convergents P_n/Q_n and P_{n-1}/Q_{n-1}. We have:

$$\frac{P_n}{Q_n} - \frac{P_{n-1}}{Q_{n-1}} = \frac{P_nQ_{n-1} - Q_nP_{n-1}}{Q_{n-1}Q_n}$$

Substituting for P_n and Q_n with the help of equation (1.2), we obtain

$$\frac{P_n}{Q_n} - \frac{P_{n-1}}{Q_{n-1}} = \frac{1}{Q_{n-1}Q_n} [(b_nP_{n-1} + a_nP_{n-2})\, Q_{n-1} -$$
$$- (b_nQ_{n-1} + a_nQ_{n-2})\, P_{n-1}] = -a_n \frac{P_{n-1}Q_{n-2} - Q_{n-1}P_{n-2}}{Q_{n-1}Q_n}$$

Applying the same transformation to $P_{n-1}Q_{n-2} - Q_{n-1}P_{n-2}$, we obtain

$$\frac{P_n}{Q_n} - \frac{P_{n-1}}{Q_{n-1}} = (-1)^2\, a_na_{n-1} \frac{P_{n-2}Q_{n-3} - Q_{n-2}P_{n-3}}{Q_{n-1}Q_n}$$

Repeating similar transformations, we have

$$\frac{P_n}{Q_n} - \frac{P_{n-1}}{Q_{n-1}} = (-1)^3\, a_na_{n-1}a_{n-2} \frac{P_{n-3}Q_{n-4} - Q_{n-3}P_{n-4}}{Q_{n-1}Q_n}$$
$$= (-1)^n\, a_na_{n-1} \dots a_1 \frac{P_0Q_{-1} - Q_0P_{-1}}{Q_{n-1}Q_n}$$
$$= (-1)^n\, a_na_{n-1} \dots a_1 \frac{-1}{Q_{n-1}Q_n}.$$

Thus. for any positive integer n, we have the equation[1]

$$\frac{P_n}{Q_n} - \frac{P_{n-1}}{Q_{n-1}} = (-1)^{n+1} \frac{a_1a_2 \dots a_n}{Q_{n-1}Q_n} \tag{1.3}$$

i.e.

$$P_nQ_{n-1} - Q_nP_{n-1} = (-1)^{n+1}\, a_1a_2 \dots a_n. \tag{1.4}$$

[1] The validity of formula (1.3) may easily be verified by an appeal to the method of mathematical induction.

In particular, from (1.3) we have:

$$\frac{P_1}{Q_1} - \frac{P_0}{Q_0} = \frac{a_1}{Q_0 Q_1},$$

$$\frac{P_2}{Q_2} - \frac{P_1}{Q_1} = -\frac{a_1 a_2}{Q_1 Q_2}$$

. . . .

$$\frac{P_n}{Q_n} - \frac{P_{n-1}}{Q_{n-1}} = (-1)^{n+1} \frac{a_1 a_2 \ldots a_n}{Q_{n-1} Q_n}.$$

Adding these equations and remembering that $P_0/Q_0 = b_0$, we obtain:

$$\frac{P_n}{Q_n} = b_0 + \frac{a_1}{Q_0 Q_1} - \frac{a_1 a_2}{Q_1 Q_2} + \ldots + (-1)^{n+1} \frac{a_1 a_2 \ldots a_n}{Q_{n-1} Q_n}. \tag{1.5}$$

5. We now study the behaviour of the convergents more deeply. With this object in view we consider the difference between two convergents, the difference of whose indices is equal to two. Replacing n by $n + 1$ in (1.3), we obtain:

$$\frac{P_{n+1}}{Q_{n+1}} - \frac{P_n}{Q_n} = (-1)^n \frac{a_1 a_2 \ldots a_n a_{n+1}}{Q_n Q_{n+1}}, \tag{1.6}$$

since $(-1)^{n+2} = (-1)^n$.

Adding (1.3) and (1.6), we have:

$$\frac{P_{n+1}}{Q_{n+1}} - \frac{P_{n-1}}{Q_{n-1}} = (-1)^n \frac{a_1 a_2 \ldots a_n}{Q_n} \left(\frac{a_{n+1}}{Q_{n+1}} - \frac{1}{Q_{n-1}} \right)$$

$$= (-1)^n \frac{a_1 a_2 \ldots a_n}{Q_{n-1} Q_n Q_{n+1}} (a_{n+1} Q_{n-1} - Q_{n+1}).$$

Substituting for Q_{n+1} in the numerator of the right hand side of this relationship with the help of equation (1.2), we obtain

$$\frac{P_{n+1}}{Q_{n+1}} - \frac{P_{n-1}}{Q_{n-1}} = (-1)^{n+1} \frac{a_1 a_2 \ldots a_n b_{n+1}}{Q_{n-1} Q_{n+1}}. \tag{1.7}$$

6. At this point we relate successive convergents of odd order. Replacing n by $2k$ in (1.7), we have:

$$\frac{P_{2k+1}}{Q_{2k+1}} - \frac{P_{2k-1}}{Q_{2k-1}} = -\frac{a_1a_2 \ldots a_{2k}b_{2k+1}}{Q_{2k-1}Q_{2k+1}}.$$

In particular,

$$\frac{P_3}{Q_3} - \frac{P_1}{Q_1} = -\frac{a_1a_2b_3}{Q_1Q_3},$$

$$\frac{P_5}{Q_5} - \frac{P_3}{Q_3} = -\frac{a_1a_2a_3a_4b_5}{Q_3Q_5},$$

. . . .

$$\frac{P_{2k+1}}{Q_{2k+1}} - \frac{P_{2k-1}}{Q_{2k-1}} = -\frac{a_1a_2 \ldots a_{2k}b_{2k+1}}{Q_{2k-1}Q_{2k+1}}.$$

Adding these equations and remembering that

$$\frac{P_1}{Q_1} = b_0 + \frac{a_1}{b_1},$$

we obtain

$$\frac{P_{2k+1}}{Q_{2k+1}} = b_0 + \frac{a_1}{b_1} - \frac{a_1a_2b_3}{Q_1Q_3} - \frac{a_1a_2a_3a_4b_5}{Q_3Q_5} - \ldots - \frac{a_1a_2 \ldots a_{2k}b_{2k+1}}{Q_{2k-1}Q_{2k+1}}. \quad (1.8)$$

7. We carry out analogous calculations for convergents of even order. For this we replace n by $2k - 1$ in (1.7). We have

$$\frac{P_{2k}}{Q_{2k}} - \frac{P_{2k-2}}{Q_{2k-2}} = \frac{a_1a_2 \ldots a_{2k-1}b_{2k}}{Q_{2k-2}Q_{2k}}.$$

In particular,

$$\frac{P_2}{Q_2} - \frac{P_0}{Q_0} = \frac{a_1b_2}{Q_0Q_2}$$

$$\frac{P_4}{Q_4} - \frac{P_2}{Q_2} = \frac{a_1a_2a_3b_4}{Q_2Q_4},$$

. . . .

$$\frac{P_{2k}}{Q_{2k}} - \frac{P_{2k-2}}{Q_{2k-2}} = \frac{a_1a_2 \ldots a_{2k-1}b_{2k}}{Q_{2k-2}Q_{2k}}.$$

Adding these equations and remembering that $P_0/Q_0 = b_0$, we obtain:

$$\frac{P_{2k}}{Q_{2k}} = b_0 + \frac{a_1 b_2}{Q_0 Q_2} + \frac{a_1 a_2 a_3 b_4}{Q_2 Q_4} + \dots + \frac{a_1 a_2 \dots a_{2k-1} b_{2k}}{Q_{2k-2} Q_{2k}}. \qquad (1.9)$$

8. Let all the coefficients of a continued fraction be positive. In such a case the denominators of all its convergents are positive. Then from (1.9) it follows that the convergents of even order generate a monotonically increasing sequence. But from the form of the continued fraction (1.1) it is clear that all its convergents of even order are less than $b_0 + (a_1/b_1)$. Consequently, when all the coefficients are positive numbers, the convergents of even order generate a monotonically increasing sequence, with, as an upper bound, the number $b_0 + (a_1/b_1)$. Such a sequence has a limit. Hence $\lim\limits_{k\to\infty} P_{2k}/Q_{2k}$ exists.

Further it follows from (1.8) that when the coefficients are positive numbers the convergents of odd order generate a monotonically decreasing sequence. But from the form of the continued fraction (1.1) it is clear that all its convergents of odd order are greater than b_0. Consequently, when all the coefficients are positive numbers, the convergents of odd order generate a monotonically decreasing sequence with lower bound b_0. Such a sequence has a limit. Hence, $\lim\limits_{k\to\infty} P_{2k-1}/Q_{2k-1}$ exists.

Thus, for any natural k, the inequalities

$$\frac{P_{2k}}{Q_{2k}} \leqslant \lim_{k\to\infty} \frac{P_{2k}}{Q_{2k}} \leqslant \lim_{k\to\infty} \frac{P_{2k-1}}{Q_{2k-1}} \leqslant \frac{P_{2k-1}}{Q_{2k-1}}. \qquad (1.10)$$

are satisfied[1].

From this it does not yet follow that

$$\lim_{k\to\infty} \frac{P_{2k}}{Q_{2k}} = \lim_{k\to\infty} \frac{P_{2k-1}}{Q_{2k-1}}.$$

[1]) It is consequence of (1.6) that for any k we have

$$\frac{P_{2k}}{Q_{2k}} - \frac{P_{2k-1}}{Q_{2k-1}} < 0,$$

(if all the coefficients of the continued fraction are positive) and thus

$$\lim_{k\to\infty} \left(\frac{P_{2k}}{Q_{2k}} - \frac{P_{2k-1}}{Q_{2k-1}} \right) \leqslant 0.$$

Thus the middle inequality in (1.10) is valid.

In the general case the following situation prevails

$$\frac{P_0}{Q_0} \quad \frac{P_2}{Q_2} \quad \frac{P_{2k}}{Q_{2k}} \to \lim \frac{P_{2k}}{Q_{2k}} \qquad \lim \frac{P_{2k-1}}{Q_{2k-1}} \leftarrow \frac{P_{2k-1}}{Q_{2k-1}} \quad \frac{P_3}{Q_3} \quad \frac{P_1}{Q_1}$$

Applying this remark to the continued fraction expansion for $\sqrt{2}$ we see, for example, that

$$\frac{7}{5} < \sqrt{2} < \frac{3}{2}, \quad \frac{41}{29} < \sqrt{2} < \frac{99}{70}, \quad \text{and so on.}$$

In this way a continued fraction provides a means for estimating an irrational number in terms of ordinary fractions.

9. If

$$\lim_{k\to\infty} \frac{P_{2k}}{Q_{2k}} = \lim_{k\to\infty} \frac{P_{2k-1}}{Q_{2k-1}} \neq \infty$$

i.e. if

$$\lim_{n\to\infty} \frac{P_n}{Q_n}$$

exists and is finite, then the continued fraction is called convergent. In this case, with positive number coefficients, its value

$$K = \lim_{n\to\infty} \frac{P_n}{Q_n}$$

is greater than any of its even order convergents and less than any of its odd order convergents. With this, it follows from (1.3), that

$$\left| K - \frac{P_n}{Q_n} \right| < \frac{a_1 a_2 \ldots a_n}{Q_{n-1} Q_n}, \tag{1.11}$$

and thus, in this case, the identity (c.f. (1.5))

$$b_0 + \frac{a_1}{b_1} + \frac{a_2}{b_2} + \ldots + \frac{a_n}{b_n} + \ldots =$$

$$= b_0 + \frac{a_1}{Q_0 Q_1} - \frac{a_1 a_2}{Q_1 Q_2} + \ldots + (-1)^{n-1} \frac{a_1 a_2 \ldots a_n}{Q_{n-1} Q_n} + \ldots \tag{1.12}$$

is valid.

Seidel [88] called series and continued fractions satisfying equation (1.12), *equivalent.*

§ 2. Transformations of Continued Fractions

1. We multiply a_m, b_m and a_{m+1} by an arbitrary finite number $p_m (m = 0, 1, \ldots, n, \ldots)$, differing from zero. It is clear that as a result of this, the value of the continued fraction is unaltered. Therefore the following identity is valid:

$$b_0 + \frac{a_1}{b_1} + \frac{a_2}{b_2} + \ldots + \frac{a_n}{b_n} + \ldots =$$

$$= b_0 + \frac{p_1 a_1}{p_1 b_1} + \frac{p_1 p_2 a_2}{p_2 b_2} + \ldots + \frac{p_{n-1} p_n a_n}{p_n b_n} + \ldots \quad (2.1)$$

With this P_1 and Q_1 are replaced by $p_1 P_1$ and $p_1 Q_1$ respectively; P_2 and Q_2 – by $p_1 p_2 P_2$ and $p_1 p_2 Q_2$, ..., P_n and Q_n – *by* $p_1 p_2 \ldots p_n P_n$ and $p_1 p_2 \ldots p_n Q_n$.

By means of this transformation all partial denominators $b_1, b_2, \ldots$ of the continued fraction (1.1) can always be made positive.

2. With the help of transformation (2.1) we reduce the continued fraction (1.1) to a form in which all partial numerators are equal to 1. For this, we determine $p_1, p_2, \ldots$ to be such that the equations $p_1 a_1 = 1$ and $p_{n-1} p_n a_n = 1$ $(n = 2, 3, \ldots)$ obtain. Then

$$p_1 = \frac{1}{a_1}, \quad p_2 = \frac{a_1}{a_2}, \quad p_3 = \frac{a_2}{a_1 a_3}, \ldots$$

$$p_{2k-1} = \frac{a_2 a_4 \ldots a_{2k-2}}{a_1 a_3 \ldots a_{2k-1}}, \quad p_{2k} = \frac{a_1 a_3 \ldots a_{2k-1}}{a_2 a_4 \ldots a_{2k}};$$

hence,

$$(p_1 p_2)(p_3 p_4) \ldots (p_{2k-1} p_{2k}) = \frac{1}{a_2 a_4 \ldots a_{2k}};$$

$$p_1 (p_2 p_3)(p_4 p_5) \ldots (p_{2k} p_{2k+1}) = \frac{1}{a_1 a_3 \ldots a_{2k+1}}.$$

Expansion (1.1) becomes

$$K = \alpha_0 + \frac{1}{\alpha_1} + \frac{1}{\alpha_2} + \ldots + \frac{1}{\alpha_{2k-1}} + \frac{1}{\alpha_{2k}} + \ldots, \quad (2.2)$$

where

$$\left.\begin{aligned} \alpha_0 &= b_0, \\ \alpha_{2k-1} &= \frac{a_2 a_4 \ldots a_{2k-2} b_{2k-1}}{a_1 a_3 \ldots a_{2k-1}}, \\ \alpha_{2k} &= \frac{a_1 a_3 \ldots a_{2k-1} b_{2k}}{a_2 a_4 \ldots a_{2k}} \end{aligned}\right\} \quad (k = 1, 2, \ldots) \tag{2.3}$$

With this P_{2k} and Q_{2k} are replaced by

$$\frac{P_{2k}}{a_2 a_4 \ldots a_{2k}} \quad \text{and} \quad \frac{Q_{2k}}{a_2 a_4 \ldots a_{2k}}$$

respectively; P_{2k+1} and Q_{2k+1} by

$$\frac{P_{2k+1}}{a_1 a_3 \ldots a_{2k+1}} \quad \text{and} \quad \frac{Q_{2k+1}}{a_1 a_3 \ldots a_{2k+1}}.$$

Continued fractions of the form (2.2) are called *ordinary continued fractions*. In most courses of analysis only ordinary continued fractions are considered. Lagrange [42] even asserted that all remaining continued fractions have no real interest since they are easily reduced to ordinary continued fractions. But such a reduction in many cases results in a very complicated expansion, and therefore it is not possible to be wholly in sympathy with Lagrange's statement.

The numbers $\alpha_1, \alpha_2, \ldots$ are called the *partial denominators of the ordinary continued fraction.*

Ordinary continued fractions with positive integer partial denominators are called *regular* (regelmäßig) (Perron [73]).

For ordinary continued fractions, expansion (1.8) becomes

$$K = \alpha_0 + \frac{1}{Q_1} - \frac{\alpha_3}{Q_1 Q_3} - \frac{\alpha_5}{Q_3 Q_5} - \ldots - \frac{\alpha_{2k+1}}{Q_{2k-1} Q_{2k+1}} - \ldots,$$

and expansion (1.9) becomes

$$K = \alpha_0 + \frac{\alpha_2}{Q_0 Q_2} + \frac{\alpha_4}{Q_2 Q_4} + \ldots + \frac{\alpha_{2k}}{Q_{2k-2} Q_{2k}} + \ldots.$$

3. With the help of transformation (2.1) we reduce the continued fraction (1.1) to a form in which all partial denominators

are equal to 1. For this we put $p_n = 1/b_n$ $(n = 1, 2, \dots)$. The continued fraction (1.1) becomes for $b_0 = 0$

$$\frac{c_1}{1} + \frac{c_2}{1} + \dots + \frac{c_n}{1} + \dots, \tag{2.4}$$

where

$$c_1 = \frac{a_1}{b_1}, \quad c_n = \frac{a_n}{b_{n-1}b_n} \qquad (n = 2, 3, \dots). \tag{2.5}$$

In this P_n and Q_n are replaced by

$$\frac{P_n}{b_1 b_2 \dots b_n} \quad \text{and} \quad \frac{Q_n}{b_1 b_2 \dots b_n}$$

respectively (c.f. the second paragraph of this section). From the construction of the continued fraction (2.4) it follows that

$$c_1 = \frac{1}{\alpha_1}, \quad c_n = \frac{1}{\alpha_{n-1}\alpha_n} \qquad (n = 2, 3, \dots). \tag{2.6}$$

4. Daniel Bernoulli [10] proposed and solved the following problem: to find the continued fraction the convergents of which are the prescribed values $K_0, K_1, K_2, \dots$ any three successive convergents not being equal. One can assume that K_n is the numerator of the nth convergent, so that the denominator of the latter is equal to unity. From this the coefficients of the required continued fraction are determined uniquely.

Let the continued fraction sought for have the form (1.1). Then equation (1.2) may be transcribed as

$$\begin{aligned} b_0 &= K_0, & & \\ b_0 b_1 + a_1 &= K_1, & b_1 &= 1, \\ b_n K_{n-1} + a_n K_{n-2} &= K_n, & b_n + a_n &= 1 \qquad (n = 2, 3, \dots). \end{aligned}$$

From these

$$a_1 = K_1 - K_0, \quad a_n = \frac{K_{n-1} - K_n}{K_{n-1} - K_{n-2}}, \quad b_n = \frac{K_n - K_{n-2}}{K_{n-1} - K_{n-2}}.$$

Therefore the required continued fraction may be written down in the following form:

$$K_0 + \frac{K_1 - K_0}{1} + \frac{\dfrac{K_1 - K_0}{K_1 - K_0}}{\dfrac{K_2 - K_0}{K_1 - K_0}} + \frac{\dfrac{K_2 - K_3}{K_2 - K_1}}{\dfrac{K_3 - K_1}{K_2 - K_1}} + \dots + \frac{\dfrac{K_{n-1} - K_n}{K_{n-1} - K_{n-2}}}{\dfrac{K_n - K_{n-2}}{K_{n-1} - K_{n-2}}} + \dots,$$

i.e.

$$K_0 + \frac{K_1 - K_0}{1} + \frac{K_1 - K_2}{K_2 - K_0} + \frac{(K_1 - K_0)(K_2 - K_3)}{K_3 - K_1} + \dots$$
$$\dots + \frac{(K_{n-2} - K_{n-3})(K_{n-1} - K_n)}{K_n - K_{n-2}} + \dots. \tag{2.7}$$

We construct, for example, the continued fraction for which $K_n = 1/(n+1)$ $(n = 0, 1 \dots)$. We have:

$$K = 1 + \frac{\dfrac{1}{2} - 1}{1} + \frac{\dfrac{1}{2} - \dfrac{1}{3}}{\dfrac{1}{3} - 1} + \frac{\left(\dfrac{1}{2} - 1\right)\left(\dfrac{1}{3} - \dfrac{1}{4}\right)}{\dfrac{1}{4} - \dfrac{1}{2}} + \dots$$

$$\dots + \frac{\left(\dfrac{1}{n-1} - \dfrac{1}{n-2}\right)\left(\dfrac{1}{n} - \dfrac{1}{n+1}\right)}{\dfrac{1}{n+1} - \dfrac{1}{n-1}} + \dots =$$

$$= 1 - \frac{\dfrac{1}{2}}{1} + \frac{\dfrac{1}{1.2.3}}{-\dfrac{2}{1.3}} - \frac{\dfrac{1}{1.2.3.4}}{-\dfrac{2}{2.4}} - \dots$$

$$\dots - \frac{\dfrac{1}{(n-2)(n-1)n(n+1)}}{\dfrac{-2}{(n-1)(n+1)}} - \frac{\dfrac{1}{(n-1)n(n+1)(n+2)}}{\dfrac{-2}{n(n+2)}} - \dots =$$

$$= 1 - \frac{1}{2} - \frac{1}{2} - \frac{1}{2} - \dots - \frac{1}{2} - \frac{1}{2} - \dots$$

$$\frac{1}{1} \quad \frac{1}{2} \quad \frac{1}{3} \quad \frac{1}{4}$$

The derived continued fraction satisfies the equation $K = 1 - 1/(1 + K)$, i.e. $K = K/(1 + K)$, whence $K = 0$. On the other hand $\lim_{n\to\infty} P_n/Q_n = 0$.

5. If $K_0, K_1, K_2, \ldots$ are taken to be members of a certain subsequence of the convergents of expansion (1.1), then one says that the continued fraction derived in this way is a contracted form of the continued fraction (1.1).

If $K_0, K_1, K_2, \ldots$ is taken to be a sequence including, in particular, all convergents of expansion (1.1) then one says that the continued fraction (2.7) has been derived by means of an extension of the continued fraction (1.1).

The operations of contraction and extension were introduced by Seidel [88] although special cases of them were encountered already by Lagrange [42], [43].

6. Put, in particular,

$$K_n = \frac{P_{2n}}{Q_{2n}}.$$

From (1.2) we have:

$$\begin{aligned} P_{2n} &= b_{2n}P_{2n-1} + a_{2n}P_{2n-2}, \\ P_{2n-1} &= b_{2n-1}P_{2n-2} + a_{2n-1}P_{2n-3}, \\ P_{2n-2} &= b_{2n-2}P_{2n-3} + a_{2n-2}P_{2n-4}. \end{aligned}$$

Multiplying these equations by b_{2n-2}, $b_{2n}b_{2n-2}$ and $-a_{2n-1}b_{2n}$ respectively and adding the derived products, we have:

$$\begin{aligned} b_{2n-2}P_{2n} = (a_{2n}b_{2n-2} + b_{2n}b_{2n-1}b_{2n-2} + a_{2n-1}b_{2n})\, P_{2n-2} - \\ - a_{2n-1}a_{2n-2}b_{2n}P_{2n-4} \qquad (n = 2, 3, \ldots). \end{aligned}$$

Similar relationships connect Q_{2n}, Q_{2n-2}, Q_{2n-4}. The derived relationships connect the numerators and denominators of three successive convergents of the contracted continued fraction. Therefore (c.f. (1.2)) the coefficient of P_{2n-2} divided by b_{2n-2} is the nth partial denominator of the contracted continued fraction, and the coefficient of P_{2n-4} divided by b_{2n-2} is the nth partial numerator of the contracted continued fraction. Moreover

$$\frac{P_2}{Q_2} = b_0 + \frac{a_1b_2}{b_1b_2 + a_2}.$$

From this the partial numerators of the continued fraction become

$$a_1b_2, \quad -\frac{a_2a_3b_4}{b_2}, \quad -\frac{a_4a_5b_6}{b_4}, \ldots, \quad -\frac{a_{2n-2}a_{2n-1}b_{2n}}{b_{2n-2}}, \ldots,$$

and its partial numerators become

$$b_1b_2 + a_2, \quad \frac{(b_2b_3 + a_3)\,b_4 + b_2a_4}{b_2}, \quad \frac{(b_4b_5 + a_5)\,b_6 + b_4a_6}{b_4}, \ldots$$

$$\ldots, \frac{(b_{2n-2}b_{2n-1} + a_{2n-1})\,b_{2n} + b_{2n-2}a_{2n}}{b_{2n-2}}, \ldots$$

Applying transformation (2.1) to the contracted expansion, we obtain:

$$b_0 + \frac{a_1}{b_1} + \frac{a_2}{b_2} + \ldots + \frac{a_n}{b_n} + \ldots =$$

$$= b_0 + \frac{a_1b_2}{b_1b_2 + a_2} - \frac{a_2a_3b_4}{(b_2b_3 + a_3)\,b_4 + b_2a_4} -$$

$$- \frac{a_4a_5b_2b_6}{(b_4b_5 + a_5)\,b_6 + b_4a_6} - \ldots$$

$$\ldots - \frac{a_{2n-2}a_{2n-1}b_{2n-4}b_{2n}}{(b_{n-2}b_{2n-1} + a_{2n-1})\,b_{2n} + b_{2n-2}a_{2n}} - \ldots. \tag{2.8}$$

In particular, let $b_n = x$ $(n = 1, 2, \ldots)$. Then equation (2.8) becomes

$$\frac{a_1}{x} + \frac{a_2}{x} + \ldots + \frac{a_n}{x} + \ldots = \frac{a_1x}{a_2 + x^2} - \frac{a_2a_3x}{(a_3 + a_4 + x^2)\,x} -$$

$$- \frac{a_4a_5x}{(a_5 + a_6 + x^2)\,x} - \ldots - \frac{a_{2n-2}a_{2n-1}x^2}{(a_{2n-1} + a_{2n} + x^2)\,x} - \ldots,$$

i.e.

$$\frac{a_1}{x} + \frac{a_2}{x} + \ldots + \frac{a_n}{x} + \ldots = \frac{a_1x}{a_2 + x^2} - \frac{a_2a_3}{a_3 + a_4 + x^2} -$$

$$- \frac{a_4a_5}{a_5 + a_6 + x^2} - \ldots - \frac{a_{2n-2}a_{2n-1}}{a_{2n-1} + a_{2n} + x^2} - \ldots. \tag{2.9}$$

This example shows us that contraction does not always result in an equation between two expansions. Indeed when $x = 0$ the left hand side of equation (2.9) has no meaning, but the right hand side is equal to zero.

In particular, for $\sqrt{2}$ equation (2.9) becomes

$$\sqrt{2} = 1 + \frac{1}{2} + \frac{1}{2} + \frac{1}{2} + \ldots =$$

$$= 1 + \frac{2}{5} - \frac{1}{6} - \frac{1}{6} - \ldots . \tag{2.10}$$

$$\frac{1}{1} \quad \frac{7}{5} \quad \frac{41}{29} \quad \frac{239}{169}$$

7. Putting now $K_n = P_{2n+1}/Q_{2n+1}$, we have from (1.2)

$$P_{2n+1} = b_{2n+1}P_{2n} + a_{2n+1}P_{2n-1},$$

$$P_{2n} = b_n P_{2n-1} + a_{2n}P_{2n-2},$$

$$P_{2n-1} = b_{2n-1}P_{2n-2} + a_{2n-1}P_{2n-3}.$$

Multiplying these equations by b_{2n-1}, $b_{2n+1}b_{2n-1}$, $-a_{2n}b_{2n+1}$ respectively and adding the products obtained, we have:

$$b_{2n-1}P_{2n+1} = (a_{2n+1}b_{2n-1} + b_{2n-1}b_{2n}b_{2n+1} + a_{2n}b_{2n+1})P_{2n-1} -$$

$$- a_{2n-1}a_{2n}b_{2n+1}P_{2n-3} \qquad (n = 2, 3, \ldots).$$

Similar relationships connect Q_{2n+1}, Q_{2n-1}, Q_{2n-3}. Moreover

$$\frac{P_1}{Q_1} = \frac{b_0 b_1 + a_1}{b_1}.$$

From this the partial numerators of the contracted continued fraction have, in the notation of equation (1.2), the form

$$b_0 b_1 + a_1, \quad -\frac{a_1 a_2 b_3}{b_1}, \quad -\frac{a_3 a_4 b_5}{b_3}, \ldots, \quad -\frac{a_{2n-1}a_{2n}b_{2n+1}}{b_{2n-1}}, \ldots,$$

and its partial denominators have the form

$$b_1, \quad \frac{(b_1 b_2 + a_2)\, b_3 + b_1 a_3}{b_1}, \quad \frac{(b_3 b_4 + a_4)\, b_5 + b_3 a_5}{b_3}, \ldots$$

$$\ldots, \quad \frac{(b_{2n-1}b_{2n} + a_{2n})\, b_{2n+1} + b_{2n-1}a_{2n+1}}{b_{2n-1}}, \ldots$$

Applying transformation (2.1) to the contracted continued fraction, we obtain:

$$b_0 + \frac{a_1}{b_1} + \frac{a_2}{b_2} + \dots + \frac{a_n}{b_n} + \dots = \frac{b_0 b_1 + a_1}{b_1} -$$

$$- \frac{a_1 a_2 b_3}{(b_1 b_2 + a_2)\, b_3 + b_1 a_3} - \frac{a_3 a_4 b_1 b_5}{(b_3 b_4 + a_4)\, b_5 + b_3 a_5} - \dots$$

$$\dots - \frac{a_{2n-1} a_{2n} b_{2n-3} b_{2n-1}}{(b_{2n-1} b_{2n} + a_{2n})\, b_{2n+1} + b_{2n-1} a_{2n+1}} - \dots, \qquad (2.11)$$

its convergents are $1/0$, $(b_0 b_1 + a_1)/b_1$, ... and so on.

From the latter remark, one can consider every continued fraction of the form (1.1) in which $b_0 = 0$, in two ways; as having a convergent of zero order equal to $0/1$, or as having a convergent of zero order equal to $1/0$.

In particular let $b_n = x$ $(n = 0, 1, \dots)$. Then equation (2.11) becomes

$$x + \frac{a_1}{x} + \frac{a_2}{x} + \dots + \frac{a_n}{x} + \dots =$$

$$= \frac{a_1 + x^2}{x} - \frac{a_1 a_2 x}{(a_2 + a_3 + x^2)\, x} - \frac{a_3 a_4 x^2}{(a_4 + a_5 + x_2)\, x} - \dots$$

$$\dots - \frac{a_{2n-1} a_{2n} x^2}{(a_{2n} + a_{2n+1} + x^2)\, x} - \dots$$

i.e.

$$x + \frac{a_1}{x} + \frac{a_2}{x} + \dots + \frac{a_n}{x} + \dots =$$

$$= \frac{a_1 + x^2}{x} - \frac{a_1 a_2}{a_2 + a_3 + x^2} - \frac{a_3 a_4}{a_4 + a_5 + x^2} - \dots$$

$$\dots - \frac{a_{2n-1} a_{2n}}{a_{2n} + a_{1n+1} + x^2} - \dots. \qquad (2.12)$$

In particular, for $\sqrt{2}$ equation (2.12) becomes

$$1 + \sqrt{2} = \frac{5}{2} - \frac{1}{6} - \frac{1}{6} - \frac{1}{6} - \dots - \frac{1}{6} - \dots.$$

$$\frac{1}{0} \quad \frac{5}{2} \quad \frac{29}{12} \quad \frac{169}{70} \quad \frac{985}{408}$$

If we had not known that the right hand side of this equation had been derived by means of contracting the left, then we would have obtained the convergents:

$$\frac{5}{2}-\frac{1}{6}-\frac{1}{6}-\frac{1}{6}-\ldots-\frac{1}{6}-\ldots. \tag{2.13}$$

$$\frac{0}{1}\ \frac{5}{2}\quad \frac{30}{11}\quad \frac{175}{64}\quad \frac{1020}{373}$$

We shall find the value of the latter continued fraction. For this we express the continued fraction

$$2-\frac{1}{6}-\frac{1}{6}-\ldots-\frac{1}{6}-\ldots$$

in terms of expansion (2.10):

$$\frac{\sqrt{2}-1}{2}=\frac{1}{3+2}-\frac{1}{6}-\frac{1}{6}-\ldots-\frac{1}{6}-\ldots;$$

$$\frac{2}{\sqrt{2}-1}-3=2-\frac{1}{6}-\frac{1}{6}-\ldots.$$

Then the value of the continued fraction (2.13) is

$$\frac{5}{\dfrac{2}{\sqrt{2}-1}-3}=\frac{5}{2(\sqrt{2}+1)-3}=\frac{5}{2\sqrt{2}-1}=$$

$$=\frac{5}{7}(2\sqrt{2}+1)\doteqdot 0{\cdot}714286.3{\cdot}828843\doteqdot 2{\cdot}73459.$$

The convergent of the fourth order of continued fraction (2.13) is $\frac{1020}{373}\doteqdot 2{\cdot}73458$.

We call the value K of the continued fraction

$$\frac{a_1}{b_1}+\frac{a_2}{b_2}+\ldots+\frac{a_n}{b_n}+\ldots,$$

from the assumption that $P_0/Q_0=0/1$, the *ordinary value of the continued fraction*. Correspondingly we speak of *ordinary convergents*.

We call the value $\tilde{K}$ of the same continued fraction, which is derived from the assumption that $P_0/Q_0 = 1/0$ the *singular value* of the continued fraction. Correspondingly we shall speak of *singular convergents.*

We shall use the notations

$$K = \frac{a_1}{b_1} + \frac{a_2}{b_2} + \dots + \frac{a_n}{b_n} + \dots$$

and

$$\tilde{K} \overset{*}{=} \frac{a_1}{b_1} + \frac{a_2}{b_1} + \dots + \frac{a_n}{b_n} + \dots.$$

For example

$$\frac{5}{7}(2\sqrt{2}+1) = \frac{5}{2} - \frac{1}{6} - \frac{1}{6} - \dots - \frac{1}{6} - \dots,$$

$$1 + \sqrt{2} \overset{*}{=} \frac{5}{2} - \frac{1}{6} - \frac{1}{6} - \dots - \frac{1}{6} - \dots.$$

In relationship (2.11) and (2.12) the sign of equality should be replaced by the sign $\overset{*}{=}$.

8. We produce the contracted forms of continued fraction (2.2). Transformations (2.8) and (2.11) become in this case

$$\alpha_0 + \frac{1}{\alpha_1} + \frac{1}{\alpha_2} + \dots + \frac{1}{\alpha_n} + \dots =$$

$$= \alpha_0 + \frac{\alpha_2}{\alpha_1\alpha_2 + 1} - \frac{\alpha_4}{(\alpha_2\alpha_3 + 1)\,\alpha_4 + \alpha_2} - \frac{\alpha_2\alpha_6}{(\alpha_4\alpha_5 + 1)\,\alpha_6 + \alpha_4} - \dots$$

$$\dots - \frac{\alpha_{2n-4}\alpha_{2n}}{(\alpha_{2n-2}\alpha_{2n-1} + 1)\,\alpha_{2n} + \alpha_{2n-2}} - \dots \tag{2.14}$$

and

$$\alpha_0 + \frac{1}{\alpha_1} + \frac{1}{\alpha_2} + \dots + \frac{1}{\alpha_n} + \dots \overset{*}{=}$$

$$\overset{*}{=} \frac{\alpha_0\alpha_1 + 1}{\alpha_1} - \frac{\alpha_3}{(\alpha_1\alpha_2 + 1)\,\alpha_3 + \alpha_1} - \frac{\alpha_1\alpha_5}{(\alpha_3\alpha_4 + 1)\,\alpha_5 + \alpha_3} - \dots$$

$$\dots - \frac{\alpha_{2n-3}\alpha_{2n+1}}{(\alpha_{2n-1}\alpha_{2n} + 1)\,\alpha_{2n+1} + \alpha_{2n-1}} - \dots. \tag{2.15}$$

respectively.

9. We produce the contracted forms of continued fraction (2.4) where $b_0 = 0$. Transformations (2.8) and (2.11) give

$$\frac{c_1}{1} + \frac{c_2}{1} + \dots + \frac{c_n}{1} + \dots = \frac{c_1}{1 + c_2} - \frac{c_2 c_3}{1 + c_3 + c_4} - \frac{c_4 c_5}{1 + c_5 + c_6} - \dots - \frac{c_{2n-2} c_{2n-1}}{1 + c_{2n-1} + c_{2n}} - \dots \tag{2.16}$$

and

$$\frac{c_1}{1} + \frac{c_2}{1} + \dots + \frac{c_n}{1} + \dots \overset{*}{=} \frac{c_1}{1} - \frac{c_1 c_2}{1 + c_2 + c_3} - \frac{c_3 c_4}{1 + c_4 + c_5} - \dots - \frac{c_{2n-1} c_{2n}}{1 + c_{2n} + c_{2n+1}} - \dots \tag{2.17}$$

respectively.

10. We now consider further identity transformations of the continued fraction (1.1). We write the identity

$$K \equiv b_0 + \frac{a_1}{b_1} + \frac{a_2}{b_2} + \dots = \frac{b_0}{1} + \frac{c_1}{d_1} + \frac{c_2}{d_2} + \dots \tag{2.18}$$

and discuss the relationships which exist between the coefficients of these continued fractions. For this we denote K by $b_0/(1 + K_1)$. Then

$$K = b_0 + \frac{b_0}{1 + K_1} - b_0 = b_0 - \frac{b_0 K_1}{1 + K_1} = $$

$$= b_0 - \frac{b_0}{\dfrac{1}{K_1} + 1} = b_0 - \frac{b_0 c_1 d_2}{\dfrac{c_1 d_2}{K_1} + c_1 d_2}.$$

But according to (2.8)

$$K_1 = \frac{c_1 d_2}{d_1 d_2 + c_2} - \frac{c_2 c_3 d_4}{(d_2 d_3 + c_3)\, d_4 + d_2 c_4} - \frac{c_4 c_5 d_2 d_6}{(d_4 d_5 + c_5)\, d_6 + d_4 c_6} - \dots$$

$$\dots - \frac{c_{2n-2} c_{2n-1} d_{2n-4} d_{2n}}{(d_{2n-2} d_{2n-1} + c_{2n-1})\, d_{2n} + d_{2n-2} c_{2n}} - \dots$$

Consequently

$$K = b_0 - \frac{b_0 c_1 d_2}{(d_1 + c_1)\, d_2 + c_2} - \frac{c_2 c_3 d_4}{(d_2 d_3 + c_3)\, d_4 + d_2 c_4} - \frac{c_4 c_5 d_2 d_6}{(d_4 d_5 + c_5)\, d_6 + d_4 c_6} - \ldots$$

$$\ldots - \frac{c_{2n-2} c_{2n-1} d_{2n-4} d_{2n}}{(d_{2n-2} d_{2n-1} + c_{2n-1})\, d_{2n} + d_{2n-2} c_{2n}} - \ldots . \qquad (2.19)$$

But, on the other hand, K satisfies equation (2.8). From this, assuming that as a result of transformation (2.1) corresponding coefficients of continued fractions (2.8) and (2.19) are made equal, we have:

$$\left.\begin{aligned} -b_0 c_1 d_2 &= a_1 b_2, \\ c_2 c_3 d_4 &= a_2 a_3 b_4, \\ c_{2n-2} c_{2n-1} d_{2n-4} d_{2n} &= a_{2n-2} a_{2n-1} b_{2n-4} b_{2n} \quad (n = 2, 3, \ldots) \end{aligned}\right\} \qquad (2.20)$$

and

$$\left.\begin{aligned} c_1 d_2 + d_1 d_2 + c_2 &= b_1 b_2 + a_2, \\ (d_{2n-2} d_{2n-1} + c_{2n-1})\, d_{2n} + d_{2n-2} c_{2n} &= \\ = (b_{2n-2} b_{2n-1} + a_{2n-1})\, b_{2n} + b_{2n-2} a_{2n} & \quad (n = 2, 3, \ldots) \end{aligned}\right\} \qquad (2.21)$$

It is clear that in the general case equations (2.20) and (2.21) do not allow us to express c_n and d_n $(n = 1, 2, \ldots)$ in terms of $a_1, a_2, \ldots$ or conversely a_n, b_n $(n = 1, 2, \ldots)$ in terms of $c_1, c_2, \ldots, d_1, d_2, \ldots$. But this one can do with the help of supplementary assumptions.

11. We apply transformation (2.18) to a special case of the continued fraction (1.1). Let

$$b_0 = 1, \qquad c_1 = -a_1, \qquad d_n = b_n,$$
$$c_{2n+1} = a_{2n}, \qquad c_{2n} = a_{2n+1} \qquad (n = 1, 2, \ldots).$$

Then equations (2.20) evolve into identities, and equations (2.21) become

$$-a_1 b_2 + a_3 = a_2$$
$$a_{2n-2} b_{2n} + a_{2n+1} b_{2n-2} = a_{2n-1} b_{2n} + a_{2n} b_{2n-2} \qquad (n = 2, 3, \ldots).$$

From this

$$a_1 = \frac{a_3 - a_2}{b_2}, \quad \frac{a_{2n-1} - a_{2n-2}}{b_{2n-2}} = \frac{a_{2n+1} - a_{2n}}{b_{2n}} \quad (n = 2, 3, \ldots).$$

Hence with the conditions

$$a_1 = \frac{a_3 - a_2}{b_1} = \frac{a_5 - a_4}{b_4} = \ldots = \frac{a_{2n+1} - a_{2n}}{b_{1n}} = \ldots \tag{2.22}$$

the identity

$$1 + \frac{a_1}{b_1} + \frac{a_2}{b_2} + \ldots + \frac{a_n}{b_n} + \ldots =$$

$$= \frac{1}{1} - \frac{a_1}{b_1} + \frac{a_3}{b_1} + \frac{a_2}{b_3} + \ldots + \frac{a_{2n+1}}{b_{2n}} + \frac{a_{2n}}{b_{2n+1}} + \ldots \tag{2.23}$$

obtains.

Transformation (2.23) will be exploited by us in the second chapter, when continued fraction expansions of elementary functions are being studied.

12. We consider a further special case of transformation (2.18). Let

$$b_0 = 1, \quad c_n = -a_n, \quad d_{2n} = b_{2n}, \quad d_{2n-1} = \lambda_n b_{2n-1}$$
$$(n = 1, 2, \ldots; \quad \lambda_n \neq 1).$$

Then equations (2.20) degenerate into identities, and equations (2.21) become

$$-a_1 b_2 + \lambda_1 b_1 b_2 - a_2 = b_1 b_2 + a_2,$$

$$(\lambda_n b_{2n-2} b_{2n-1} - a_{2n-1})\, b_{2n} - b_{2n-2} a_{2n} =$$
$$= (b_{2n-2} b_{2n-1} + a_{2n-1})\, b_{2n} + b_{2n-2} a_{2n} \quad (n = 2, 3. \ldots).$$

From this

$$\lambda_1 b_1 = \frac{a_1 b_2 + b_1 b_2 + 2a_2}{b_2},$$

$$\lambda_n b_{2n-1} = \frac{b_{2n-2} b_{2n-1} b_{2n} + 2a_{2n-1} b_{2n} + 2a_{2n} b_{2n-2}}{b_{2n-2} b_{2n}}.$$

In this way, equation (2.18) becomes

$$1+\frac{a_1}{b_1}+\frac{a_2}{b_2}+\ldots=\frac{1}{1}-\frac{a_1}{\dfrac{a_1b_2+b_1b_2+2a_2}{b_2}}-\frac{a_2}{b_2}-$$

$$-\frac{a_3}{\dfrac{b_2b_3b_4+2a_3b_4+2a_4b_2}{b_2b_4}}-\frac{a_4}{b_4}-\frac{a_5}{\dfrac{b_4b_5b_6+2a_5b_6+2a_6b_4}{b_4b_6}}-\frac{a_6}{b_6}-\ldots$$

$$\ldots-\frac{a_{2n-1}}{\dfrac{b_{2n-2}b_{2n-1}b_{2n}+2a_{2n-1}b_{2n}+2a_{2n}b_{2n-2}}{b_{2n-2}b_{2n}}}-\frac{a_{2n}}{b_{2n}}-\ldots,$$

i.e.

$$1+\frac{a_1}{b_1}+\frac{a_2}{b_2}+\ldots=$$

$$=\frac{1}{1}-\frac{a_1b_2}{a_1b_2+b_1b_2+2a_2}-\frac{a_2}{1}-\frac{a_3b_4}{b_2b_3b_4+2a_3b_4+2a_4b_2}-$$

$$-\frac{a_4b_2}{1}-\frac{a_5b_6}{b_4b_5b_6+2a_5b_6+2a_6b_4}-\frac{a_6b_4}{1}-\ldots$$

$$\ldots-\frac{a_{2n-1}b_{2n}}{b_{2n-2}b_{2n-1}b_{2n}+2a_{2n-1}b_{2n}+2a_{2n}b_{2n-2}}-\frac{a_{2n}b_{2n-2}}{1}-\ldots. \quad (2.24)$$

In particular it follows from (2.24) that

$$\sqrt{2}=1+\frac{1}{2}+\frac{1}{2}+\frac{1}{2}+\ldots=$$

$$=\frac{1}{1}-\frac{2}{8}-\frac{1}{1}-\frac{2}{16}-\frac{2}{1}-\frac{2}{16}-\frac{2}{1}-\ldots=$$

$$=\frac{1}{1}-\frac{2}{8}-\frac{1}{1}-\frac{1}{8}-\frac{1}{1}-\frac{1}{8}-\frac{1}{1}-\ldots$$

$$\frac{0}{1}\quad\frac{1}{1}\quad\frac{8}{6}\quad\frac{7}{5}\quad\frac{48}{34}\quad\frac{41}{29}\quad\frac{280}{198}\quad\frac{239}{169}$$

For the continued fraction (2.2) (with $\alpha_0 = 1$) identity (2.24) becomes

$$1 + \frac{1}{\alpha_1 +} \frac{1}{\alpha_2 +} \dots + \frac{1}{\alpha_n +} \dots = \frac{1}{1 -} \frac{\alpha_2}{\alpha_1\alpha_2 + \alpha_2 + 2 -} \frac{1}{1 -}$$

$$- \frac{\alpha_4}{\alpha_2\alpha_3\alpha_4 + 2\alpha_2 + 2\alpha_4 -} \frac{\alpha_2}{1 -} \frac{\alpha_6}{\alpha_4\alpha_5\alpha_6 + 2\alpha_4 + 2\alpha_6 -}$$

$$- \frac{\alpha_4}{1 -} \dots - \frac{\alpha_{2n}}{\alpha_{2n-2}\alpha_{2n-1}\alpha_{2n} + 2\alpha_{2n-2} + 2\alpha_{2n} -} \frac{\alpha_{2n-2}}{1 -} \dots . \quad (2.25)$$

For the continued fraction (2.4) identity (2.24) becomes

$$1 + \frac{c_1}{1 +} \frac{c_2}{1 +} \dots + \frac{c_n}{1 +} \dots = \frac{1}{1 -} \frac{c_1}{c_1 + 2c_2 + 1 -}$$

$$- \frac{c_2}{1 -} \frac{c_3}{2c_3 + 2c_4 + 1 -} \frac{c_4}{1 -} \frac{c_5}{2c_5 + 2c_6 + 1 -}$$

$$- \frac{c_6}{1 -} \dots - \frac{c_{2n-1}}{2c_{2n-1} + 2c_{2n} + 1 -} \frac{c_{2n}}{1 -} \dots . \quad (2.26)$$

§ 3. The Transformation of Series into Continued Fractions

1. We shall distinguish the forms in which a given power or numerical series may be transformed into a continued fraction. In § 1 we showed numerical series and continued fractions which are equivalent to one another. As an example of the transformation of power series into an equivalent continued fraction we may quote the following identity of Euler [15], [16], [19]:

$$c_0 + c_1 x + c_2 x^2 + \dots + c_n x^n + \dots =$$

$$= c_0 + \frac{c_1 x}{1} \; \frac{\frac{c_2}{c_1} x}{- 1 + \frac{c_2}{c_1} x -} \; \frac{\frac{c_3}{c_2} x}{1 + \frac{c_3}{c_2} x -} \dots - \frac{\frac{c_n}{c_{n-1}} x}{1 + \frac{c_n}{c_{n-1}} x -} \dots .$$

One can write this formula as:

$$\sum_{n=0}^{\infty} c_n x^n =$$

$$= \frac{c_0}{1} \, \frac{\frac{c_1}{c_0} x}{-1+\frac{c_1}{c_0} x} \, - \, \frac{\frac{c_2}{c_1} x}{1+\frac{c_2}{c_1} x} \, - \, \frac{\frac{c_3}{c_2} x}{1+\frac{c_3}{c_2} x} \, - \ldots - \, \frac{\frac{c_n}{c_{n-1}} x}{1+\frac{c_n}{c_{n-1}} x} \, - \ldots$$

Applying transformation (2.1) to the right hand side of this second identity, we obtain the formula

$$\sum_{n=0}^{\infty} c_n x^n = c_0 + \frac{c_1 x}{1} \, - \, \frac{c_2 x}{c_1 + c_2 x} \, - \, \frac{c_1 c_3 x}{c_2 + c_3 x} \, - \ldots$$

$$\ldots - \frac{c_{n-2} c_n x}{c_{n-1} + c_n x} \, - \ldots = \frac{c_0}{1} \, - \, \frac{c_1 x}{c_0 + c_1 x} \, -$$

$$- \, \frac{c_0 c_2 x}{c_1 + c_2 x} \, - \, \frac{c_1 c_3 x}{c_2 + c_3 x} \, - \ldots - \, \frac{c_{n-2} c_n x}{c_{n-1} + c_n x} \, - \ldots . \quad (3.1)$$

Since this series has been transformed into an equivalent continued fraction, then the nth convergent of the continued fraction standing on the right hand side of identity (3.1) is identically equal to the sum of the first $n + 1$ terms of the series standing on the left hand side.

2. For example

$$\arctan = x - \frac{x^3}{3} + \frac{x^5}{5} - \frac{x^7}{7} + \ldots =$$

$$= \frac{x}{1} \, \frac{\frac{x^2}{3}}{+1-\frac{x^2}{3}} \, \frac{\frac{3}{5} x^2}{+1-\frac{3}{5} x^2} + \ldots + \, \frac{\frac{2n-1}{2n+1} x^2}{1-\frac{2n-1}{2n+1} x^2} + \ldots ,$$

i.e.

$$\arctan x = \frac{x}{1} \, + \, \frac{x^2}{3 - x^2} \, + \, \frac{9x^2}{5 - 3x^2} \, + \ldots$$

$$\ldots + \frac{(2n-1)^2 x^2}{2n + 1 - (2n-1) x^2} + \ldots . \quad (3.2)$$

From this, when $x = 1$, we have;

$$\frac{\pi}{4} = \frac{1}{1} + \frac{1}{2} + \frac{3^2}{2} + \frac{5^2}{2} + \frac{7^2}{2} + \ldots + \frac{(2n-1)^2}{2} + \ldots \quad (3.3)$$

$$\frac{0}{1} \quad \frac{1}{1} \quad \frac{2}{3} \quad \frac{13}{15} \quad \frac{76}{105} \quad \frac{789}{945}$$

Expansion (3.3) was first derived by Lord Brouncker (Wallis [104], [105]), by transforming an infinite product in which Wallis had expanded π. This was the first time that a transcendental number had been expanded as a continued fraction.

Applying identity (2.24) to (3.2) we obtain:

$$\frac{\arctan x}{x} = \frac{1}{1} + \frac{x^2}{3-x^2} + \frac{9x^2}{5-3x^2} + \ldots =$$

$$= 1 - \frac{x^2(5-3x^2)}{(5-3x^2)\,x^2 + (3-x^2)(5-3x^2) + 18x^2} - \frac{9x^2}{1} - \ldots =$$

$$= 1 - \frac{5x^2-3x^4}{15+9x^2} - \frac{9x^2}{1} - \ldots,$$

i.e.

$$\arctan x = x - \frac{5x^3-3x^5}{15+9x^2} - \frac{9x^2}{1} - \ldots.$$

$$\frac{x}{1} \quad \frac{15x+4x^3+3x^5}{15+9x^2} \quad \frac{15x-5x^3+3x^5}{15}$$

In this way we have, as a result of the transformation of a power series into an equivalent continued fraction, derived rational function approximations for $\arctan x$. In view of the complexity we shall not set out the general term of the expansion derived. But for expansion (3.3) we quote the result in full:

$$\frac{4}{\pi} = 1 + \frac{1}{2} + \frac{3^2}{2} + \ldots + \frac{(2n-1)^2}{2} + \ldots =$$

$$= \frac{1}{1} - \frac{2.1}{2+4+18} - \frac{9}{1} - \frac{2.25}{8+4.25+4.49} -$$

$$-\frac{2.49}{1}-\frac{2.81}{8+4.81+4.121}-\ldots-\frac{2(4n-1)^2}{1}-$$

$$-\frac{2(4n+1)^2}{8+4(4n+1)^2+4(4n+3)^2}-\ldots.$$

From this

$$\frac{\pi}{4}=1-\frac{2}{24}-\frac{9}{1}-\frac{25}{152}-\frac{49}{1}-\frac{81}{408}-\ldots$$

$$\frac{1}{1}\quad\frac{22}{24}\quad\frac{13}{15}\quad\frac{1426}{1680}\quad\frac{789}{945}$$

$$\ldots-\frac{(4n-1)^2}{1}-\frac{(4n+1)^2}{8(8n^2+8n+3)}-\ldots.$$

3. From the power series

$$A_0+A_1x+A_2x^2+\ldots$$

one can find a continued fraction such that the expansion of its nth convergent in a power series will coincide with the original power series as far as the term containing x^n. Such a continued fraction is spoken of as *corresponding* (korrespondierende) (Perron [73]) to the given series. Customarily it is expressed in one of the following forms

$$b_0+\frac{a_1x}{b_1}+\frac{a_2x}{b_2}+\ldots;\quad \frac{b_0}{1}+\frac{c_1x}{d_1}+\frac{c_2x}{d_2}+\ldots.$$

Contracting the corresponding continued fractions, we obtain a continued fraction, the expansion of the nth convergent of which in a power series coincides with the original series as far as the term in x^{2n}. Such continued fractions are said to be *associated* (assoziierte) (Perron [73]) with the given series. The relationship between corresponding and associated continued fractions was considered by Heilermann [30].

4. Great importance attaches to the fact that the convergence behaviour of a power or numerical series and that of its corresponding continued fraction is quite different. Both may converge,

both diverge, or one may converge whilst the other diverges. Perron [73] cites an example of a continued fraction for which, as the argument varies, all these special cases are encountered. In this Perron assumes that (in the general case an unsolved problem) corresponding series and continued fractions both converge to one and the same value if they both converge.

It is important to remark that one can even transform a power series with a convergence radius equal to zero into a corresponding continued fraction which converges in a certain domain. Examples of such transformations will be given in chapter II.

5. One can express the coefficients of the corresponding and associated continued fractions in terms of the coefficients in the terms of the original power series, but these expressions involve determinants of high orders (Heilermann [25], [29], Muir [54], [55], Frobenius [23], Stieltjes [92], Hankel [27]). This means that in most cases such expressions are not suitable for immediate application. Therefore we shall not dwell upon these formulae, referring those interested to the book of Perron [73], and proceed to the exposition of a direct method for the transformation of a given power series into a corresponding continued fraction. This procedure was in principle proposed by V. Viskovatoff [103]; we have merely developed a more convenient notation for this method of calculation.

6. Let

$$f(x) = \frac{\alpha_{10} + \alpha_{11}x + \alpha_{12}x^2 + \alpha_{13}x^3 + \dots}{\alpha_{00} + \alpha_{01}x + \alpha_{02}x^2 + \alpha_{03}x^3 + \dots}.$$

Then

$$f(x) = \frac{1}{\dfrac{\alpha_{00}}{\alpha_{10}} + \dfrac{\alpha_{00} + \alpha_{01}x + \alpha_{02}x^2 + \dots}{\alpha_{10} + \alpha_{11}x + \alpha_{12}x^2 + \dots} - \dfrac{\alpha_{00}}{\alpha_{10}}} =$$

$$= \frac{\alpha_{10}}{\alpha_{00} + x\dfrac{(\alpha_{10}\alpha_{01} - \alpha_{00}\alpha_{11}) + (\alpha_{10}\alpha_{02} - \alpha_{00}\alpha_{12})\,x + \dots}{\alpha_{10} + \alpha_{11}x + \alpha_{12}x^2 + \dots}} =$$

$$= \frac{\alpha_{10}}{\alpha_{00} + x\dfrac{\alpha_{20} + \alpha_{21}x + \alpha_{22}x^2 + \dots}{\alpha_{10} + \alpha_{11}x + \alpha_{12}x^2 + \dots}} =$$

$$= \cfrac{\alpha_{10}}{\alpha_{00} + x \cfrac{\alpha_{20}}{\alpha_{10} + x \cfrac{(\alpha_{20}\alpha_{11} - \alpha_{10}\alpha_{21}) + (\alpha_{20}\alpha_{12} - \alpha_{10}\alpha_{22})\, x + \dots}{\alpha_{20} + \alpha_{21}x + \alpha_{22}x^2 + \dots}}} =$$

$$= \frac{\alpha_{10}}{\alpha_{00}} + \frac{\alpha_{20}x}{\alpha_{10}} + \frac{\alpha_{30}x}{\alpha_{20}} + \dots.$$

The computations are conveniently set out in the following scheme:

$$\begin{array}{llll} \alpha_{00} & \alpha_{01} & \alpha_{02} & \cdots \\ \alpha_{10} & \alpha_{11} & \alpha_{12} & \cdots \\ \alpha_{20} & \alpha_{21} & \alpha_{22} & \cdots \\ \alpha_{30} & \alpha_{31} & \alpha_{32} & \cdots \\ \cdots & \cdots & \cdots & \cdots \end{array}$$

Here

$$\alpha_{mn} = \alpha_{m-1,0}\alpha_{m-2,\,n+1} - \alpha_{m-2,0}\alpha_{m-1,\,n+1}.$$

7. Consider for example the continued fraction expansion of the expression

$$\frac{1-x}{1-5x+6x^2} \; (x < \tfrac{1}{3}).$$

We have:

$$\begin{array}{rrr} 1 & -5 & 6 \\ 1 & -1 & \\ -4 & 6 & \\ -2 & & \\ -12 & & \end{array}$$

$$\frac{1-x}{1-5x+6x^2} = \frac{1}{1} - \frac{4x}{1} - \frac{2x}{-4} - \frac{12x}{-2} =$$

$$= \frac{1}{1} - \frac{4x}{1} + \frac{x}{2} - \frac{3x}{1}.$$

$$\frac{0}{1} \quad \frac{1}{1} \quad \frac{1}{1-4x} \quad \frac{2+x}{2-7x} \quad \frac{2-2x}{2-10x+12x^2}$$

8. Consider the continued fraction expansion of the expression

$$\frac{1}{1-3x+3x^2-x^3} \; (x < 1).$$

We have:

$$\begin{array}{rrrr}
1 & -3 & 3 & -1 \\
1 & & & \\
-3 & 3 & -1 & \\
-3 & 1 & & \\
-6 & 3 & & \\
3 & & & \\
9 & & &
\end{array}$$

$$\frac{1}{(1-x)^3} = \frac{1}{1} - \frac{3x}{1} - \frac{3x}{-3} - \frac{6x}{-3} + \frac{3x}{-6} + \frac{9x}{3} =$$

$$= \frac{1}{1} - \frac{3x}{1} + \frac{x}{1} - \frac{2x}{3} + \frac{x}{2} - \frac{x}{1}.$$

$$\frac{0}{1}\quad \frac{1}{1}\quad \frac{1}{1-3x}\quad \frac{1+x}{1-2x}\quad \frac{3+x}{3-8x+6x^2}\quad \frac{6+3x+x^2}{6-15x+10x^2}\quad \frac{6}{6-18x+18x^2-6x^3}$$

9. Let $\alpha_{2,0} = 0$. Then

$$f(x) = \cfrac{\alpha_{10}}{\alpha_{00} + x^2 \cfrac{\alpha_{21} + \alpha_{22}x + \dots}{\alpha_{10} + \alpha_{11}x + \alpha_{12}x^2 + \dots}}.$$

The fraction

$$\frac{\alpha_{21} + \alpha_{22}x + \dots}{\alpha_{10} + \alpha_{11}x + \alpha_{12}x^2 + \dots}$$

is expanded as in section 6, and thus we come to the identity

$$f(x) = \frac{\alpha_{10}}{\alpha_{00}} + \frac{\alpha_{21}x^2}{\alpha_{10}} + \frac{\alpha'_{31}x}{\alpha_{21}} + \frac{\alpha'_{41}x}{\alpha'_{31}} + \dots.$$

The computations are set out in the following scheme:

$$\begin{array}{llll}
\alpha_{00} & \alpha_{01} & \alpha_{02} & \dots \\
\alpha_{10} & \alpha_{11} & \alpha_{12} & \dots \\
0 & \alpha_{21} & \alpha_{22} & \dots \\
\alpha_{21} & \alpha_{22} & \alpha_{23} & \dots \\
\alpha'_{31} & \alpha'_{32} & \alpha'_{33} & \dots \\
\alpha'_{41} & \alpha'_{42} & \alpha'_{43} & \dots
\end{array}$$

Here

$$\alpha'_{31} = \alpha_{21}\alpha_{11} - \alpha_{10}\alpha_{22},$$
$$\alpha'_{32} = \alpha_{21}\alpha_{12} - \alpha_{10}\alpha_{23},$$
$$\cdots\cdots\cdots\cdots\cdots\cdots\cdots\cdots$$
$$\alpha'_{41} = \alpha'_{31}\alpha_{22} - \alpha'_{32}\alpha_{21},$$
$$\cdots\cdots\cdots\cdots\cdots\cdots\cdots\cdots$$

Thus, if $\alpha_{20} = 0$, then the fourth row of the scheme is derived by means of a displacement of the third row by one place to the left, the fifth row is derived from a combination of the fourth and second rows by means of the general rule, the sixth row – by a combination of the fifth and fourth, and so on.

Exactly in the same way, if $\alpha_{k,0} = 0$ then the $(k+2)^{\text{th}}$ row of the scheme is derived by means of a displacement of the $(k+1)^{\text{th}}$ row by one place to the left; the $(k+3)^{\text{rd}}$ row is derived by a combination of the $(k+2)^{\text{nd}}$ and k^{th} by means of the general rule, the $(k+4)^{\text{th}}$ row from a combination of the $(k+3)^{\text{rd}}$ and $(k+2)^{\text{nd}}$, and so on. The expansion in this case becomes

$$f(x) = \frac{\alpha_{10}}{\alpha_{00}} + \frac{\alpha_{20}x}{\alpha_{10}} + \frac{\alpha_{30}x}{\alpha_{20}} + \cdots$$
$$\cdots + \frac{\alpha_{k-1,0}x}{\alpha_{k-2,0}} + \frac{\alpha_{k,1}x^2}{\alpha_{k-1,0}} + \frac{\alpha'_{k+1,1}x}{\alpha_{k,1}} + \frac{\alpha'_{k+2,1}x}{\alpha'_{k+1,1}} + \cdots.$$

10. We consider the continued fraction expansion of the expression

$$\frac{1-3x^2}{1-x^2-4x^4}\left(x^2 < \frac{\sqrt{17}-1}{8}\right).$$

We have:

$$\begin{array}{rrrrr}
1 & 0 & -1 & 0 & -4 \\
1 & 0 & 0 & -3 & \\
0 & -1 & 3 & -4 & \\
-1 & 3 & -4 & & \\
-3 & 4 & 3 & & \\
-5 & 15 & & & \\
25 & -15 & & & \\
300 & & & & \\
-300.15 & & & &
\end{array}$$

$$\frac{1-3x^3}{1-x^2-4x^4} = \frac{1}{1} - \frac{x^2}{1} - \frac{3x}{-1} - \frac{5x}{-3} + \frac{25x}{-5} + \frac{300x}{25} - \frac{15x}{1} =$$

$$= \frac{1}{1} - \frac{x^2}{1} + \frac{3x}{1} - \frac{5x}{3} +$$

$$\frac{0}{1} \quad \frac{1}{1} \quad \frac{1}{1-x^2} \quad \frac{1+3x}{1+3x-x^2} \quad \frac{3+4x}{3+4x-3x^2+5x^3}$$

$$+ \frac{5x}{1} - \frac{12x}{5} - \frac{3x}{1}.$$

$$\frac{3+9x+15x^2}{3+9x+12x^2} \quad \frac{15+9x+27x^2}{15+9x+12x^2+36x^3-60x^4} \quad \frac{15-45x^3}{15-15x^2-60x^4}$$

Further methods for decomposing rational fraction expressions into continued fractions were proposed by Kausler [35], [36], and Schubert [85].

§ 4. General Considerations in the Convergence Theory of Continued Fractions

1. We have already remarked that continued fractions for which $\lim_{n\to\infty} P_n/Q_n$ exists and is finite are called *convergent*. The value of the continued fraction is then equal to this limit. But from the convergence of the continued fraction it does not yet follow that $\lim_{n\to\infty} P_n/Q_n$ is equal to the quantity which we originally expanded as a continued fraction

2. If $\lim_{n\to\infty} P_n/Q_n = \infty$ or $\lim_{n\to\infty} P_n/Q_n = -\infty$, then the continued fraction is called *inessentially divergent*. If $\lim_{n\to\infty} P_n/Q_n$ does not exist then the continued fraction is called *essentially divergent.* The concepts of essential and inessential divergence were introduced by Perron [73].

3. The convergence of a series or of an infinite product is not influenced by neglecting a finite number of the first few terms. But for a continued fraction such an omission (excepting the

neglect of b_0) may result in an inessentially divergent continued fraction. Therefore we are led to introduce the following considerations (Pringsheim [76]): the continued fraction $\left[\frac{a_\nu}{b_\nu}\right]_1^\infty$ is called *absolutely convergent* if for all $m \geqslant 1$ the continued fractions $\left[\frac{a_\nu}{b_\nu}\right]_m^\infty$ converge. However, if for any value of m the latter continued fraction diverges, then the continued fraction $\left[\frac{a_\nu}{b_\nu}\right]_1^\infty$ is called *conditionally convergent.* The distinction between absolute and conditional convergence was also made by Stern [91].

4. From this it follows that for continued fractions, generally speaking, it is impossible to give a convergence criterion in the form of a limit, as is the case for infinite series. The conditions for convergence, relating to a_n and b_n for example, must be satisfied for all natural n.

5. If the continued fraction $\left[\frac{a_\nu}{b_\nu}\right]_1^\infty$ converges, the continued fractions $\left[\frac{a_\nu}{b_\nu}\right]_m^\infty$ may diverge only in the sense that reciprocals of the values of their convergents tend to zero for increasing ν. Hence for the convergence of the continued fraction $\left[\frac{a_\nu}{b_\nu}\right]_1^\infty$ there may be only two cases: all continued fractions $\left[\frac{a_\nu}{b_\nu}\right]_m^\infty$ converge (absolute convergence), or certain of the continued fractions $\left[\frac{a_\nu}{b_\nu}\right]_m^\infty$ are inessentially divergent (conditional convergence). It remains to mention that Sleshinskii [5], [6], [7] understood by the convergence of a continued fraction also inessential divergence. Therefore Pringsheim [76], not being familiar with these papers by Sleshinskii, incorrectly reproached him with confusing the concepts of conditional and absolute convergence.

6. We now discuss the restrictions which must be imposed on the coefficients of the continued fraction $\left[\frac{1}{\alpha_\nu}\right]_1^\infty$ in order that the latter should converge. For this we prove the following theorem (Koch [37], [38]).

The convergence of the series $\sum_{n=1}^{\infty} |\alpha_n|$ *is sufficient for finite limits*

$$\lim_{n\to\infty} P_{2n} = P, \quad \lim_{n\to\infty} P_{2n+1} = P', \quad \lim_{n\to\infty} Q_{2n} = Q, \quad \lim_{n\to\infty} Q_{2n+1} = Q'$$

to exist and for these to satisfy the relationship $P'Q - PQ' = 1$.

For the proof, we note that according to equation (1.2)

$$P_{2n} = \alpha_{2n}P_{2n-1} + P_{2n-2} = \\ = \alpha_{2n}P_{2n-1} + \alpha_{2n-2}P_{2n-3} + \dots + \alpha_2 P_1 + P_0. \tag{4.1}$$

Without loss of generality we may assume that $P_0 = 1$. Futhermore, as we know, $P_{-1} = 1$. Therefore

$$|P_1| \leqslant |\alpha_1|\,|P_0| + |P_{-1}| = 1 + |\alpha_1|,$$

$$|P_2| \leqslant |\alpha_2|\,|P_1| + |P_0| \leqslant \\ \leqslant |\alpha_2|\,(1 + |\alpha_1|) + 1 < (1 + |\alpha_1|)(1 + |\alpha_2|),$$

....

$$|P_n| < (1 + |\alpha_1|)(1 + |\alpha_2|) \dots (1 + |\alpha_n|)^{1} < e^{|\alpha_1| + |\alpha_2| + \dots + |\alpha_n|}.$$

But it has been assumed that the series $\sum_{n=1}^{\infty} |\alpha_n|$ converges. Hence $\prod_{n=1}^{\infty} (1 + |\alpha_n|)$ also converges. Therefore

$$|P_n| < \prod_{n=1}^{\infty} (1 + |\alpha_n|) \equiv c < \infty. \tag{4.2}$$

According to a theorem of Bolzano and Cauchy (Fichtengoltz [8], vol 1, *p.* 100, Whittaker and Watson [109], Ch. 2, p. 13.), for P_{2n} to have a finite limit it is necessary and sufficient that for every $\varepsilon > 0$ there exists a number N such that the inequality $|P_{2n+2m} - P_{2n}| < \varepsilon$ is satisfied for $n > N$ and $m > 0$. According to (4.1) we have:

$$|P_{2n+2m} - P_{2n}| = |\alpha_{2n+2m}P_{2n+2m-1} + \\ + \alpha_{2n+2m-2}P_{2n+2m-3} + \dots + \alpha_{2n+2}P_{2n+1}| \leqslant \\ \leqslant |\alpha_{2n+2m}|\,|P_{2n+2m-1}| + \\ + |\alpha_{2n+2m-2}|\,|P_{2n+2m-3}| + \dots + |\alpha_{2n+2}|\,|P_{2n+1}|.$$

From this, in consequence of (4.2),

$$|P_{2n+2m} - P_{2n}| < c(|\alpha_{2n+2m}| + |\alpha_{2n+2m-2}| + \dots + |\alpha_{2n+2}|)$$

But it has been assumed that the series $\sum_{n=1}^{\infty} |\alpha_n|$ converges. Hence

[1] This inequality is proved by the method of mathematical induction.

the series $\sum_{n=1}^{\infty} |\alpha_{2n}|$ converges. But according to the theorem of Bolzano and Cauchy

$$|\alpha_{2n+2m}| + |\alpha_{2n+2m-2}| + \dots + |\alpha_{2n+2}| < \varepsilon \qquad (n > N, \qquad m > 0).$$

Hence P – the limit of P_{2n}, is finite. In exactly the same way we prove the finiteness of P', Q and Q'. But from (1.4) we have:

$$P_{2n+1}Q_{2n} - P_{2n}Q_{2n+1} = 1 \qquad (n = 1, 2, \dots).$$

Proceeding to the limit, we obtain:

$$P'Q - PQ' = 1.$$

From this, P_n/Q_n has two distinct limits: P/Q and P'/Q'. Hence the continued fraction (2.2) diverges.

Thus the divergence of the series $\sum_{n=1}^{\infty} |\alpha_n|$ is *necessary* for the convergence of the continued fraction (2.2).

We note that on the strength of the inequality

$$1 + \sum_{k=1}^{n} |\alpha_k| < \prod_{k=1}^{n} (1 + |\alpha_k|) < e^{\sum_{k=1}^{n} |\alpha_k|} \tag{4.3}$$

the convergence of the infinite product $\prod_{n=1}^{\infty} (1 + |\alpha_n|)$ is necessary and sufficient for the convergence of the series $\sum_{n=1}^{\infty} |\alpha_n|$. Therefore one may replace $\sum_{n=1}^{\infty} |\alpha_n|$ by $\prod_{n=1}^{\infty} (1 + |\alpha_n|)$ in the conditions of the above theorem.

7. The concept of the uniform convergence of a continued fraction is extremely important. One can formulate it in the following way.

If the coefficients of a continued fraction are functions of a finite or infinite number of variables, then this continued fraction is called *uniformly convergent* over a set E of variation of these variables if its convergents P_n/Q_n are in E and converge uniformly to a limit, i.e. if for any $\varepsilon > 0$, one can find a number N such that for $n \geqslant N$, $Q_n \neq 0$ and the inequality

$$\left| \frac{P_n}{Q_n} - \lim_{\lambda \to \infty} \frac{P_\lambda}{Q_\lambda} \right| < \varepsilon \tag{4.4}$$

is satisfied over *all the set* E. As a consequence of this definition it follows that the series (c.f. (1.3))

$$\frac{P_N}{Q_N} + \sum_{\lambda=N+1}^{\infty} \left(\frac{P_\lambda}{Q_\lambda} - \frac{P_{\lambda-1}}{Q_{\lambda-1}} \right) \equiv$$

$$\equiv \frac{P_N}{Q_N} + \sum_{\lambda=N+1}^{\infty} (-1)^{\lambda-1} \frac{a_1 a_2 \ldots a_\lambda}{Q_{\lambda-1} Q_\lambda} \qquad (4.5)$$

converges uniformly over E to $\lim_{n\to\infty} P_n/Q_n$, since P_n/Q_n is the partial sum of the series and $\lim_{n\to\infty} P_n/Q_n$ is its sum. Conversely, from the uniform convergence of this series, condition (4.4) follows, i.e. the continued fraction converges uniformly. From this definition it also follows that the value of the continued fraction and that of the series (4.5) agree with one another for any $x \in E$, i.e. that the continued fraction and the series (4.5) are identically equal to one another over the set E.

8. The concept of the uniform convergence of a continued fraction helps in clearing up the question as to whether a given continued fraction converges to that function of which it is the continued fraction expansion. Before doing anything else we shall prove the following theorem, which is a more precise formulation of a theorem given by Pringsheim [79].

The uniform convergence of the continued fraction

$$\frac{c_1}{1} + \frac{c_2 x}{1} + \ldots + \frac{c_n x}{1} + \ldots \qquad (c_n \neq 0;\ n = 1, 2, \ldots) \qquad (4.6)$$

over the set E is sufficient for the convergence over the set E of the continued fraction to the function $K(x)$ of which it is the continued fraction expansion.

Since the continued fraction (4.6) obtained by expanding the function $K(x)$ converges over the set E, then $\lim_{n\to\infty} P_n(x)/Q_n(x)$ exists and is finite for any $x \in E$. Since the expansion (4.6) is uniformly convergent over the set E, then by definition $P_n(x)/Q_n(x)$ $(n \geqslant N)$ tends uniformly to $\lim_{n\to\infty} P_n(x)/Q_n(x)$ for all x in E. This means that for all $x \in E$ $\lim_{n\to\infty} P_n(x)/Q_n(x)$ is the sum of the uniformly convergent series (4.5) which is itself identically equal to the continued fraction (4.8) over the set E and in the given case becomes

$$\frac{P_N(x)}{Q_N(x)} + \sum_{\lambda=N+1}^{\infty} (-1)^{\lambda-1} \frac{c_1 c_2 \dots c_\lambda}{Q_{\lambda-1}(x)\, Q_\lambda(x)} x^{\lambda-1} \tag{4.7}$$

Since the series (4.7) is identically equal to the continued fraction (4.6), and the continued fraction (4.6) is derived by expanding the function $K(x)$, then the series (4.7) may also be derived by expanding the function $K(x)$. But the series (4.7) is uniformly convergent over the set E. Hence it converges to $K(x)$ over the given set E, whence $\lim_{n\to\infty} P_n(x)/Q_n(x) = K(x)$ for all $x \in E$.

9. Since by assumption the continued fraction (4.6) converges uniformly over E, then only a finite number of the functions Q_n become zero in E. Let the set E be connected and let the point $x = 0$ be an interior point of it. $Q_n(0) = 1$ for any n since $P_n(0)/Q_n(0) = c_1/1$. Therefore in E there exists a certain circle, $|x| < \rho$, inside which not one of the $Q_n(x)$ has a zero. This circle is an open connected set, i.e. is a domain. In this domain the series (4.7) converges uniformly, and its terms are regular (i.e. not having singularities) rational functions of x for $n = 1, 2, \dots$. From this, the terms of this series are analytic functions of x for $|x| < \rho$. But according to Weierstrass' first theorem (Markushevitch [27] p. 201, Titchmarsh [108] Ch. 2, p. 95) if the terms of a series which is uniformly convergent inside a domain $|x| < \rho$ are analytic functions inside this domain, then the sum of this series is also analytic in this domain. But the sum of the series (4.7) is $K(x)$. Therefore $K(x)$ is a regular single – valued analytic function for $|x| < \rho$.

Moreover, since when $|x| < \rho$ not one of the $Q_n(x)$ has a zero, then inside this circle all $P_n(x)/Q_n(x)$ are regular analytic functions, i.e. the series

$$\frac{P_n(x)}{Q_n(x)} = \sum_{\nu=1}^{\infty} c_\nu^{(n)} x^{\nu-1} \qquad (n = 2, 3, \dots) \tag{4.8}$$

converges uniformly for $|x| < \rho$. Furthermore $\dfrac{P_n(0)}{Q_n(0)} = \dfrac{c_1^{(n)}}{1} = \dfrac{c_1}{1}$, i.e. $c_1^{(n)} = c_1 (n = 2, 3, \dots)$.

10. According to the assumptions, not one of the $Q_n(x)$ has a zero for $|x| < \rho$. Therefore, when $|x| < \rho$ one can expand the

function $1/(Q_{n-1}(x)\,Q_n(x))$ in a convergent series for any n, and $R_n(0) = 1/(Q_{n-1}(0)\,Q_n(0)) = 1$. Then from (4.7) it follows that

$$\frac{P_n(x)}{Q_n(x)} - \frac{P_{n-1}(x)}{Q_{n-1}(x)} = (-1)^{n-1} \frac{c_1c_2 \dots c_n}{Q_{n-1}(x)\,Q_n(x)} x^{n-1} =$$

$$= (-1)^{n-1} c_1c_2 \dots c_nR_n(x)\,x^{n-1}. \tag{4.9}$$

But according to (4.8)

$$\frac{P_n(x)}{Q_n(x)} - \frac{P_{n-1}(x)}{Q_{n-1}(x)} = \sum_{\nu=1}^{\infty} (c_\nu^{(n)} - c_\nu^{(n-1)})\,x^{\nu-1}. \tag{4.10}$$

According to equation (4.9), expansion (4.10) commences with a term containing x^{n-1}. Therefore $c_\nu^{(n)} = c_\nu^{(n-1)}$ for $\nu = 1, 2, \dots, n-1$. Replacing n by $n-1$, we have:

$$c_\nu^{(n)} = c_\nu^{(n-1)} \quad \text{for} \quad \nu = 1, 2, \dots, n-2.$$

Finally we obtain

$$c_1^{(n)} = c_1^{(n-1)} = \dots = c_1^{(1)},$$
$$c_2^{(n)} = c_2^{(n-1)} = \dots = c_2^{(2)},$$
$$\dots\dots\dots\dots\dots\dots\dots\dots\dots\dots$$
$$c_{n-1}^{(n)} = c_{n-1}^{(n-1)}.$$

From this, the series (4.8) becomes

$$\frac{P_n(x)}{Q_n(x)} = \sum_{\nu=1}^{n-1} c_\nu^{(\nu)}x^{\nu-1} + \sum_{\nu=n}^{\infty} c_\nu^{(n)}x^{\nu-1}. \tag{4.11}$$

But from (4.7) it follows that when $|x| < \rho$

$$K(x) = \frac{P_n(x)}{Q_n(x)} + \sum_{\nu=n+1}^{\infty} (-1)^{\nu-1} \frac{c_1c_2 \dots c_\nu}{Q_{\nu-1}(x)\,Q_\nu(x)} x^{\nu-1} \tag{4.12}$$

$$(n = 1, 2, \dots).$$

Comparing expansions (4.11) and (4.12) we see that the power series development of $K(x)$ coincides as far as the term $c_{n-1}^{(n-1)}x^{n-2}$ with the power series development of $P_n(x)/Q_n(x)$. We note that (4.12) is not a power series, since $Q_{\nu-1}(x)\,Q_\nu(x)$ is a polynomial in x. But letting n tend to infinity, we obtain the result that when $|x| < \rho$

$$K(x) = \sum_{\nu=1}^{\infty} c_\nu^{(\nu)}x^{\nu-1},$$

where $\sum_{\nu=1}^{\infty} c_{\nu}^{(\nu)} x^{\nu-1}$ is the series corresponding to the continued fraction (4.6).

In this way we have proved that if the continued fraction (4.6) converges uniformly for $|x| < \rho$, then it converges for $|x| < \rho$ to a regular single-valued analytic function which we have developed in this continued fraction. This function may be expanded as a power series, which converges for $|x| < \rho$ and is the power series corresponding to the continued fraction (4.6). Thus we have derived the conditions under which a continued fraction and a power series which correspond to one another both converge to one and the same function.

We note that one can replace the domain $|x| < \rho$, by any domain T containing the origin.

11. If the origin is a boundary point of the set E, then $\rho = 0$, i.e. the power series corresponding to the continued fraction (4.6) diverges everywhere except at the origin. But the continued fraction (4.6) nevertheless converges uniformly over the set E, to the function which we have developed as a continued fraction. This function, in the case under consideration, may be expanded in the neighbourhood of the origin in a divergent power series, i.e. it is not analytic. From this, the convergents of the continued fraction (4.6) are approximating expressions to a non-analytic function, and this, to a certain extent, provides a solution to the problem of the approximate computation of non-analytic functions.

12. We have discussed the questions involved in the conditions under which a continued fraction converges to the regular single-valued analytic function in which it has been expanded as a continued fraction. Now we are able to put the question: under what conditions are two uniformly convergent continued fractions identically equal? The answer to this question is contained in the follow theorem of Pringsheim [79].

If the values of two continued fractions, uniformly convergent in a domain T which contains the origin as an interior point, coincide in a domain S which is wholly contained in T, then these continued fractions are identically equal to one another over the domain T.

According to the theorem of section 8 these continued fractions converge in T to regular single-valued analytic functions. But analytic functions which are identically equal to one an other in the arbitrary small domain S are identically equal to each other everywhere in T. Therefore the values of the continued fractions $K(x) = \left[\frac{c_1}{1}; \frac{c_\nu x}{1}\right]_2^\infty$ and $K_1(x) = \left[\frac{c'_1}{1}; \frac{c'_\nu x}{1}\right]_2^\infty$ are equal inside T. From the equality of the analytic functions to which they converge, it follows that $c'_1 = c_1$. Taking this into account, from the equation $K(x) = K_1(x)$, we deduce that

$$\left[\frac{c_\nu x}{1}\right]_2^\infty = \left[\frac{c'_\nu x}{1}\right]_2^\infty \tag{4.13}$$

for all values of x for which these continued fractions converge. They may not converge for certain values of x, since nothing was said, in the conditions of the theorem, about the absolute or conditional convergence of the continued fractions $K(x)$ and $K_1(x)$. But if the continued fractions contained in equation (4.13) have points of divergence, then they may only be zeros of $K(x)$ or $K_1(x)$, i.e. there may only be a finite number of such points in T. But since $K(0)$ and $K_1(0)$ are not equal to zero, then $K(x)$ and $K_1(x)$ are not equal to zero in a certain neighbourhood of the point $x = 0$. In this neighbourhood, equation (4.13) is satisfied at all points, and since

$$\left[\frac{c_\nu x}{1}\right]_2^\infty = \frac{c_1 - K(x)}{K(x)}, \qquad \left[\frac{c'_\nu x}{1}\right]_2^\infty = \frac{c'_1 - K_1(x)}{K_1(x)},$$

then $\left[\frac{c_\nu x}{1}\right]_2^\infty$ and $\left[\frac{c'_\nu x}{1}\right]_2^\infty$ converge in T to analytic functions. Therefore $c'_2 = c_2$. Continuing this process, we see that $c'_n = c_n$ ($n = 1, 2, \ldots$).

From this it follows, taking into account the assumptions stated at the beginning of this section, that both continued fractions $K(x)$ and $K_1(x)$ must be infinite.

13. We now discuss the connection of formulae for expanding functions in continued fractions, with the theorem set out above. Expanding the quotient of two power series $F_1(x)$ and $F_2(x)$ as a continued fraction we have:

$$\frac{F_1(x)}{F_2(x)} = \left[\frac{c_1}{1}; \frac{c_\nu x}{1}\right]_2^\infty. \tag{4.14}$$

If the continued fraction standing on the right hand side of this equation converges for some value of x, then it does not yet follow from this that the value of this continued fraction is equal to the value of $F_1(x)/F_2(x)$. (Most of the examples described in papers of the 18th and 19th centuries were restricted to formal expansions of this type.)

But from the theorem of section 8 it follows that if the continued fraction occurring equation in (4.14) is uniformly convergent in a certain neighbourhood of the point $x = 0$, then in this neighbourhood its value coincides with the value of $F_1(x)/F_2(x)$.

It is clear that this remains true when one of the series $F_1(x)$ and $F_2(x)$ is equal to unity.

But if $F_1(x)$ and $F_2(x)$ are polynomials, then the continued fraction (4.14) terminates. Therefore in the theorem of section 8 the function $K(x)$ must be non-rational, otherwise the continued fraction (4.6) will terminate, which contradicts the assumptions of the theorem.

14. Let the continued fraction $K_m(x) = \left[\frac{c_p x}{1}\right]_{m+1}^{\infty}$ be uniformly convergent in a domain T containing the origin as an interior point. Then according to the theorem of section 8, $K_m(x)$ converges in T to a regular single-valued analytic function.

Denote the convergents of the continued fraction $K_m(x)$ by $P_{m,n}(x)/Q_{m,n}(x)$. Then, in particular

$$\frac{P_{m,0}(x)}{Q_{m,0}(x)} = \frac{0}{1}, \qquad \frac{P_{m,1}(x)}{Q_{m,1}(x)} = \frac{c_{m+1}x}{1}.$$

Hence

$$\frac{P_m(x)}{Q_m(x)} = \frac{Q_{m,0}(x)\, P_m(x) + P_{m,0}(x)\, P_{m-1}(x)}{Q_{m,0}(x)\, Q_m(x) + P_{m,0}(x)\, Q_{m-1}(x)}.$$

Further, according to (1.2)

$$\frac{P_{m+1}(x)}{Q_{m+1}(x)} = \frac{1.P_m(x) + c_{m+1}x\, P_{m-1}(x)}{1.Q_m(x) + c_{m+1}x\, Q_{m-1}(x)} =$$

$$= \frac{Q_{m,1}(x)\, P_m(x) + P_{m,1}(x)\, P_{m-1}(x)}{Q_{m,1}(x)\, Q_m(x) + P_{m,1}(x)\, Q_{m-1}(x)}.$$

Let

$$\frac{P_{m+k}(x)}{Q_{m+k}(x)} = \frac{Q_{m,k}(x)\, P_m(x) + P_{m,k}(x)\, P_{m-1}(x)}{Q_{m,k}(x)\, Q_m(x) + P_{m,k}(x)\, Q_{m-1}(x)} \tag{4.15}$$

$$(k = 0, 1, \ldots, n).$$

Then

$$\frac{P_{m+n+1}(x)}{Q_{m+n+1}(x)} = \frac{P_{m+n}(x) + c_{m+n+1}x\, P_{m+n-1}(x)}{Q_{m+n}(x) + c_{m+n+1}x\, Q_{m+n-1}(x)} =$$

$$= \frac{Q_{m,n}(x)\, P_m(x) + P_{m,n}(x)\, P_{m-1}(x) + c_{m+n+1}x \times \{Q_{m,n-1}(x)\, P_m(x) + P_{m,n-1}(x)\, P_{m-1}(x)\}}{Q_{m,n}(x)\, Q_m(x) + P_{m,n}(x)\, Q_{m-1}(x) + c_{m+n+1}x \times \{Q_{m,n-1}(x)\, Q_m(x) + P_{m,n-1}(x)\, Q_{m-1}(x)\}} =$$

$$= \frac{\{Q_{m,n}(x) + c_{m-n+1}xQ_{m,n-1}(x)\}\, P_m(x) + \{P_{m,n}(x) + c_{m+n+1}x\, P_{m,n-1}(x)\}\, P_{m-1}(x)}{\{Q_{m,n}(x) + c_{m+n+1}x\, Q_{m,n-1}(x)\}\, Q_m(x) + \{P_{m,n}(x) + c_{m+n+1}x\, P_{m,n-1}(x)\}\, Q_{m-1}(x)}.$$

But, as a consequence of (1.2)

$$Q_{m,n}(x) + c_{m+n+1}x\, Q_{m,n-1}(x) = Q_{m,n+1}(x),$$
$$P_{m,n}(x) + c_{m+n+1}x\, P_{m,n-1}(x) = P_{m,n+1}(x).$$

Consequently, equation (4.15) is valid for $k = n + 1$. From this, as a consequence of the principle of mathematical induction, it is valid for all natural values of n. Thus

$$\frac{P_{m+n}(x)}{Q_{m+n}(x)} = \frac{P_m(x) + \dfrac{P_{m,n}(x)}{Q_{m,n}(x)} P_{m-1}(x)}{Q_m(x) + \dfrac{P_{m,n}(x)}{Q_{m,n}(x)} Q_{m-1}(x)}.$$

But

$$\lim_{n\to\infty} \frac{P_{m,n}(x)}{Q_{m,n}(x)} = K_m(x),$$

since, from the notation, $P_{m,n}(x)/Q_{m,n}(x)$ is the nth order convergent of the continued fraction $K_m(x)$. Therefore

$$\lim_{n\to\infty} \frac{P_{m+n}(x)}{Q_{m+n}(x)} = \frac{P_m(x) + K_m(x)\, P_{m-1}(x)}{Q_m(x) + K_m(x)\, Q_{m-1}(x)}. \tag{4.16}$$

The expression standing on the right hand side of equation (4.16) loses meaning when

$$Q_m(x) + Q_{m-1}(x)\, K_m(x) = 0. \tag{4.17}$$

But since the right hand side of equation (4.16) is an analytic function, then equation (4.17) obtains only for a finite number of points in the domain T. Otherwise

$$K_m(x) \equiv -\frac{Q_m(x)}{Q_{m-1}(x)},$$

i.e. $K(x)$ is a terminating continued fraction.

At the points at which equation (4.17) is satisfied, it is not possible that the relation

$$P_m(x) + P_{m-1}(x)\, K_m(x) = 0$$

should also be satisfied, since it would then follow that

$$\frac{P_m(x)}{Q_m(x)} = \frac{P_{m-1}(x)}{Q_{m-1}(x)},$$

which is impossible according to the assumptions of the theorem. Therefore the roots of the equation (4.17) may only be poles of the analytic function (4.16), i.e. points of inessential divergence of the continued fraction $K(x)$. In this way we have proved the following theorem (Pringsheim [79]).

The uniform convergence of the continued fraction $\left[\frac{c_p x}{1}\right]_{m+1}^{\infty}$ *in a domain T having the origin as an interior point, is sufficient for the uniform convergence in T of the continued fraction* $K(x) = \left[\frac{c_1}{1}; \frac{c_p x}{1}\right]_2^{\infty}$, *with the possible exception of a finite number of points x' of inessential divergence. The continued fraction* $\left[\frac{c_1}{1}; \frac{c_p x}{1}\right]_2^{\infty}$ *converges in the interior of T to a single-valued analytic function $K(x)$, regular in T, except at the points x' which are poles of this function.*

§ 5. Convergence Test for Continued Fractions with Positive Coefficients

1. In the preceding section we saw that the divergence of the series $\sum_{n=1}^{\infty} |\alpha_n|$ is *necessary* for the convergence of the continued fraction (2.2). Seidel [87], and independently of him Stern [95], proved that for positive $\alpha_n (n = 1, 2, \ldots)$ the divergence of the series $\sum_{n=1}^{\infty} \alpha_n$ is *necessary and sufficient* for the convergence of the continued fraction (2.2).

We have already demonstrated the necessity of the condition. We now prove that it is sufficient. In the given case

$$Q_1 = \alpha_1,$$
$$Q_2 = \alpha_1\alpha_2 + 1,$$
$$\dots\dots\dots\dots\dots\dots\dots\dots$$
$$Q_{2k} = \alpha_{2k}Q_{2k-1} + Q_{2k-2},$$
$$Q_{2k+1} = \alpha_{2k+1}Q_{2k} + Q_{2k-1},$$
$$\alpha_n > 0 \qquad (n = 1, 2, \dots).$$

Hence

$$Q_2 > 1,\ Q_4 > 1, \dots,\ Q_{2k} > 1;\quad Q_3 > \alpha_1,\ Q_5 > \alpha_1, \dots,\ Q_{2k+1} > \alpha_1.$$

Therefore

$$Q_{2k} > Q_{2k-2} + \alpha_1\alpha_{2k}, \quad Q_{2k+1} > Q_{2k-1} + \alpha_{2k+1}.$$

From this

$$\left.\begin{aligned} Q_{2k} &> \alpha_1(\alpha_2 + \alpha_4 + \dots + \alpha_{2k}), \\ Q_{2k+1} &> \alpha_1 + \alpha_3 + \dots + \alpha_{2k+1}. \end{aligned}\right\} \tag{5.1}$$

Thus, since the divergence of the series $\sum_{n=1}^{\infty} \alpha_n$ implies the divergence of at least one of the series $\sum_{k=1}^{\infty} \alpha_{2k}$, $\sum_{k=1}^{\infty} \alpha_{2k-1}$, $\lim_{k\to\infty} Q_{2k}Q_{2k+1} = \infty$. In this way, taking equation (1.3) into account, Seidel's criterion is established.

2. Opperman [63] proved that the divergence of the infinite product $\prod_{n=1}^{\infty} (1 + \alpha_n)$ is necessary and sufficient for the convergence of the continued fraction (2.2) with positive coefficients. On account of the inequality (4.3), this test coincides with Seidel's test.

3. According to Seidel's test, the expansion

$$\sqrt{2} = 1 + \frac{1}{2} + \frac{1}{2} + \dots + \frac{1}{2} + \dots$$

converges, since the series $2 + 2 + \dots$ diverges.

The continued fraction

$$\frac{1}{x} + \frac{1}{x^2} + \frac{1}{x^3} + \dots + \frac{1}{x^n} + \dots$$

converges when $x \geqslant 1$ and diverges when $0 < x < 1$, since the series $\sum_{n=1}^{\infty} x^n$ diverges when $x \geqslant 1$ and converges when $0 < x < 1$.

4. When $\alpha_1, \alpha_2, \ldots$ are positive integers the continued fraction (2.2) converges since the series, the terms of which are positive whole numbers, diverges.

In exactly the same way, when $\alpha_1 > 0, \alpha_2 > 0, \ldots$ and $\lim_{n\to\infty} \alpha_n > 0$ the continued fraction (2.2) converges.

We note that the convergence of a continued fraction with positive coefficients depends on the divergence of a certain series i.e. upon the behaviour of the whole ensemble of coefficients, and not upon each one of them. Therefore the convergence of continued fractions with positive coefficients is absolute convergence.

5. Using relationships (2.3), we arrive at the following convergence theorem of Seidel (Stern [90]).

The divergence of at least one of the series

$$\sum_{n=1}^{\infty} \frac{a_1 a_3 \ldots a_{2n-1}}{a_2 a_4 \ldots a_{2n}} b_{2n}, \qquad \sum_{n=1}^{\infty} \frac{a_2 a_4 \ldots a_{2n}}{a_1 a_3 \ldots a_{2n+1}} b_{2n+1} \tag{5.2}$$

is necessary and sufficient for the convergence of the continued fraction (1.1) *with positive coefficients.*

6. From the relationships $\sqrt{u_n v_n} \leqslant (u_n + v_n)/2$, it follows that the divergence of the series $\sum_{n=1}^{\infty} \sqrt{u_n v_n}$ is sufficient for the divergence of at least one of the series $\sum_{n=1}^{\infty} u_n$, $\sum_{n=1}^{\infty} v_n$, since

$$\sum_{n=1}^{\infty} \sqrt{u_n v_n} \leqslant \tfrac{1}{2} \sum_{n=1}^{\infty} u_n + \tfrac{1}{2} \sum_{n=1}^{\infty} v_n.$$

Putting $u_{2n} = \alpha_{2n}$, $v_{2n} = \alpha_{2n+1}$, we have from equation (2.3):

$$u_{2n} v_{2n} = \frac{b_{2n} b_{2n+1}}{a_{2n+1}},$$

$$\sum_{n=1}^{\infty} \sqrt{\frac{b_{2n} b_{2n+1}}{a_{2n+1}}} \leqslant \tfrac{1}{2} \sum_{n=1}^{\infty} \alpha_{2n} + \tfrac{1}{2} \sum_{n=1}^{\infty} \alpha_{2n+1}.$$

Putting $u_{2n-1} = \alpha_{2n}$, $v_{2n-1} = \alpha_{2n-1}$, we have from equation (2.3)

$$u_{2n-1}v_{2n-1} = \frac{b_{2n-1}b_{2n}}{a_{2n}}$$

$$\sum_{n=1}^{\infty} \sqrt{\frac{b_{2n-1}b_{2n}}{a_{2n}}} \leqslant \tfrac{1}{2}\sum_{n=1}^{\infty} \alpha_{2n} + \tfrac{1}{2}\sum_{n=1}^{\infty} \alpha_{2n-1}.$$

Thus

$$\sum_{n=2}^{\infty} \sqrt{\frac{b_{n-1}b_n}{a_n}} \leqslant \sum_{n=1}^{\infty} \alpha_{2n} + \sum_{n=1}^{\infty} \alpha_{2n-1} - \frac{\alpha_1}{2} = \sum_{n=1}^{\infty} \alpha_n - \frac{\alpha_1}{2}$$

Hence (Pringsheim [77]), the divergence of the series $\sum_{n=2}^{\infty} \sqrt{\frac{b_{n-1}b_n}{a_n}}$ is necessary and sufficient for the convergence of the continued fraction (1.1) with positive coefficients.

From this test, for example, the expansion

$$\sqrt{3} = 1 + \sqrt{3} - 1 = 1 + \frac{2}{1+\sqrt{3}} =$$

$$= 1 + \frac{2}{2} + \frac{2}{2} + \dots + \frac{2}{2} + \dots$$

converges.

7. We note that if

$$K = b_0 + \frac{a_1}{b_1} + \frac{a_2}{b_2} + \dots + \frac{a_n}{b_n} + \dots,$$

then

$$-K = -b_0 + \frac{a_1}{-b_1} + \frac{a_2}{-b_2} + \dots + \frac{a_n}{-b_n} + \dots.$$

Therefore all convergence criteria relating to continued fractions with positive coefficients are easily extended to continued fractions in which all partial numerators are positive and all partial denominators negative.

8. Identity (2.24) frequently permits the transformation of one continued fraction into another in which all coefficients are positive. This sometimes enables us to apply convergence criteria relating to continued fractions with positive coefficients to continued fractions with arbitrary coefficients.

§ 6. Convergence Test for Continued Fractions with Arbitrary Coefficients

1. Let numbers $r_1, r_2, \ldots$ satisfy the following conditions

$$\left.\begin{array}{ll} 1) & r_1 |1 + c_2| \geqslant |c_2|, \\ 2) & r_2 |1 + c_2 + c_3| \geqslant c_3, \\ 3) & r_n |1 + c_n + c_{n+1}| \geqslant r_n r_{n-2} |c_n| + |c_{n+1}| \qquad (n \geqslant 3), \\ 4) & r_n \geqslant 0 \qquad (n \geqslant 3). \end{array}\right\} \quad (6.1)$$

Scott and Wall [86] assume further that the numbers r_1 and r_2 are non-negative, but this already follows from the first two conditions (6.1).

By $c_1, c_2, \ldots$ we shall understand the partial numerators of the continued fraction

$$K = \frac{1}{1} + \frac{c_2}{1} + \frac{c_3}{1} + \ldots + \frac{c_n}{1} + \ldots. \qquad (6.2)$$

From condition 3) of (6.1) the equation $r_n = 0$ is possible only when $c_{n+1} = 0$, i.e. the continued fraction (6.2) terminates. Therefore from condition 3) of (6.1) it follows that if (6.2) is to be an infinite continued fraction

$$r_{n-2} \leqslant \left| \frac{1 + c_n + c_{n+1}}{c_n} \right| - \frac{|c_{n+1}|}{r_n |c_n|},$$

i.e.

$$0 < r_{n-2} < \left| \frac{1 + c_n + c_{n+1}}{c_n} \right|.$$

By imposing various restrictions upon the numbers $r_1, r_2, \ldots$ and $c_1, c_2, \ldots$ one can obtain a series of criteria which are sufficient for the convergence of the continued fraction (6.2).

2. We prove the following theorem (Scott and Wall [86]).

If the numbers $r_1, r_2, \ldots$ *satisfy the conditions* (6.1) *and the series* $\sum_{n=1}^{\infty} r_1 r_2 \ldots r_n$ *converges, then the continued fraction* (6.2) *converges and furthermore satisfies the inequality*

$$|K| \leqslant 1 + \sum_{n=1}^{\infty} r_1 r_2 \ldots r_n. \qquad (6.3)$$

From condition (6.1) it follows that

$$Q_2 \equiv 1 + c_2 \neq 0, \qquad Q_3 = 1 + c_2 + c_3 \neq 0.$$

We put $c_{n+1}Q_{n-1}/Q_{n+1} = d_n$, then

$$|d_1| = \left| \frac{c_2}{1 + c_2} \right| \leqslant r_1, \qquad |d_2| = \left| \frac{c_3}{1 + c_2 + c_3} \right| \leqslant r_2.$$

But from equation (1.2) we have for the continued fraction (6.2)

$$Q_{n+2} = Q_{n+1} + c_{n+2}Q_n,$$
$$Q_{n+1} = Q_n + c_{n+1}Q_{n-1},$$
$$Q_n = Q_{n-1} + c_nQ_{n-2}.$$

Multiplying the third of these equations by $-c_{n+1}$ and adding it to the first two, we obtain:

$$Q_{n+2} = (1 + c_{n+1} + c_{n+2})\, Q_n - c_nc_{n+1}Q_{n-2}. \tag{6.4}$$

Then when $c_{k+2} \neq 0$,

$$\frac{1}{|d_{k+1}|} \equiv \left| \frac{Q_{k+2}}{c_{k+2}Q_k} \right| \geqslant \left| \frac{1 + c_{k+1} + c_{k+2}}{c_{k+2}} \right| - \left| \frac{c_kc_{k+1}Q_{k-2}}{c_{k+2}Q_k} \right| \equiv$$

$$\equiv \left| \frac{1 + c_{k+1} + c_{k+2}}{c_{k+2}} \right| - \left| \frac{c_{k+1}}{c_{k+2}} \right| |d_{k-1}|.$$

Let $Q_{n+1} \neq 0$ and $|d_n| \leqslant r_n$ when $n = 1, 2, \ldots, k \quad (k \geqslant 2)$. Then

$$\frac{1}{|d_{k+1}|} \geqslant \left| \frac{1 + c_{k+1} + c_{k+2}}{c_{k+2}} \right| - \left| \frac{c_{k+1}}{c_{k+2}} \right| r_{k-1}.$$

Since we have assumed that the continued fraction (6.2) is infinite then $r_{n+1} > 0$. But according to condition 3) of (6.1)

$$r_{k+1}\, |1 + c_{k+1} + c_{k+2}| \geqslant r_{k+1}r_{k-1}\, |c_{k+1}| + |c_{k+2}|.$$

Therefore

$$\frac{1}{|d_{k+1}|} \geqslant r_{k-1} \left| \frac{c_{k+1}}{c_{k+2}} \right| + \frac{1}{r_{k+1}} - \left| \frac{c_{k+1}}{c_{k+2}} \right| r_{k-1} = \frac{1}{r_{k+1}} > 0.$$

Consequently $Q_{k+2} \neq 0$ and $|d_{k+1}| \leqslant r_{k+1}$. Thus for all positive integers n we have the inequalities $Q_n \neq 0$ and $|d_n| \leqslant r_n$.

But solving for d_n we have

$$d_1 = \frac{c_2 Q_0}{Q_2} = \frac{c_2}{Q_1 Q_2}, \quad \text{since} \quad Q_0 = Q_1 = 1.$$

$$d_1 d_2 = \frac{c_2}{Q_1 Q_2} \frac{c_3 Q_1}{Q_3} = \frac{c_2 c_3}{Q_2 Q_3},$$

$$d_1 d_2 d_3 = \frac{c_2 c_3}{Q_2 Q_3} \frac{c_4 Q_2}{Q_4} = \frac{c_2 c_3 c_4}{Q_3 Q_4},$$

....

$$d_1 d_2 \dots d_n = \frac{c_2}{Q_1 Q_2} \frac{c_3 Q_1}{Q_3} \frac{c_4 Q_2}{Q_4} \dots \frac{c_n Q_{n-2}}{Q_n} \frac{c_{n+1} Q_{n-1}}{Q_{n+1}} = \frac{c_2 c_3 \dots c_{n+1}}{Q_n Q_{n+1}}.$$

But according to (1.6)

$$|K| \leqslant \left| \frac{P_1}{Q_1} \right| + \left| \frac{P_2}{Q_2} - \frac{P_1}{Q_1} \right| + \left| \frac{P_3}{Q_3} - \frac{P_2}{Q_2} \right| + \dots$$

$$\dots + \left| \frac{P_{n+1}}{Q_{n+1}} - \frac{P_n}{Q_n} \right| + \dots = 1 + \left| \frac{c_2}{Q_1 Q_2} \right| + \left| \frac{c_2 c_3}{Q_2 Q_3} \right| + \dots$$

$$\dots + \left| \frac{c_2 c_3 \dots c_{n+1}}{Q_n Q_{n+1}} \right| + \dots = 1 + |d_1| + |d_1 d_2| + \dots$$

$$\dots + |d_1 d_2 \dots d_n| + \dots \leqslant 1 + \sum_{n=1}^{\infty} r_1 r_2 \dots r_n.$$

Therefore if the series $\sum_{n=1}^{\infty} r_1 r_2 \dots r_n$ converges, then the series (1.5) converges, which proves the convergence of the continued fraction (6.2), and that it satisfies the inequality (6.3).

3. If $c_{k+2} = 0$ then $Q_{k+2} = Q_{k+1} \neq 0$ and $d_{k+1} = 0$, i.e. $|d_{k+1}| < < r_{k+1}$.

Hence

$$|K| \leqslant 1 + |d_1| + |d_1 d_2| + \dots + |d_1 d_2 \dots d_k|,$$

i.e. the continued fraction (6.2) converges. Therefore we have the following theorem (Scott and Wall [86]).

If numbers $r_1, r_2, \ldots$ fulfil conditions (6.1) *and at least one of the c_n is equal to zero, then the continued fraction* (6.2) *converges.*

4. Now let $c_1, c_2, \ldots$ be functions of a certain variable. Then the terms of the series

$$\frac{P_1}{Q_1} + \left(\frac{P_2}{Q_2} - \frac{P_1}{Q_1}\right) + \ldots + \left(\frac{P_{n+1}}{Q_{n+1}} - \frac{P_n}{Q_n}\right) + \ldots \tag{6.5}$$

will, as before, satisfy the relationships

$$\left|\frac{P_1}{Q_1}\right| = 1, \quad \left|\frac{P_2}{Q_2} - \frac{P_1}{Q_1}\right| = |d_1| \leqslant r_1, \ldots, \quad \left|\frac{P_{n+1}}{Q_{n-1}} - \frac{P_n}{Q_n}\right| =$$

$$= |d_1 d_2 \ldots d_n| \leqslant r_1 r_2 \ldots r_n.$$

But the following convergence test of Weierstrass is known.

If, over the set E, the terms of the functional series $\sum_{n=1}^{\infty} u_n(x)$ satisfy the inequality $|u_n(x)| \leqslant q_n$ $(n = 1, 2, \ldots)$ where q_n are the terms of a certain convergent numerical series $\sum_{n=1}^{\infty} q_n$, then the series $\sum_{n=1}^{\infty} u_n(x)$ is uniformly convergent over E.

Hence the series (6.5) is uniformly convergent over E. But by definition the continued fraction (6.2) is uniformly convergent over E.

Therefore we have the following theorem (Scott and Wall [86]).

If numbers $r_1, r_2, \ldots$ fulfil conditions (6.1) *and the series $\sum_{n=1}^{\infty} r_1 r_2 \ldots r_n$ converges over a certain set E then the continued fraction* (6.2) *converges uniformly over E, and satisfies the inequality* (6.3).

5. A particular choice of the set E may be based on the following theorem (Scott and Wall [86]).

The set of conditions

$$p_1 > 1, \quad |c_n| \leqslant \frac{p_n - 1}{p_{n-1} p_n} \qquad (n = 2, 3, \ldots) \tag{6.6}$$

where $p_1, p_2, \ldots$ are the terms of a certain numerical sequence, is sufficient for the uniform convergence of the continued fraction (6.2) *and for the inequality*

$$|K| \leqslant \frac{p_1}{p_1 - 1}\left[1 - \frac{1}{1 + \sum\limits_{n=1}^{\infty}(p_1 - 1)(p_2 - 1)\dots(p_n - 1)}\right]. \qquad (6.7)$$

to be satisfied.

From the inequality (6.6) it follows that if (6.2) is to be an infinite continued fraction then the inequalities $p_n > 1$ $(n = 2, 3, \dots)$ obtain.

The inequality (6.7) goes over into equality if $c_n = (1 - p_n)/(p_{n-1}p_n)$ $(n = 2, 3, \dots)$. For the proof of the theorem we put $(p_n - 1)/(p_{n-1}p_n) = t_n$ and consider the continued fraction

$$\frac{1}{1} - \frac{t_2}{1} - \frac{t_3}{1} - \dots.$$

Denote its nth convergent by G_n/H_n, and put $p_1p_2\dots p_nH_n = H'_n$ $(n = 1, 2, \dots)$; $H'_0 = 1$. Then the relationship $H_n = H_{n-1} - t_nH_{n-2}$ becomes

$$H'_n = p_nH'_{n-1} - p_np_{n-1}t_nH'_{n-2} = p_nH'_{n-1} - (p_n - 1)\,H'_{n-2}$$
$$(n = 2, 3, \dots),$$

whence

$$\begin{aligned} H'_n - H'_{n-1} &= (p_n - 1)(H'_{n-1} - H'_{n-2}) = \\ &= (p_n - 1)(p_{n-1} - 1)\dots(p_2 - 1)(H'_1 - H'_0) = \\ &= (p_n - 1)(p_{n-1} - 1)\dots(p_2 - 1)(p_1H_1 - 1) = \\ &= (p_n - 1)(p_{n-1} - 1)\dots(p_2 - 1)(p_1 - 1) > 0, \end{aligned}$$
$$(n = 1, 2, \dots),$$

since $H_1 = 1$. Hence $H'_n > H'_{n-1} > \dots > H'_0 = 1$ and $H_n > 0$ for $n = 1, 2, \dots$.

Now we put in the theorem of section 2,

$$r_n = \frac{t_{n+1}H_{n-1}}{H_{n+1}} \qquad (n = 1, 2, \dots).$$

One may transcribe equation (6.4) as

$$H_{n+1} = (1 - t_n - t_{n+1})\,H_{n-1} - t_{n-1}t_nH_{n-3} \qquad (n \geqslant 3),$$
$$H_3 = 1 - t_2 - t_3, \quad H_2 = 1 - t_2.$$

Multiplying this equation by t_{n+1}/H_{n+1}, we have :

$$t_{n+1} = (1 - t_n - t_{n-1}) \frac{t_{n+1}H_{n-1}}{H_{n+1}} - \frac{t_{n-1}t_n t_{n+1} H_{n-1} H_{n-3}}{H_{n-1}H_{n+1}} \qquad (n \geqslant 3),$$

$$t_3 = (1 - t_2 - t_3) \frac{t_3 H_1}{H_3}, \quad t_2 = (1 - t_2) \frac{t_2 H_0}{H_2} \quad (H_0 = H_1 = 1),$$

i.e.

$$r_n(1 - t_n - t_{n-1}) = r_n r_{n-2} t_n + t_{n+1} \qquad (n \geqslant 3).$$

$$r_2(1 - t_2 - t_3) = t_3, \qquad r_1(1 - t_2) = t_2.$$

But according to condition (6.6) $|c_n| \leqslant t_n$. Therefore

$$r_1 |1 + c_2| > r_1(1 - |c_2|) > r_1(1 - t_2) = t_2 \geqslant |c_2|,$$
$$r_2 |1 + c_2 + c_3| > r_2(1 - |c_2| - |c_3|) > r_2(1 - t_2 - t_3) = t_3 \geqslant |c_3|,$$
$$r_n |1 + c_n + c_{n+1}| > r_n(1 - |c_n| - |c_{n+1}|) \geqslant r_n(1 - t_n - t_{n+1}) =$$
$$= r_n r_{n-2} t_n + t_{n+1} \geqslant r_n r_{n-2} |c_n| + |c_{n+1}| \qquad (n \geqslant 3).$$

Thus the numbers $r_1, r_2, \ldots$ fulfil conditions (6.1). Further

$$r_1 r_2 \ldots r_n = \frac{t_2 \ldots t_{n+1}}{H_n H_{n+1}} =$$

$$= \frac{(p_2-1)(p_3-1)\ldots(p_{n+1}-1)}{p_1 p_2^2 p_3^2 \ldots p_n^2 p_{n+1} H_n H_{n+1}} = \frac{p_1(p_1-1)(p_2-1)\ldots(p_{n+1}-1)}{(p_1-1)\, H'_n H'_{n+1}} =$$

$$= \frac{p_1}{p_1 - 1} \cdot \frac{H'_{n+1} - H'_n}{H'_n H'_{n+1}} = \frac{p_1}{p_1 - 1} \left(\frac{1}{H'_n} - \frac{1}{H'_{n+1}} \right).$$

Hence the series $\sum_{n=1}^{\infty} r_1 r_2 \ldots r_n$ converges. Therefore from the theorem of section 4, the continued fraction (6.2) is uniformly convergent.

To estimate the absolute value of this continued fraction K, we note that

$$\sum_{n=1}^{\infty} r_1 r_2 \ldots r_n = \frac{p_1}{p_1 - 1} \left(\frac{1}{H'_1} - \frac{1}{\lim\limits_{n\to\infty} H'_n} \right).$$

From this, since

$$H'_n = H'_{n-1} + (p_1 - 1)(p_2 - 1) \ldots (p_n - 1) =$$
$$= 1 + \sum_{r=1}^{n} (p_1 - 1)(p_2 - 1) \ldots (p_r - 1),$$

we see that

$$|K| \leqslant 1 + \frac{p_1}{p_1 - 1} \cdot$$

$$\cdot \left[\frac{1}{p_1} - \frac{1}{1 + \sum_{n=1}^{\infty} (p_1 - 1)(p_2 - 1) \ldots (p_n - 1)} \right] =$$

$$= \frac{p_1}{p_1 - 1} \left[1 - \frac{1}{1 + \sum_{n=1}^{\infty} (p_1 - 1)(p_2 - 1) \ldots (p_n - 1)} \right].$$

When $c_n = (1 - p_n)/(p_{n-1}p_n)$ the ratter relationship goes over into equality, i.e. when

$$K = \frac{1}{1} - \frac{\frac{p_2 - 1}{p_1 p_2}}{1} - \frac{\frac{p_3 - 1}{p_2 p_3}}{1} - \frac{\frac{p_n - 1}{p_{n-1} p_n}}{1} - \ldots$$

$$(p_n > 1, \; n = 1, 2. 3, \ldots)$$

we have

$$K = \frac{p_1}{p_1} - \frac{p_2 - 1}{p_2} - \frac{p_3 - 1}{p_3} - \ldots - \frac{p_n - 1}{p_n} - \ldots$$

$$= \frac{p_1}{p_1 - 1} \left[1 - \frac{1}{1 + \sum_{n=1}^{\infty} (p_1 - 1)(p_2 - 1) \ldots (p_n - 1)} \right]. \quad (6.8)$$

Perron [73] proved this criterion without the estimation of K and with the further stringent requirement that the series

$$\sum_{n=1}^{\infty} (p_1 - 1)(p_2 - 1) \ldots (p_n - 1)$$

should diverge.

6. We now consider the case $p_1 = 1$. It is clear that in this case the estimate (6.7) becomes indeterminate. But when $p_1 = 1$ we have from the equation $H_n' - H_{n-1}' = (p_1 - 1) \ldots (p_n - 1)$ $(n = 1, 2, \ldots)$

$$H_n' = H_{n-1}' = \ldots = H_0' = 1 \qquad (n = 1, 2, \ldots).$$

From this

$$H_n = \frac{1}{p_1 p_2 \dots p_n}.$$

We now verify the equation

$$H_{n+1} = (1 - t_n - t_{n+1})\, H_{n-1} - t_{n-1} t_n H_{n-3} \qquad (n \geqslant 3).$$

Here it becomes

$$\frac{1}{p_1 p_2 \dots p_{n+1}} = \left(1 - \frac{p_n - 1}{p_n p_{n+1}} - \frac{p_{n+1} - 1}{p_n p_{n+1}}\right) \frac{1}{p_1 \dots p_{n-1}} - \\ - \frac{(p_{n-1} - 1)(p_n - 1)}{p_{n-2} p_{n-1}^2 p_n p_1 p_2 \dots p_{n-3}} \qquad (n \geqslant 3).$$

i.e.

$$\frac{1}{p_n p_{n+1}} = \frac{\begin{gathered} p_{n-1} p_n p_{n+1} - p_{n+1}(p_n - 1) - p_{n-1}(p_{n+1} - 1) - \\ - p_{n+1} p_{n-1}(p_n - 1) + p_{n+1}(p_n - 1) \end{gathered}}{p_{n-1} p_n p_{n+1}}:$$

Further, verifying the equations $H_3 = 1 - t_2 - t_3$ and $H_2 = 1 - - t_2$, we have

$$\frac{1}{p_1 p_2 p_3} = 1 - \frac{p_2 - 1}{p_1 p_2} - \frac{p_3 - 1}{p_2 p_3},$$

$$1 \equiv p_1 p_2 p_3 - (p_2 - 1) p_3 - p_1(p_3 - 1) \qquad (p_1 = 1),$$

$$\frac{1}{p_1 p_2} \equiv 1 - \frac{p_2 - 1}{p_1 p_2} \qquad (p_1 = 1).$$

Thus all the equations are satisfied. Further, when

$$H_n = \frac{1}{p_1 p_2 \dots p_n}$$

we have

$$r_n = t_{n+1} \frac{1}{p_1 p_2 \dots p_{n-1}} p_1 p_2 \dots p_{n+1} = t_{n+1} p_n p_{n+1} = p_{n+1} - 1.$$

Therefore the convergence of the series $\sum_{n=1}^{\infty} r_1 r_2 \dots r_n$ is equivalent to the convergence of the series

$$\sum_{n=1}^{\infty} (p_2 - 1)(p_3 - 1) \dots (p_{n+1} - 1).$$

From this we have the following theorem:

The set of conditions

1) $p_1 = 1$,

2) $|c_n| \leqslant \dfrac{p_n - 1}{p_{n-1}p_n} \qquad (n = 2, 3, \dots)$,

3) *the series* $\sum_{n=1}^{\infty} (p_2 - 1)(p_3 - 1) \dots (p_{n+1} - 1)$ *converges*

is sufficient for the uniform convergence of the continued fraction (2.4) *and for the inequality*

$$|K| \leqslant 1 + \sum_{n=1}^{\infty} (p_2 - 1) \dots (p_{n+2} - 1)$$

to be valid.

When $c_n = (1 - p_n)/(p_{n-1}p_n)$ the latter relationship goes over into equality, i.e. when

$$K = \frac{1}{1} - \frac{\dfrac{p_2 - 1}{p_2}}{1} - \frac{\dfrac{p_3 - 1}{p_2 p_3}}{1} - \dots - \frac{\dfrac{p_n - 1}{p_{n-1}p_n}}{1} - \dots$$

$$(p_n > 1;\ n = 2, 3, \dots)$$

we have

$$K = \frac{1}{1} - \frac{p_2 - 1}{p_2} - \frac{p_3 - 1}{p_3} - \dots - \frac{p_n - 1}{p_n} - \dots =$$

$$= 1 + \sum_{n=1}^{\infty} (p_2 - 1)(p_3 - 1) \dots (p_{n+1} - 1).$$

7. We write $p_n = (2n + 1)/(n + k)$. From the condition $p_n > 1$ $(n = 2, 3, \dots)$ we have $2n + 1 \geqslant n + k$ $(n = 2, 3, \dots)$, i.e. $k < 3$. Further

$$\frac{p_n - 1}{p_{n-1}p_n} = \frac{\dfrac{2n + 1}{n + k} - 1}{\dfrac{2n - 1}{n + k - 1} \cdot \dfrac{2n + 1}{n + k}} =$$

$$= \frac{(n+1-k)(n+k-1)}{4n^2-1} = \frac{n^2-(k-1)^2}{4n^2-1}.$$

From this, the condition

$$|c_n| \leqslant \frac{n^2-(k-1)^2}{4n^2-1} \qquad (n = 2, 3, \ldots) \tag{6.9}$$

is sufficient for the uniform convergence of the continued fraction (2.4), whence, when $k \neq 2$

$$|K| \leqslant \frac{3}{2-k}\left[1 - \frac{1}{1 + \sum\limits_{n=1}^{\infty} \frac{2-k}{1+k} \cdot \frac{3-k}{2+k} \cdots \frac{n+1-k}{n+k}}\right], \tag{6.10}$$

since

$$\frac{p_1}{p_1-1} = \frac{3}{(1+k)\left(\frac{3}{1+k}-1\right)} = \frac{3}{2-k}, \quad p_n - 1 = \frac{n+1-k}{n+k}.$$

From (6.9) it follows that k must satisfy the inequality $4-(k-1)^2 > 0$, i.e. $(3-k)(1+k) < 0$, $-1 < k < 3$.

8. Denote the general term of the series

$$s = \sum_{n=1}^{\infty} \frac{2-k}{1+k} \cdot \frac{3-k}{2+k} \cdots \frac{n+1-k}{n+k}.$$

by u_n. Then

$$\frac{u_n}{u_{n+1}} = \frac{n+1+k}{n+2-k} = \frac{1+\frac{1+k}{n}}{1+\frac{2-k}{n}} = 1 + \frac{\alpha_1}{n} + \frac{\alpha_2}{n^2} + \ldots,$$

where

$$\alpha_1 + 2 - k = 1 + k, \quad \alpha_1 = 2k-1.$$

But from Gauss' test the series $\sum\limits_{n=1}^{\infty} u_n$ converges when $2k-1 > 1$ and diverges when $2k-1 \leqslant 1$, i.e. converges when $k > 1$ and diverges when $k \leqslant 1$.

Therefore, when $-1 < k \leqslant 1$ the estimate (6.10) becomes

$$|K| \leqslant \frac{3}{2-k} \tag{6.11}$$

and preserves the form (6.10) only when $1 < k < 3$.

9. When $k = 2$ we have $p_n = (2n+1)/(n+2)$, whence in particular $p_1 = 1$. In this case condition (6.9) becomes

$$|c_n| \leqslant \frac{n^2-1}{4n^2-1} \qquad (n = 2, 3, \ldots),$$

whence (c.f. section 6)

$$|K| \leqslant 1 + \sum_{n=2}^{\infty} \frac{1}{4} \cdot \frac{2}{5} \cdots \frac{n-1}{n+2} =$$

$$= 1 + 6 \sum_{n=2}^{\infty} \frac{1}{n(n+1)(n+2)} = 1 + 6\left(\frac{1}{4} - \frac{1}{6}\right) = \frac{3}{2}.$$

In particular, when $c_n = (1-n^2)/(4n^2-1)$ we have:

$$\frac{3}{2} = \frac{1}{1} - \frac{\frac{3}{3.5}}{1} - \frac{\frac{8}{5.7}}{1} - \frac{\frac{15}{7.9}}{1} - \ldots - \frac{\frac{n^2-1}{(2n-1)(2n+1)}}{1} - \ldots,$$

i.e.

$$\frac{1}{2} = \frac{1}{3} - \frac{3}{5} - \frac{8}{7} - \frac{15}{9} - \ldots - \frac{n^2-1}{2n+1} - \ldots.$$

10. When $k = \frac{1}{2}$ we have $p_n = 2$. In this case condition (6.9) becomes

$$|c_n| \leqslant \tfrac{1}{4} \qquad (n = 2, 3, \ldots) \tag{6.12}$$

from which, according to the estimate (6.11), $|K| \leqslant 2$. Condition (6.12) was given by Worpitzky [107], Sleshinskii [7] and Pringsheim [78], but without the estimate. In particular, when $c_n = -\frac{1}{4}$

$$2 = \frac{1}{1} - \frac{\frac{1}{4}}{1} - \frac{\frac{1}{4}}{1} + \ldots,$$

i.e.

$$1 = \frac{1}{2} - \frac{1}{2} - \ldots - \frac{1}{2} - \ldots . \qquad (6.13)$$

We note that when condition (6.12) is fulfilled, one can sharpen the estimate of the continued fraction. Indeed one can present the continued fraction K in the form

$$K = \frac{1}{1 + \frac{1}{4}w},$$

where

$$w = \frac{4c_2}{1} + \frac{c_3}{1} + \frac{c_4}{1} + \ldots .$$

The continued fraction

$$\frac{w}{4c_2} = \frac{1}{1} + \frac{c_3}{1} + \frac{c_4}{1} + \ldots$$

fulfils condition (6.12) and therefore $|w/4c_2| \leqslant 2$, whence $|w| \leqslant 8\,|c_2|$. But according to condition (6.12), $|c_2| \leqslant \frac{1}{4}$. Hence $|w| \leqslant 2$. Therefore, from the equation $1 + (w/4) = 1/K$, we have $|w| = 4\,|(K - 1)/K|$, whence $|(K - 1)/K| \leqslant \frac{1}{2}$. Let $K = x + iy$, then the equation $|(K - 1)/K| \leqslant \frac{1}{2}$ becomes

$$(x - 1)^2 + y^2 \leqslant \frac{x^2 + y^2}{4}, \quad 3x^2 - 8x + 4 + 3y^2 \leqslant 0,$$

$$x^2 - \frac{8}{3}x + \frac{4}{3} + y^2 \leqslant 0, \quad \left(x - \frac{4}{3}\right)^2 + y^2 + \frac{4}{3} - \frac{16}{9} \leqslant 0,$$

$$\left(x - \frac{4}{3}\right)^2 + y^2 \leqslant \frac{4}{9}.$$

Consequently the inequality $|(K - 1)/K| \leqslant \frac{1}{2}$ is equivalent to the inequality

$$\left|K - \frac{4}{3}\right| \leqslant \frac{2}{3}. \qquad (6.14)$$

Hence if the coefficients of the continued fraction (6.2) fulfil conditions (6.12) then this continued fraction satisfies conditions (6.14).

11. From conditions (6.12) follows the theorem (Van Vleck [102], Pringsheim [79]):

The condition

$$0 \leqslant c_n \leqslant g \quad (n = 2, 3, \ldots) \tag{6.15}$$

is sufficient for the continued fraction $K = \left[\frac{1}{1}; \frac{c_n z}{1}\right]_2^\infty$ *to converge in the circle* $|z| < 1/4g$ *to a regular analytic non-rational function, and for the series corresponding to this continued fraction to do the same, and furthermore for* $|K - \frac{4}{3}| \leqslant \frac{2}{3}$.

In the event the condition (6.12) becomes, for this continued fraction,

$$|c_n z| \leqslant \tfrac{1}{4} \quad (n = 2, 3, \ldots).$$

But according to the conditions of the theorem, $|c_n| \leqslant g$. Therefore condition (6.12) obtains here only for those values of z which satisfy the inequality $|gz| < \frac{1}{4}$, i.e. $|z| < 1/4g$, which proves the theorem.

§ 7. Convergence Tests for Continued Fractions which are Periodic in the Limit

1. Continued fractions of the form $\left[\frac{a_\nu}{b_\nu}\right]_1^\infty$ for which $a_\nu \neq 0$, $\lim_{\nu\to\infty} a_\nu = a$, $\lim_{\nu\to\infty} b_\nu = b$, are called *periodic in the limit*. Such continued fractions are very important in the context of practical application.

2. Theorem: *The condition* $\limsup_{\nu\to\infty} |c_\nu| \leqslant g$ *is sufficient for the continued fraction*

$$\left[\frac{c_1}{1}; \frac{c_\nu z}{1}\right]_2^\infty \tag{7.1}$$

to be convergent in the circle $|z| < 1/4g$ *(excepting possibly at certain poles) to a regular analytic function, the poles of the latter being points of inessential divergence of the continued fraction* (7.1). *In the neighbourhood of the origin this function is equal to the series corresponding to the continued fraction* (7.1) (van Vleck [102], Pringsheim [79]).

Proof: Since by assumption $\limsup_{\nu\to\infty} |c_\nu| \leqslant g$, then there exists an n such that for $\nu \geqslant n$ the inequality $|c_\nu| \leqslant g + \varepsilon$ obtains. Therefore according to the theorem of section 11 § 6, when $|z| < 1/4(g + \varepsilon)$ the continued fraction $\left[\frac{c_\nu z}{1}\right]_{n+1}^{\infty}$ converges to a regular non-rational function which, when $|z| < 1/4(g + \varepsilon)$, is equal to the series corresponding to this continued fraction. But according to the theorem of section 14 § 4 the continued fraction (7.1) converges uniformly in the circle $|z| < 1/4(g + \varepsilon)$ (and, consequently in the circle $|z| < 1/4g$, since one can make ε arbitrarily small), with the possible exception of a finite number of points of inessential divergence, to a single valued analytic function, regular in the circle $|z| < 1/4g$ with the exception of a finite number of points which are the poles of this function.

3. Choosing as g any arbitrarily small positive number in the theorem of section 2, we arrive at the following theorem (Pringsheim [79]).

The condition $\lim_{\nu \to \infty} c_\nu = 0$ *is sufficient for the continued fraction* (7.1) *to converge uniformly in any finite domain with the exception of a finite number of points of inessential divergence, to an analytic function which is regular in the neighbourhood of the origin, and in the remaining part of the domain is regular, with the exception of the above mentioned points of inessential divergence of the continued fraction* (7.1), *which are poles of the function. The point* $z = \infty$ *is an essential singularity of this function.*

4. Now let $\lim_{\nu \to \infty} c_\nu = c \neq 0$. For the exposition of this case we shall follow the work of Pringsheim [79]. We first consider the convergence of the continued fraction

$$\frac{cz}{1} + \frac{cz}{1} + \frac{cz}{1} + \dots \tag{7.2}$$

For this continued fraction, formulae (1.2) become

$$P_0 = 0, \quad P_1 = cz, \quad P_{n+1} = P_n + czP_{n-1} \quad (n \geqslant 1),$$
$$Q_0 = 1, \quad Q_1 = 1, \quad Q_{n+1} = Q_n + czQ_{n-1} \quad (n \leqslant 1).$$

Hence when $n \geqslant 1$ P_{n+1} and Q_{n+1} satisfy one and the same relationships

$$D_{n+1} - D_n - czD_{n-1} = 0. \tag{7.3}$$

Denote by u and u' the roots of the quadratic equation $y^2 - y - cz = 0$, and assume that $|u'| \leqslant |u|$. Then

$$u + u' = 1, \quad uu' = -cz. \tag{7.4}$$

Therefore relationships (7.3) become

$$D_{n+1} - (u + u')D_n + uu'D_{n-1} = 0,$$

i.e.

$$D_{n+1} - uD_n = u'(D_n - uD_{n-1}).$$

From this

$$\begin{aligned} D_n - uD_{n-1} &= u'^{n-1}(D_1 - uD_0), \\ D_{n-1} - uD_{n-2} &= u'^{n-2}(D_1 - uD_0), \\ D_{n-2} - uD_{n-3} &= u'^{n-3}(D_1 - uD_0), \\ &\dots\dots\dots\dots \\ D_1 - uD_0 &= D_1 - uD_0. \end{aligned}$$

Multiply the first of these equations by 1, the second by u, the third by u^2, and so on and add these equations, we obtain

$$D_n - u^n D_0 = $$
$$= (u'^{n-1} + u'^{n-2}u + \dots + u'u^{n-2} + u^{n-1}).(D_1 - uD_0);$$

If here $u \neq u'$, then one may write this expression in the form

$$D_n - u^n D_0 = \frac{u^n - u'^n}{u - u'}(D_1 - uD_0).$$

In particular, taking into account $P_0 = 0$, $P_1 = cz$, $Q_0 = Q_1 = 1$, we obtain

$$P_n = \frac{u^n - u'^n}{u - u'} cz = -\frac{u^n - u'^n}{u - u'} uu',$$

$$Q_n = u^n + \frac{u^n - u'^n}{u - u'}(1 - u) = u^n + \frac{u^n - u'^n}{u - u'} u' = \frac{u^{n+1} - u'^{n+1}}{u - u'}.$$

Consequently,

$$\frac{P_n}{Q_n} = -\frac{u^n - u'^n}{u^{n+1} - u'^{n+1}} uu' = -\frac{1 - \left(\frac{u'}{u}\right)^n}{1 - \left(\frac{u'}{u}\right)^{n+1}} u'.$$

From this, when $|u'| < |u|$, we have $\lim_{n\to\infty} P_n/Q_n = -u'$.

When $|u| = |u'|$, it follows from the relation $u + u' = 1$ that either $u = u' = \frac{1}{2}$ or that u and u' are complex conjugate numbers.

In the case $u = u' = \frac{1}{2}$ we have

$$P_n = -n(\tfrac{1}{2})^{n+1}, \quad Q_n = (n + 1)(\tfrac{1}{2})^n$$

and

$$\lim_{n\to\infty} \frac{P_n}{Q_n} = \lim_{n\to\infty} \left(- \frac{n}{2(n + 1)}\right) = -\frac{1}{2},$$

i.e. $\lim\limits_{n\to\infty} (P_n/Q_n) = -u'$ as before.

In the case of complex conjugate u and u', $\lim\limits_{n\to\infty} P_n/Q_n$ does not exist, i.e. the continued fraction diverges. The case $|u'| > |u|$ is not possible, since from the notation, $|u'| \leqslant |u|$.

5. Since u and u' are the roots of the quadratic equation $y^2 - y - cz = 0$, then

$$u = \frac{1 + \sqrt{1 + 4cz}}{2}, \quad u' = \frac{1 - \sqrt{1 + 4cz}}{2}.$$

When $|u'| = |u|$, the equation $|1 + \sqrt{1 + 4cz}| = |1 - \sqrt{1 + 4cz}|$ is satisfied. This is possible either when $1 + 4cz = 0$, or when $1 + 4cz < 0$ since then u and u' are complex conjugate numbers.

Thus in the case of the non-existence of the limit $\lim\limits_{n\to\infty} P_n/Q_n$, cz is a negative real number satisfying the inequality $cz < -\frac{1}{4}$. Consequently the continued fraction converges throughout the complex z-plane cut along that segment of the line $\arg(z) = -\arg(c)$ which joins the point $(-4c)^{-1}$ and the point at infinity and which does not pass through the origin. The continued fraction (7.2) then converges uniformly inside any finite domain lying wholly in its domain of convergence.

6. We shall prove that the continued fraction (7.1) for which $\lim\limits_{\nu\to\infty} c_\nu = c \neq 0$ converges under the very same conditions as those relating to the continued fraction (7.2). For the continued fraction (7.1) formulae (1.2) give

$$P_0 = 0, \quad P_1 = c_1, \quad P_{n+1} = P_n + c_{n+1}zP_{n-1} \quad (n \geqslant 1),$$
$$Q_0 = 1, \quad Q_1 = 1, \quad Q_{n+1} = Q_n + c_{n+1}zQ_{n-1} \quad (n \geqslant 1).$$

Hence when $n \geqslant 1$, P_{n+1} and Q_{n+1} satisfy one and the same relationship

$$D_{n+1} - D_n - c_{n+1} z D_{n-1} = 0. \tag{7.5}$$

We consider the sequence of numbers u_ν, u'_ν, where $\nu \geqslant n_0 > 0$, satisfying the equations

$$u_\nu + u'_\nu = u_{\nu+1} + u'_{\nu+1} = 1, \quad u_\nu u'_{\nu+1} = -c_{\nu+1} z. \tag{7.6}$$

We shall further stipulate that for all ν the inequality $|u'_\nu| \leqslant |u_\nu|$ is satisfied. Making use of equation (7.6) we may write relationship (7.5) in the form

$$D_{n+1} - (u_{n+1} + u'_{n+1}) D_n + u_n u'_{n+1} D_{n-1} = 0,$$

i.e.

$$D_{n+1} - u_{n+1} D_n = u'_{n+1}(D_n - u_n D_{n-1}). \tag{7.7}$$

7. We shall prove that for a proper choice of the number n_0 the sequence of numbers u_ν and u'_ν are uniquely determined, and that as ν increases without limit u_ν and u'_ν converge uniformly in the domain of uniform convergence of the continued fraction (7.2). For this we assume that $\lim\limits_{\nu\to\infty} u_\nu$ and $\lim\limits_{\nu\to\infty} u'_\nu$ exist, and introduce the notation $\lim\limits_{\nu\to\infty} u_\nu = u$, $\lim\limits_{\nu\to\infty} u'_\nu = u'$. Then, according to equation (7.6), u and u' satisfy equation (7.4).

From (7.6) it follows that

$$u_\nu(1 - u_{\nu+1}) = -c_{\nu+1} z,$$

i.e.

$$u_{\nu+1} = \frac{u_\nu + c_{\nu+1} z}{u_\nu}.$$

From this, taking equation (7.4) into account, follows the transformation

$$u - u_{\nu+1} = \frac{u_\nu(u-1) - c_{\nu+1} z}{u_\nu} = \frac{-u_\nu u' + uu' + cz - c_{\nu+1} z}{u_\nu} =$$

$$= \frac{u'(u - u_\nu) + \dfrac{c - c_{\nu+1}}{c} cz}{u - (u - u_\nu)} = \frac{u'(u - u_\nu) - \dfrac{c - c_{\nu+1}}{c} uu'}{u - (u - u_\nu)} =$$

$$= u' \frac{1 - \dfrac{u_\nu}{u} - \dfrac{c - c_{\nu+1}}{c}}{1 - \left(1 - \dfrac{u_\nu}{u}\right)},$$

$$1 - \frac{u_{\nu+1}}{u} = \frac{u'}{u} \frac{\left(1 - \dfrac{u_\nu}{u}\right) - \left(1 - \dfrac{c_{\nu+1}}{c}\right)}{1 - \left(1 - \dfrac{u_\nu}{u}\right)}.$$

Denote by T the domain of uniform convergence of the continued fraction (7.2.). According to the definition the inequality $|u'/u| < 1$ obtains for all $z \in T$. Denoting max $|u/u'|$ by M, we have for all $z \in T$ the inequality $0 < M < 1$. Hence for all $z \in T$ the inequality

$$\left|1 - \frac{u_{\nu+1}}{u}\right| \leqslant M \frac{\left|1 - \dfrac{u_\nu}{u}\right| + \left|1 - \dfrac{c_{\nu+1}}{c}\right|}{\left|1 - \left|1 - \dfrac{u_\nu}{u}\right|\right|} \tag{7.8}$$

obtains.

8. For a certain ν and for all $z \in T$, let the inequality

$$\left|1 - \frac{u_\nu}{u}\right| \leqslant 1 - N \tag{7.9}$$

be valid, where for the time being N is understood to be a certain number satisfying the inequality $0 < N < 1$. Then

$$1 - \left|1 - \frac{u_\nu}{u}\right| \geqslant N,$$

and (7.8) becomes

$$\left|1 - \frac{u_{\nu+1}}{u}\right| \leqslant \frac{M}{N}\left(\left|1 - \frac{u_\nu}{u}\right| + \left|1 - \frac{c_{\nu+1}}{c}\right|\right). \tag{7.10}$$

9. We choose an increasing sequence of natural numbers n_λ ($\lambda = 0, 1, 2, \ldots$) such that for $\nu \geqslant n_\lambda$

$$\left|1 - \frac{c_{\nu+1}}{c}\right| \leqslant N^{\lambda-1}(1 - N)^2.$$

It is always possible to do this since $\lim_{\nu\to\infty} c_\nu = c$. Then (7.10) becomes

$$\left|1 - \frac{u_{\nu+1}}{u}\right| \leqslant \frac{M}{N}\left|1 - \frac{u_\nu}{u}\right| + MN^{\lambda-2}(1 - N)^2. \qquad (7.11)$$

10. Until now we have not yet chosen u_{n_0} and have not established the connection between M and N. Define u_{n_0} by means of the equation $u_{n_0} = Nu$ and put $M = N^3$. Then the inequality (7.9), in particular, becomes $|1 - (u_{n_0}/u)| = 1 - N$. Therefore from (7.11) there follows:

$$\left|1 - \frac{u_{n_0+1}}{u}\right| \leqslant N^2(1 - N) + N(1 - N)^2 = N(1 - N),$$

whence, since $0 < N < 1$, $|1 - (u_{n_0+1}/u)| < 1 - N$.

Putting $\nu = n_0 + 1, n_0 + 2, \ldots, n_1 - 1$ in (7.11), we obtain in exactly the same way the inequality

$$\left|1 - \frac{u_{n_0+2}}{u}\right| < N(1 - N),$$

$$\left|1 - \frac{u_{n_1+3}}{u}\right| < N(1 - N), \ldots, \left|1 - \frac{u_{n_1}}{u}\right| < N(1 - N).$$

But from (7.11) it follows (since in this case $\lambda = 1$) that

$$\left|1 - \frac{u_{n_1+1}}{u}\right| < N^3(1 - N) + N^2(1 - N)^2 = N^2(1 - N),$$

and moreover that

$$\left|1 - \frac{u_{n_1+1}}{u}\right| < N(1 - N).$$

In exactly the same way

$$\left|1 - \frac{u_{n_1+2}}{u}\right| < N^2(1 - N),$$

$$\left|1 - \frac{u_{n_1+3}}{u}\right| < N^2(1 - N), \ldots, \left|1 - \frac{u_{n_2}}{u}\right| < N^2(1 - N).$$

But from (7.11) there follows:

$$\left|1 - \frac{u_{n_2+1}}{u}\right| < N^3(1 - N)$$

and so on. After trivial manipulations we obtain

$$\left|1 - \frac{u_{n_\lambda+\mu}}{u}\right| < N^{\lambda+1}(1 - N) \quad (\mu = 1, 2, \ldots, n_{\lambda+1} - n_\lambda).$$

From this, denoting max $|u|$ in the domain T by q, we have for $\nu > n_\lambda$

$$|u - u_\nu| < N^{\lambda+1}(1 - N)q$$

for all points in the domain T. Consequently in T, $\lim_{\nu\to\infty} u_\nu = u$, and further u_ν converges to u uniformly.

11. It remains to prove the same for u'_ν and u'_ν/u_ν. But

$$u' - u'_\nu = (1 - u) - (1 - u_\nu) = -(u - u_\nu),$$

whence in T $\lim_{\nu\to\infty} u'_\nu = u'$, and u'_ν converges uniformly to u'. Furthermore

$$\frac{u'}{u} - \frac{u'_\nu}{u_\nu} = \frac{1-u}{u} - \frac{1-u_\nu}{u_\nu} = \frac{1}{u} - \frac{1}{u_\nu} = -\frac{u - u_\nu}{uu_\nu}.$$

But from the relationship

$$\left|\frac{u'}{u}\right| = \left|\frac{1}{u} - 1\right| < 1$$

it follows that $|1/u| - 1 < 1$, i.e. $|1/u| < 2$ and $|1/u_\nu| < 2$. Therefore $|(u'/u) - (u'_\nu/u_\nu)| < 4\,|u - u_\nu|$, whence in T $\lim_{\nu\to\infty} u'_\nu/u_\nu = u'/u$, and u'_ν/u_ν converges uniformly to u'/u.

12. Using the formula $u_\nu(1 - u_{\nu+1}) = -c_{\nu+1}z$, which follows from (7.6), one can, when $\nu < n_0$, determine u_ν as long as the quantity $1 - u_{\nu+1}$ does not become zero. In this way we have proved the uniqueness of u_ν. But with the help of the relationship $u'_\nu = 1 - u_\nu$ the uniqueness of u'_ν has also been proved.

13. We now return to equation (7.7). Replacing n by ν, letting ν take the values $m, m + 1, \ldots, n - 1$ and multiplying together

the equations obtained, we derive

$$\prod_{\nu=m}^{n-1} (D_{\nu+1} - u_{\nu+1}D_\nu) = \prod_{\nu=m}^{n-1} u'_{\nu+1} \prod_{\nu=m}^{n-1} (D_\nu - u_\nu D_{\nu-1}),$$

i.e.

$$D_n - u_n D_{n-1} =$$
$$= u_{m+1}u_{m+2} \dots u_n(D_m - u_m D_{m-1}) \frac{u'_{m+1}}{u_{m+1}} \frac{u'_{m+2}}{u_{m+2}} \dots \frac{u'_n}{u_n}. \qquad (7.12)$$

We shall assume that $n_0 \leqslant m < n - 1$.

Replacing n by $n - 1$, $n - 2$, ..., $m + 1$ in (7.12) we derive the series of equations

$$D_{n-1} - u_{n-1}D_{n-2} =$$
$$= u_{m+1}u_{m+2} \dots u_{n-1}(D_m - u_m D_{m-1}) \frac{u'_{m+1}}{u_{m+1}} \frac{u'_{m+2}}{u_{m+2}} \dots \frac{u'_{n-1}}{u_{n-1}},$$

$$D_{n-2} - u_{n-2}D_{n-3} =$$
$$= u_{m+1}u_{m+2} \dots u_{n-2}(D_m - u_m D_{m-1}) \frac{u'_{m+1}}{u_{m+1}} \frac{u'_{m+2}}{u_{m+2}} \dots \frac{u'_{n-2}}{u_{n-2}},$$

. . . .

$$D_{m+1} - u_{m+1}D_m = u_{m+1}(D_m - u_m D_{m-1}) \frac{u'_{m+1}}{u_{m+1}}.$$

Multiplying these equations by u_n, $u_{n-1}u_n$, ..., $u_{m+2}u_{m+3} \dots u_n$ respectively, and adding them to (7.12), we obtain

$$D_n - u_{m+1}u_{m+2} \dots u_n D_m = u_{m+1}u_{m+2} \dots u_n(D_m - u_m D_{m-1})\sigma_{m,n},$$

where

$$\sigma_{m,n} = \frac{u'_{m+1}}{u_{m+1}} + \frac{u'_{m+1}}{u_{m+1}} \frac{u'_{m+2}}{u_{m+2}} + \dots + \frac{u'_{m+1}}{u_{m+1}} \frac{u'_{m+2}}{u_{m+2}} \dots \frac{u'_n}{u_n}.$$

From this

$$\frac{D_n}{u_{m+1}u_{m+2} \dots u_n} = D_m + (D_m - u_m D_{m-1})\sigma_{m,n}. \qquad (7.13)$$

This is the solution of the difference equation (7.7).

14. We recall that by D_n we understood P_n as well as Q_n. Therefore from (7.13) we obtain:

$$\frac{P_n}{Q_n} = \frac{P_m + (P_m - u_m P_{m-1})\sigma_{m,n}}{Q_m + (Q_m - u_m Q_{m-1})\sigma_{m,n}}. \qquad (7.14)$$

But, according to d'Alembert's test, the series

$$\sum_{n=m+1}^{\infty} \sigma_{m,n} \qquad (7.15)$$

converges in T, since $\lim\limits_{n\to\infty} |u_n'/u_n| \leqslant M < 1$. We now show that as a consequence of the uniform convergence of u_n'/u_n to u'/u this series converges uniformly in T. On account of the inequality $M < 1$ one can always choose $\delta > 0$ such that $M + \delta < 1$. Then in consequence of the uniform convergence of u_n'/u_n to u'/u one can choose m such that, for $\nu \geqslant m$,

$$\left|\frac{u_\nu'}{u_\nu}\right| \leqslant \left|\frac{u'}{u}\right| + \delta \leqslant M + \delta,$$

whence

$$|\sigma_{m,n+p} - \sigma_{m,n}| = \left| \frac{u_{m+1}'}{u_m} \cdots \frac{u_{n+1}'}{u_{n+1}} + \dots + \frac{u_{m+1}'}{u_{m+1}} \cdots \frac{u_{n+p}'}{u_{n+p}} \right| \leqslant$$

$$\leqslant (M+\delta)^{n+1-m} + (M+\delta)^{n+2-m} + \dots + (M+\delta)^{n+p-m} <$$

$$< \frac{(M+\delta)^{n-m+1}}{1-(M+\delta)}.$$

With appropriately chosen n the right hand side of this inequality becomes as small as we wish *throughout* the domain T, independent of p. Thus the uniform convergence of the series (7.15) in T has been proved.

15. Denoting by σ_n the sum of the series (7.16), we have from (7.14):

$$\lim_{n\to\infty} \frac{P_n}{Q_n} = \frac{P_m + (P_m - u_m P_{m-1})\sigma_m}{Q_m + (Q_m - u_m Q_{m-1})\sigma_m}.$$

Hence the continued fraction (7.1) is uniformly convergent in any domain lying wholly in T and in which

$$Q_m + (Q_m - u_m Q_{m-1})\sigma_m \neq 0.$$

16. We remark that the system of equations

$$P_m + (P_m - u_m P_{m-1})\sigma_m = 0,$$
$$Q_m + (Q_m - u_m Q_{m-1})\sigma_m = 0,$$

is incompatible. Indeed it follows from it that when $\sigma_m = 0$, then $P_m = Q_m = 0$, and when $\sigma_m \neq 0$ that $P_m/Q_m = P_{m-1}/Q_{m-1}$. But such an equation is impossible because of the construction of the continued fraction (7.1).

17. Further the equation $Q_m + (Q_m - u_m Q_{m-1})\sigma_m = 0$ may not be identically satisfied in any finite domain lying in T, since $Q_m + (Q_m - u_m Q_{m-1})\sigma_m$ is an analytic function of z, and therefore has only a finite number of zeros in T. Thus we have proved the following theorem:

The condition $\lim_{\nu\to\infty} c_\nu = c \neq 0$ *is sufficient for the uniform convergence of the continued fraction* (7.1), *with the exception of a finite number of points of inessential divergence, in any domain* $T \subset \overline{T}$, *where* $\overline{T}$ *is the complex z-plane cut along that segment of the line* $\arg(z) = -\arg(c)$ *which joins the point* $-(4c)^{-1}$ *and the point at infinity and which does not pass through the origin.*

18. We now proceed to consider the case when the continued fraction diverges on the negative real axis. As a preliminary we prove the following lemma (van Vleck [101], Ince [34]).

We introduce, in the continued fraction $\left[\frac{1}{\alpha_\nu}\right]_1^\infty$ the notation $\alpha_\nu = |\alpha_\nu|\, e^{iv_\nu}$. Then the set of conditions

1) $-\frac{\pi}{2} + \varepsilon \leqslant v_\nu \leqslant \frac{\pi}{2} - \varepsilon \quad (\varepsilon > 0, \nu = 1, 2, \ldots),$

2) $\alpha_1, \alpha_3, \alpha_5, \ldots$ not all equal to zero

is sufficient for the existence of the limits $\lim_{n\to\infty} P_{2n}/Q_{2n}$, $\lim_{n\to\infty} P_{2n+1}/Q_{2n+1}$.

We denote by $\bar{Q}_m$ the complex conjugate of Q_m. Then from equation (1.2)

$$Q_n = \alpha_n Q_{n-1} + Q_{n-2}$$

we have

$$Q_n \bar{Q}_{n-1} = \alpha_n |Q_{n-1}|^2 + \bar{Q}_{n-1} Q_{n-2},$$

i.e.

$$\operatorname{Re}(Q_n \bar{Q}_{n-1}) = |Q_{n-1}|^2 \operatorname{Re}(\alpha_n) + \operatorname{Re}(Q_{n-1}\bar{Q}_{n-2}), \qquad (7.16)$$

from which

$$\operatorname{Re}(Q_n\bar{Q}_{n-1}) = \\ = |Q_0|^2 \operatorname{Re}(\alpha_1) + |Q_1|^2 \operatorname{Re}(\alpha_2) + \dots + |Q_{n-1}|^2 \operatorname{Re}(\alpha_n). \quad (7.17)$$

Let $\alpha_{2\nu+1}$ be the first of the numbers $\alpha_1, \alpha_3, \dots$ not equal to zero. According to condition 2), such a number exists. Then

$$Q_0 = Q_2 = \dots = Q_{2\nu} = 1,$$
$$Q_1 = Q_3 = \dots = Q_{2\nu-1} = 0,$$
$$Q_{2\nu+1} = \alpha_{2\nu+1}.$$

According to condition 1), $\operatorname{Re}(\alpha_\nu) > 0$ $(\nu = 1, 2, \dots)$ if $\alpha_\nu \neq 0$. Then from (7.16) we have

$$\operatorname{Re}(Q_n\bar{Q}_{n-1}) \geqslant \operatorname{Re}(Q_{n-1}\bar{Q}_{n-2}) \geqslant \dots \geqslant \operatorname{Re}(Q_{2\nu+1}\bar{Q}_{2\nu}) = \\ = \operatorname{Re}(\alpha_{2\nu+1}) > 0.$$

Therefore the convergents beginning with the $2\nu^{\text{th}}$ have meaning. Hence, according to (1.7), when $n \geqslant 2\nu + 1$ we have

$$\left|\frac{P_{n+1}}{Q_{n+1}} - \frac{P_{n-1}}{Q_{n-1}}\right| = \left|\frac{\alpha_{n+1}}{Q_{n-1}Q_{n+1}}\right|.$$

But

$$|\alpha_n| = \left||\alpha_n| \cos v_n + i\,|\alpha_n| \sin v_n\right| \leqslant |\alpha_n| \cos v_n + |\alpha_n| \sin v_n = \\ = \operatorname{Re}(\alpha_n)(1 + |\tan v_n|).$$

From condition 1) we have

$$|\tan v_n| \leqslant \left|\tan\left(\frac{\pi}{2} - \varepsilon\right)\right| = \cot \varepsilon.$$

This implies that

$$|\alpha_n| \leqslant (1 + \cot \varepsilon) \operatorname{Re}(\alpha_n). \quad (7.18)$$

From this, according to (7.16)

$$\left|\frac{P_{n+1}}{Q_{n+1}} - \frac{P_{n-1}}{Q_{n-1}}\right| \leqslant \frac{|Q_n|^2(1 + \cot \varepsilon) \operatorname{Re}(\alpha_{n+1})}{|Q_{n+1}\bar{Q}_n|\,|Q_n\bar{Q}_{n-1}|} \leqslant \\ \leqslant \frac{\operatorname{Re}(Q_{n+1}\bar{Q}_n) - \operatorname{Re}(Q_n\bar{Q}_{n-1})}{\operatorname{Re}(Q_{n+1}\bar{Q}_n)\operatorname{Re}(Q_n\bar{Q}_{n-1})}(1 + \cot \varepsilon) =$$

$$= \left(\frac{1}{\operatorname{Re}(Q_n \bar{Q}_{n-1})} - \frac{1}{\operatorname{Re}(Q_n \bar{Q}_{n+1})} \right) (1 + \cot \varepsilon) \leqslant$$

$$\leqslant \left(\frac{1}{\operatorname{Re}(Q_n \bar{Q}_{n-1})} - \frac{1}{\operatorname{Re}(Q_{n+2} \bar{Q}_{n+1})} \right) (1 + \cot \varepsilon).$$

Thus the differences

$$\frac{P_{2n+1}}{Q_{2n+1}} - \frac{P_{2n-1}}{Q_{2n-1}} \quad \text{and} \quad \frac{P_{2n}}{Q_{2n}} - \frac{P_{2n-2}}{Q_{2n-2}}$$

are the terms of an absolutely convergent series. Consequently

$$\lim_{n\to\infty} \frac{P_{2n+1}}{Q_{2n+1}} \quad \text{and} \quad \lim_{n\to\infty} \frac{P_{2n}}{Q_{2n}} \quad \text{exist.}$$

19. We estimate a lower bound for $\operatorname{Re}(Q_n \bar{Q}_{n-1})$. When $n - 2 \geqslant 2\nu$ we have

$$\left| \frac{Q_n}{Q_{n-2}} \right| = \left| \frac{\alpha_n Q_{n-1} + Q_{n-2}}{Q_{n-2}} \right| \leqslant 1 + \left| \frac{\alpha_n Q_{n-1} \bar{Q}_{n-1}}{\bar{Q}_{n-1} Q_{n-2}} \right|.$$

From this, using (7.18), we obtain

$$\left| \frac{Q_n}{Q_{n-2}} \right| \leqslant 1 + \frac{|Q_{n-1}|^2 (1 + \cot \varepsilon) \operatorname{Re}(\alpha_n)}{\operatorname{Re}(Q_{n-1} \bar{Q}_{n-2})}.$$

Taking (7.16) into account and remembering that $\operatorname{Re}(Q_{n-1}\bar{Q}_{n-2}) \geqslant$ $\geqslant \operatorname{Re}(Q_{2\nu+1}\bar{Q}_{2\nu})$, we obtain the latter inequality in the form

$$\left| \frac{Q_n}{Q_{n-2}} \right| \leqslant 1 + \frac{\operatorname{Re}(Q_n \bar{Q}_{n-1}) - \operatorname{Re}(Q_{n-1} \bar{Q}_{n-2})}{\operatorname{Re}(Q_{2\nu+1} \bar{Q}_{2\nu})} (1 + \cot \varepsilon).$$

But since, by assumption, $Q_{2\nu} = 1$, $Q_{2\nu+1} = \alpha_{2\nu+1}$, then with the help of (7.18) we derive

$$\frac{1}{\operatorname{Re}(Q_{2\nu+1} \bar{Q}_{2\nu})} = \frac{1}{\operatorname{Re}(\alpha_{2\nu+1})} \leqslant \frac{1 + \cot \varepsilon}{|\alpha_{2\nu+1}|}.$$

Hence

$$\left| \frac{Q_n}{Q_{n-2}} \right| \leqslant e^{\frac{(1+\cot \varepsilon)^2}{|\alpha_{2\nu+1}|} [\operatorname{Re}(Q_n \bar{Q}_{n-1}) - \operatorname{Re}(Q_{n-1} \bar{Q}_{n-2})]}.$$

From this

$$\left|\frac{Q_n}{Q_{n-2}}\right|\left|\frac{Q_{n-2}}{Q_{n-4}}\right|\dots^{1} \leqslant e^{\frac{(1+\cot\varepsilon)^2}{|\alpha_{2\nu+1}|}\{[\mathrm{Re}(Q_n\bar{Q}_{n-1})-\mathrm{Re}(Q_{n-1}\bar{Q}_{n-2})]+\dots\}}.$$

But

$$\begin{aligned}[\mathrm{Re}\,(Q_n\bar{Q}_{n-1}) &- \mathrm{Re}\,(Q_{n-1}\bar{Q}_{n-2})] + \\ &+ [\mathrm{Re}\,(Q_{n-2}\bar{Q}_{n-3}) - \mathrm{Re}\,(Q_{n-3}\bar{Q}_{n-4})] + \dots = \\ &= \mathrm{Re}\,(Q_n\bar{Q}_{n-1}) - [\mathrm{Re}\,(Q_{n-1}\bar{Q}_{n-2}) - \mathrm{Re}\,(Q_{n-2}\bar{Q}_{n-3})] - \\ &- [\mathrm{Re}\,(Q_{n-3}\bar{Q}_{n-4}) - \mathrm{Re}\,(Q_{n-4}\bar{Q}_{n-5})] + \dots.\end{aligned}$$

According to (7.16) the differences standing in square brackets are $\geqslant 0$; the latter summand is $-\,\mathrm{Re}\,(Q_{2\nu+2}\bar{Q}_{2\nu+1})$ or $-\,\mathrm{Re}\,(Q_{2\nu+1}\bar{Q}_{2\nu})$, which (also on account of (7.16)) is non-positive, therefore

$$\begin{aligned}[\mathrm{Re}\,(Q_n\bar{Q}_{n-1}) &- \mathrm{Re}\,(Q_{n-1}\bar{Q}_{n-2})] + \\ &+ [\mathrm{Re}\,(Q_{n-2}\bar{Q}_{n-3} - \mathrm{Re}\,(Q_{n-3}\bar{Q}_{n-4})] + \dots \leqslant \mathrm{Re}\,(Q_n\bar{Q}_{n-1}).\end{aligned}$$

Consequently,

$$\left|\frac{Q_n}{Q_{n-2}}\right|\left|\frac{Q_{n-2}}{Q_{n-4}}\right|\dots \leqslant e^{\frac{(1+\cot\varepsilon)^2}{|\alpha_{2\nu+1}|}\mathrm{Re}(Q_n\bar{Q}_{n-1})} \equiv \lambda_n.$$

Thus

$$|Q_n| \leqslant |Q_{2\nu}|\,\lambda_n \qquad (n \text{ even}),$$
$$|Q_n| \leqslant |Q_{2\nu+1}|\,\lambda_n \qquad (n \text{ odd}).$$

But since $Q_{2\nu} = 1$, $Q_{2\nu+1} = \alpha_{2\nu+1}$, then for any $n \geqslant 2\nu + 2$

$$|Q_n| < (1 + |\alpha_{2\nu+1}|)\lambda_n. \tag{7.19}$$

We note that

$$|Q_{2\nu+1}| = |\alpha_{2\nu+1}| < (1 + |\alpha_{2\nu+1}|)\,e^{(1+\cot\varepsilon)^2},$$

whence (7.19) is valid when $n = 2\nu + 1$.

Further, according to (7.16), (7.18) and (7.19), we have

$$\begin{aligned}\mathrm{Re}\,(Q_n\bar{Q}_{n-1}) &- \mathrm{Re}\,(Q_{n-1}\bar{Q}_{n-2}) = \\ &= |Q_{n-1}|^2\,\mathrm{Re}\,(\alpha_n) = \frac{|Q_{n-1}Q_n|^2\,\mathrm{Re}\,(\alpha_n)}{|Q_n|^2} \geqslant\end{aligned}$$

[1] In the case of even n the last factor in the given product is $|Q_{2\nu+2}/Q_{2\nu}|$, in the case of uneven n — $|Q_{2\nu+3}/Q_{2\nu+1}|$.

$$\geqslant \frac{[\mathrm{Re}\,(Q_n\bar{Q}_{n-1})]^2\,\mathrm{Re}\,(\alpha_n)}{(1+|\alpha_{2\nu+1}|)^2\lambda_n^2} \geqslant \frac{[\mathrm{Re}\,(Q_{2\nu+1}\bar{Q}_{2\nu})]^2\,|\alpha_n|}{(1+\cot\varepsilon)(1+|\alpha_{2\nu+1}|)^2\lambda_n^2} \geqslant$$

$$\geqslant \frac{[\mathrm{Re}\,(\alpha_{2\nu+1})]^2\,|\alpha_n|}{(1+\cot\varepsilon)(1+|\alpha_{2\nu+1}|)^2\lambda_n^2} \geqslant \frac{|\alpha_{2\nu+1}|^2\,|\alpha_n|}{(1+\cot\varepsilon)^3(1+|\alpha_{2\nu+1}|^2)\lambda_n^2} =$$

$$= \frac{|\alpha_{2\nu+1}|^2\,|\alpha_n|}{(1+\cot\varepsilon)^3(1+|\alpha_{2\nu+1}|)^2}\, e^{-\frac{2(1+\cot\varepsilon)^2}{|\alpha_{2\nu+1}|}\mathrm{Re}(Q_n\overline{Q}_{n-1})}.$$

From this, since $e^{x_1} - e^{x_2} \geqslant x_1 - x_2$ when $x_1 \geqslant x_2 > 0$,

$$e^{\mathrm{Re}(Q_n\overline{Q}_{n-1})} - e^{\mathrm{Re}(Q_{n-1}\overline{Q}_{n-2})} \geqslant$$

$$\geqslant \frac{|\alpha_{2\nu+1}|^2\,|\alpha_n|}{(1+\cot\varepsilon)^3(1+|\alpha_{2\nu+1}|)^2}\, e^{-\frac{2(1+\cot\varepsilon)^2}{|\alpha_{2\nu+1}|}\mathrm{Re}(Q_n\overline{Q}_{n-1})} \qquad (n \geqslant 2\nu+1).$$

Multiplying both sides of this inequality by

$$e^{\frac{2(1+\cot\varepsilon)^2}{|\alpha_{2\nu+1}|}\mathrm{Re}(Q_n\overline{Q}_n-1)},$$

we obtain:

$$e^{\left[1+\frac{2(1+\cot\varepsilon)^2}{|\alpha_{2\nu+1}|}\right]\mathrm{Re}(Q_n\overline{Q}_{n-1})} \geqslant e^{\mathrm{Re}(Q_{n-1}\overline{Q}_{n-2})+\frac{2(1+\cot\varepsilon)^2}{|\alpha_{2\nu+1}|}\mathrm{Re}(Q_n\overline{Q}_{n-1})} +$$

$$+ \frac{|\alpha_{2\nu+1}|^2\,|\alpha_n|}{(1+\cot\varepsilon)^3(1+|\alpha_{2\nu+1}|)^2} \geqslant e^{\left[1+\frac{2(1+\cot\varepsilon)^2}{|\alpha_{2\nu+1}|}\right]\mathrm{Re}(Q_{n-1}\overline{Q}_{n-2})} +$$

$$+ \frac{|\alpha_{2\nu+1}|^2\,|\alpha_n|}{(1+\cot\varepsilon)^3(1+|\alpha_{2\nu+1}|)^2}.$$

Adding such inequalities with $n = 2\nu+1,\ 2\nu+2,\ \ldots$, we obtain

$$e^{\left[1+\frac{2(1+\cot\varepsilon)^2}{|\alpha_{2\nu+1}|}\right]\mathrm{Re}(Q_n\overline{Q}_{n-1})} \geqslant \frac{|\alpha_{2\nu+1}|^2}{(1+\cot\varepsilon)^3(1+|\alpha_{2\nu+1}|)^2} \sum_{k=2\nu+1}^{n} |\alpha_k|.$$

From this

$$\mathrm{Re}\,(Q_n\bar{Q}_{n-1}) \geqslant \frac{|\alpha_{2\nu+1}|}{|\alpha_{2\nu+1}|+2(1+\cot\varepsilon)^2} \times$$

$$\times \left[\ln \frac{|\alpha_{2\nu+1}|^2}{(1+\cot\varepsilon)^3(1+|\alpha_{2\nu+1}|)^2} + \ln \sum_{k=2\nu+1}^{n} |\alpha_k|\right] \qquad (n \geqslant 2\nu+1).$$

Thus the divergence of the series $\sum_{k=1}^{\infty} |\alpha_k|$ is sufficient for the unbounded increase of $\mathrm{Re}\,(Q_n\bar{Q}_{n-1})$ as $n \to \infty$.

20. We now prove that when the conditions of the lemma of section 18 are satisfied, the continued fraction $\left[\dfrac{1}{\alpha_k}\right]_1^\infty$ converges (diverges) if the series $\sum\limits_{k=1}^{\infty} \alpha_k$ diverges (converges) (van Vleck [101], Jensen [34], Stolz and Gmeiner [94]).

We know from section 6 of § 4 that the convergence of the series $\sum\limits_{k=1}^{\infty} \alpha_k$ is always sufficient for the divergence of the continued fraction $\left[\dfrac{1}{\alpha_k}\right]_1^\infty$. Let the series $\sum\limits_{k=1}^{\infty} \alpha_k$ diverge. From (1.3) we have:

$$\left|\frac{P_n}{Q_n} - \frac{P_{n-1}}{Q_{n-1}}\right| = \frac{1}{|Q_n Q_{n-1}|} = \frac{1}{|Q_n \bar{Q}_{n-1}|} \leqslant \frac{1}{\operatorname{Re}(Q_n \bar{Q}_{n-1})}.$$

But we have only just seen that the divergence of the series $\sum\limits_{k=1}^{\infty} \alpha_k$ is sufficient for the unbounded increase of $\operatorname{Re}(Q_n \bar{Q}_{n-1})$ as $n \to \infty$. Hence it is sufficient for the convergence of the continued fraction $\left[\dfrac{1}{\alpha_k}\right]_1^\infty$.

If all α_k are positive, then all v_k are equal to zero and we derive anew the criterion of Seidel.

21. Let $\alpha_1, \alpha_2, \ldots$ be functions of an arbitrary number of variables in a certain domain S. Then when the conditions of the lemma of section 18 are satisfied, and $0 < A < |\alpha_{2\nu+1}| < B$ throughout the domain S, the uniform divergence of the series $\sum\limits_{k=1}^{\infty} \alpha_k$ in this domain is sufficient for the uniform convergence of the continued fraction $\left[\dfrac{1}{\alpha_k}\right]_1^\infty$ in this domain (Perron [73]).

We note that from the lemma of section 18 there follows:

$$\left|\frac{P_{n-1}}{Q_{n-1}} - \lim_{\mu\to\infty} \frac{P_{n-1+2\mu}}{Q_{n-1+2\mu}}\right| \leqslant \sum_{\mu=0}^{\infty} \left|\frac{P_{n-1+2\mu}}{Q_{n-1+2\mu}} - \frac{P_{n+1+2\mu}}{Q_{n+1+2\mu}}\right| \leqslant$$

$$\leqslant (1 + \cot \varepsilon) \sum_{\mu=0}^{\infty} \left[\frac{1}{\operatorname{Re}(Q_{n+2\mu}\bar{Q}_{n-1+2\mu})} - \frac{1}{\operatorname{Re}(Q_{n+2+2\mu}\bar{Q}_{n+1+2\mu})}\right] =$$

$$= (1 + \cot \varepsilon) \left[\frac{1}{\operatorname{Re}(Q_n \bar{Q}_{n-1})} - \lim_{\mu\to\infty} \frac{1}{\operatorname{Re}(Q_{n+2\mu}\bar{Q}_{n-1+2\mu})}\right].$$

From this, in the case of the convergence of the continued fraction $\left[\frac{1}{\alpha_k}\right]_1^\infty$

$$\left|\frac{P_{n-1}}{Q_{n-1}} - \lim_{\mu\to\infty}\frac{P_\mu}{Q_\mu}\right| \leqslant \frac{1+\cot\varepsilon}{\operatorname{Re}(Q_n\bar{Q}_{n-1})}.$$

But

$\operatorname{Re}(Q_n\bar{Q}_{n-1}) >$

$$> \frac{A}{2(1+\cot\varepsilon)^2+B}\left[\ln\frac{A^2}{(1+\cot\varepsilon)^3(1+B)^2} + \ln\sum_{k=2\nu+1}^{n}|\alpha_k|\right].$$

If the series $\sum_{k=1}^{\infty}|\alpha_k|$ diverges uniformly in the domain S, then for any arbitrarily large positive number M one can select such an index m, that for all $n > m$ the inequality $\sum_{k=1}^{n}|\alpha_k| > M$ obtains in all the domain S. Thus the continued fraction is uniformly convergent in the domain S.

22. From this we have the following convergence test (Stieltjes [92]).

The set of conditions

1) $\alpha_1, \alpha_2, \ldots$ *real and negative,*

2) $\alpha_1, \alpha_3, \ldots$ *not all equal to zero,*

3) *the series* $\sum_{k=1}^{\infty}\alpha_k$ *diverges,*

is sufficient for the uniform convergence of the continued fraction $\left[\frac{re^{i\varphi}}{\alpha_k}\right]_{k=1}^{\infty}$ *in any domain U of the form* $0 < r \leqslant R$, $-\pi+\varepsilon \leqslant \varphi \leqslant \pi-\varepsilon$ $(\varepsilon > 0)$.

For the proof we present the continued fraction in the equivalent form

$$\cfrac{\sqrt{r}\,e^{i\varphi/2}}{\frac{\alpha_1}{\sqrt{r}}e^{-i\varphi/2} + \cfrac{1}{\frac{\alpha_2}{\sqrt{r}}e^{-i\varphi/2} + \ldots + \cfrac{1}{\frac{\alpha_n}{\sqrt{r}}e^{-i\varphi/2} + \ldots}}}. \tag{7.20}$$

Since $0 < r \leqslant R$ then the series $\sum_{n=1}^{\infty}(\alpha_n/\sqrt{r})$ diverges uniformly in U. The continued fraction (7.20), divided by $\sqrt{r}\, e^{i\varphi/2}$ satisfies the conditions of the theorem of section 21 and is therefore uniformly convergent. But since $|\sqrt{r}\, e^{i\varphi/2}| \leqslant R$, this factor does not affect the uniform convergence. Hence Stieltjes test has been proved.

One may formulate this test in the following way:

The set of conditions

1) $\alpha_1, \alpha_2, \ldots$ *real and negative,*

2) $\alpha_1, \alpha_3, \ldots, \alpha_{2n+1}, \ldots$ *not all equal to zero,*

3) *the series* $\sum_{k=1}^{\infty} \alpha_k$ *diverges*

is sufficient for the uniform convergence of the continued fraction $\left[\dfrac{z}{\alpha_k}\right]_1^{\infty}$ *in any finite domain lying in the complex z-plane, cut along the negative real axis.*

CHAPTER II

CONTINUED FRACTION EXPANSIONS OF CERTAIN FUNCTIONS

§ 1. A Solution of a Certain Riccati Equation with the Help of Continued Functions

1. Lagrange [43] proposed the following method for the solution of differential equations with the help of continued fractions.

Let there be given a differential equation relating y and x. Let $y \to \xi_0$ for small $|x|$. Write $y = \xi_0/(1 + y_1)$ and substitute this relation into the original equation. Obtain the differential equation connecting y_1 and x. Let $y_1 \to \xi_1$ for small $|x|$. Write $y_1 = \xi_1/(1 + y_2)$ and repeat the same process. Combining these results we obtain the continued fraction expansion $\left[\dfrac{\xi_\nu}{1}\right]_1^\infty$ for the solution of the original equation. The ξ_ν are most conveniently expressed in the form $a_\nu x^{\alpha_\nu}$, where $\alpha_\nu \geqslant 0$.

2. Lagrange's method for the solution of the differential equation does not always (expressing the matter rather mildly) succeed in giving the general term of the required continued fraction expansion. It is therefore of interest to consider differential equations for whose solution the method of Lagrange presents continued fractions whose general terms are known, and to consider further related expansions. As such an equation we consider the solution, by the method of Lagrange, of the equation of Sanielivici [82]

$$y' = \frac{l}{a + bx} + \left(\frac{\lambda}{x} + \frac{\mu b}{a + bx} + \frac{\nu f}{c + fx}\right) y - \frac{g y^2}{x(a + bx)(c + fx)}, \quad (1.1)$$

where $a, b, c, f, g, l, \lambda, \mu, \nu$ are constants and $\lambda + \mu + \nu = 1$.

We note that almost all the equations, the solutions of which where expanded as continued fractions by Lagrange and Euler, appear as special cases of the equation

$$(\alpha + \alpha' x)xy' + (\beta + \beta' x)y + \gamma y^2 = \delta x, \tag{1.2}$$

where α, α', p, p', γ and δ are constants.

3. We first discuss the connection between equations (1.1) and (1.2). For this we the parameter μ from equation (1.1) and free ourselves in this equation from the denominators, assuming that $a \neq 0$, $c \neq 0$. We have

$$\begin{aligned}(a + bx)(c + fx)xy' = \\ &= [\lambda(a + bx)(c + fx) + (1 - \lambda - \nu)bx(c + fx) + \\ &+ \nu fx(a + bx)]y - gy^2 + lx(c + fx).\end{aligned}$$

Dividing the right and left hand sides by ac ($\neq 0$), we obtain after trivial manipulations

$$\begin{aligned}\left(1 + \frac{b}{a}x\right)\left(1 + \frac{f}{c}x\right)xy' - \\ &- \left[\lambda + \left(\lambda\frac{f}{c} + \frac{b}{a} - \nu\frac{b}{a} + \nu\frac{f}{c}\right)x + \frac{bf}{ac}x^2\right]y + \\ &+ \frac{g}{ac}y^2 = \frac{l}{a}x\left(1 + \frac{f}{c}x\right).\end{aligned}$$

Introducing the notation

$$\frac{b}{a} = \eta', \quad \frac{f}{c} = \eta, \quad \lambda = -\beta, \quad (\lambda + \nu)\eta + (1 - \nu)\eta' = -\beta',$$

$$\frac{g}{ac} = \gamma, \quad \frac{l}{a} = \delta,$$

the preceding equation assumes the form

$$\begin{aligned}(1 + \eta' x)(1 + \eta x)xy' + (\beta + \beta' x - \eta\eta' x^2)y + \gamma y^2 = \\ = \delta x(1 + \eta x). \quad (1.3)\end{aligned}$$

When $\eta = 0$ we obtain equation (1.2) with $\alpha = 1$, $\alpha' = \eta'$. We shall assume in the meantime that $\eta \neq \eta'$.

4. Sanielevici [82] transliterates equation (1.1) into an equation of the type (1.3) but with $\eta' = 0$, $\eta = -1$. We write for this

$$x = \frac{A\xi}{1 + B\xi}, \quad y = \frac{Y}{1 + B\xi}.$$

Then

$$dx = \frac{A}{(1 + B\xi)^2} d\xi, \quad dy = \frac{(1 + B\xi)Y' - BY}{(1 + B\xi)^2} d\xi.$$

Equation (1.3) becomes

$$\left(1 + \frac{\eta' A\xi}{1 + B\xi}\right)\left(1 + \frac{\eta A\xi}{1 + B\xi}\right)\frac{A\xi}{1 + B\xi} \; \frac{(1 + B\xi)Y' - BY}{A} + \\ + \left[\beta + \frac{\beta' A\xi}{1 + B\xi} - \frac{\eta\eta' A^2\xi^2}{(1 + B\xi)^2}\right]\frac{Y}{1 + B\xi} + \\ + \frac{\gamma Y^2}{(1 + B\xi)^2} = \frac{\delta A\xi}{(1 + B\xi)}\left(1 + \frac{\eta A\xi}{1 + B\xi}\right).$$

We reduce the equation to a common denominator and multiply throughout by this denominator

$$[1 + (B + \eta' A)\xi].[1 + (B + \eta A)\xi]\xi(1 + B\xi)Y' + \\ + \{-[1 + (B + \eta' A)\xi].[1 + (B + \eta A)\xi]B\xi + \beta(1 + B\xi)^2 + \\ + \beta' A\xi(1 + B\xi) - \eta\eta' A^2\xi^2\}Y + \gamma(1 + B\xi)Y^2 = \\ = \delta A\xi[1 + (B + \eta A)\xi].(1 + B\xi).$$

Write

$$B + \eta' A = 0, \quad B + \eta A = -1$$

and we have

$$-[1 + (B + \eta' A)\xi][1 + (B + \eta A)\xi]B\xi - \eta\eta' A^2\xi^2 = \\ = -(1 - \xi)B\xi + \eta BA\xi^2 = -B\xi[1 - \xi(1 + \eta A)] = \\ = -B\xi(1 + B\xi).$$

The equation, after cancellation by $1 + B\xi$, becomes

$$(1 - \xi)\xi Y' + [-B\xi + \beta(1 + B\xi) + \beta' A\xi]Y + \gamma Y^2 = \delta A\xi(1 - \xi)$$

or

$$(1 - \xi)\xi Y' + [\beta(1 - \xi) + (\beta - B + \beta B + \beta' A)\xi]Y + \gamma Y^2 = \\ = \delta A\xi(1 - \xi).$$

But

$$B = -\eta' A, \quad (\eta - \eta')A = -1, \quad A = \frac{1}{\eta' - \eta}, \quad B = -\frac{\eta'}{\eta' - \eta},$$

$$\beta - B + \beta B + \beta' A = \frac{\beta\eta' - \beta\eta + \eta' - \beta\eta' + \beta'}{\eta' - \eta} = \frac{\beta' + \eta' - \beta\eta}{\eta' - \eta} = \nu$$

(c.f. section 3).

Introducing the notation

$$\frac{\delta}{\eta' - \eta} = m,$$

the previous equation evolves to the form

$$Y' + \left(\frac{\beta}{\xi} + \frac{\nu}{1 - \xi}\right) Y + \frac{\gamma Y^2}{\xi(1 - \xi)} = m. \tag{1.4}$$

5. We put in (1.4)

$$Y = -\frac{\beta}{\gamma} + s\xi + \frac{\xi(1 - \xi)}{z}, \tag{1.5}$$

where the constant s in the meantime is arbitrary. Equation (1.4) becomes

$$s + \frac{(1 - 2\xi)z - \xi(1 - \xi)z'}{z^2} +$$

$$+ \left(\frac{\beta}{\xi} + \frac{\nu}{1 - \xi}\right)\left(-\frac{\beta}{\gamma} + s\xi + \frac{\xi(1 - \xi)}{z}\right) +$$

$$+ \frac{\gamma}{\xi(1 - \xi)}\left[-\frac{\beta}{\gamma} + s\xi + \frac{\xi(1 - \xi)}{z}\right]^2 = m,$$

i.e.

$$sz^2 + (1 - 2\xi)z - \xi(1 - \xi)z' + \left(\frac{\beta}{\xi} + \frac{\nu}{1 - \xi}\right) \times$$

$$\times \left[\left(-\frac{\beta}{\gamma} + s\xi\right)z + \xi(1 - \xi)\right]z + \frac{\gamma}{\xi(1 - \xi)}\left[\left(-\frac{\beta}{\gamma} + s\xi\right)^2 z^2 +\right.$$

$$\left. + 2\left(-\frac{\beta}{\gamma} + s\xi\right)\xi(1 - \xi)z + \xi^2(1 - \xi)^2\right] = mz^2.$$

We group together those terms containing identical powers of z:

$$-\xi(1-\xi)z' + \left[1 - 2\xi + \beta(1-\xi) + \nu\xi + 2\gamma\left(-\frac{\beta}{\gamma} + s\xi\right)\right]z +$$

$$+\left[-m + s - \frac{\beta^2}{\gamma\xi} - \frac{\nu\beta}{\gamma(1-\xi)} + \beta s + \frac{\nu s\xi}{1-\xi} + \frac{\beta^2}{\gamma}\left(\frac{1}{\xi} + \frac{1}{1-\xi}\right) - \right.$$

$$\left. - \frac{2\beta s}{1-\xi} + \frac{\gamma s^2\xi}{1-\xi}\right]z^2 + \gamma\xi(1-\xi) = 0;$$

this one can write down as

$$-\xi(1-\xi)z' + [(1-\beta)(1-\xi) + (-1 - 2\beta + \nu + 2\gamma s)\xi]z +$$

$$+\left[-m + s + \beta s - \nu s + \frac{\nu s}{1-\xi} - \gamma s^2 + \frac{\gamma s^2}{1-\xi} - \frac{\nu\beta}{\gamma(1-\xi)} + \right.$$

$$\left. + \frac{\beta^2}{\gamma(1-\xi)} - \frac{2\beta s}{1-\xi}\right]z^2 + \gamma\xi(1-\xi) = 0$$

or

$$-\xi(1-\xi)z' + [(1-\beta)(1-\xi) + (-1 - 2\beta + \nu + 2\gamma s)\xi]z +$$

$$+\left[-m + s(1+\beta-\nu) - \gamma s^2 + \frac{1}{\gamma(1-\xi)}(\gamma\nu s - \nu\beta + \right.$$

$$\left. + \gamma^2 s^2 - 2\beta\gamma s + \beta^2)\right]z^2 + \gamma\xi(1-\xi) = 0.$$

Dividing this expression by $-\xi(1-\xi)$ we obtain

$$z' + \left(\frac{\beta-1}{\xi} + \frac{1+2\beta-\nu-2\gamma s}{1-\xi}\right)z - \frac{1}{\xi(1-\xi)}\left\{-m + \right.$$

$$\left. + s(1+\beta-\nu) - \gamma s^2 + \frac{1}{\gamma(1-\xi)}[\nu(\gamma s - \beta) + (\gamma s - \beta)^2]\right\}z^2 = \gamma,$$

or

$$z' + \left(\frac{\beta-1}{\xi} + \frac{1+2\beta-\nu-2\gamma s}{1-\xi}\right)z +$$

$$+ \frac{1}{\xi(1-\xi)}\left[m - s(1+\beta-\nu) + \gamma s^2 - \frac{(\gamma s-\beta)(\gamma s-\beta+\nu)}{\gamma(1-\xi)}\right]z^2 = \gamma. \quad (1.6)$$

6. For equation (1.6) to have the same form as that of equation (1.4) it is sufficient to put $\gamma s = \beta$ or $\gamma s = \beta - \nu$.

We first consider the case $\gamma s = \beta$. Then the substitution (1.5) becomes

$$Y = -\frac{\beta}{\gamma}(1-\xi) + \frac{\xi(1-\xi)}{z}, \tag{1.5'}$$

and equation (1.6) may be written as

$$z' + \left(\frac{\beta - 1}{\xi} + \frac{1-\nu}{1-\xi}\right) z + \frac{1}{\xi(1-\xi)}\left[m - \frac{\beta}{\gamma}(1-\nu)\right] z^2 = \gamma,$$

or finally

$$z' + \left(\frac{\beta_1}{\xi} + \frac{\nu_1}{1-\xi}\right) z + \frac{\gamma_1 z^2}{\xi(1-\xi)} = m_1, \tag{1.7}$$

where the notation

$$\beta_1 = \beta - 1, \quad \nu_1 = 1 - \nu, \quad m_1 = \gamma, \quad \gamma_1 = m - \frac{\beta}{\gamma}(1-\nu),$$

has been introduced.

We note that

$$\gamma\gamma_1 = m\gamma - \beta(1-\nu).$$

Repeated substitutions of the form (1.5') (with corresponding values of the parameters) yields

$$\gamma Y = -\beta(1-\xi) + \frac{\gamma\xi(1-\xi)}{z} =$$

$$= -\beta(1-\xi) + \frac{\gamma\gamma_1\xi(1-\xi)}{-\beta_1(1-\xi)} + \frac{\gamma_1\gamma_2\xi(1-\xi)}{-\beta_2(1-\xi)} + \dots$$

$$\dots + \frac{\gamma_{2n-1}\gamma_{2n}\xi(1-\xi)}{-\beta_{2n}(1-\xi)} + \frac{\gamma_{2n}\gamma_{2n+1}\xi(1-\xi)}{-\beta_{2n+1}(1-\xi)} + \dots,$$

i.e.

$$\gamma Y = -\beta(1-\xi) +$$

$$+ \frac{\gamma\gamma_1\xi}{-\beta_1} + \frac{\gamma_1\gamma_2\xi}{-\beta_2(1-\xi)} + \dots + \frac{\gamma_{2n-1}\gamma_{2n}\xi}{-\beta_{2n}(1-\xi)} + \frac{\gamma_{2n}\gamma_{2n+1}\xi}{-\beta_{2n+1}} + \dots. \tag{1.8}$$

Here the constants β_n are determined from the following sequential relationships

$$\beta_1 = \beta - 1, \quad \beta_2 = \beta - 2, \ldots, \beta_n = \beta - n,$$

i.e.

$$-\beta_n = n - \beta.$$

The constants ν_n are expressed in terms of ν by

$$\nu_1 = 1 - \nu, \; \nu_2 = \nu, \; \nu_3 = 1 - \nu, \; \ldots, \; \nu_{2n} = \nu, \; \nu_{2n+1} = 1 - \nu.$$

Finally,

$$\gamma\gamma_1 = m\gamma - \beta(1 - \nu),$$

$$\begin{aligned}\gamma_1\gamma_2 &= m_1\gamma_1 - \beta_1(1 - \nu_1) = \gamma\gamma_1 - (\beta - 1)\nu = \\ &= m\gamma - \beta + \beta\nu - \beta\nu + \nu = m\gamma - \beta + \nu,\end{aligned}$$

$$\begin{aligned}\gamma_2\gamma_3 &= \gamma_1\gamma_2 - \beta_2(1 - \nu_2) = m\gamma - \beta + \nu - (\beta - 2)(1 - \nu) = \\ &= m\gamma - 2\beta - \nu + 2 + \beta\nu = m\gamma + 2(1 - \beta) - \nu(1 - \beta) = \\ &= m\gamma + (1 - \beta)(2 - \nu),\end{aligned}$$

$$\begin{aligned}\gamma_3\gamma_4 &= \gamma_2\gamma_3 - \beta_3(1 - \nu_3) = m\gamma + (1 - \beta)(2 - \nu) - (\beta - 3)\nu = \\ &= m\gamma + 2 - 2\beta - \nu + \beta\nu - \beta\nu + 3\nu = \\ &= m\gamma + 2 - 2\beta + 2\nu = m\gamma + 2(1 - \beta + \nu).\end{aligned}$$

Assume that

$$\left.\begin{aligned}\gamma_{2n-1}\gamma_{2n} &= m\gamma + n(n - 1 - \beta + \nu), \\ \gamma_{2n}\gamma_{2n+1} &= m\gamma + (n - \beta)(n + 1 - \nu).\end{aligned}\right\} \tag{1.9}$$

Then

$$\begin{aligned}\gamma_{2n+1}\gamma_{2n+2} &= m_{2n+1}\gamma_{2n+1} - \beta_{2n+1}(1 - \nu_{2n+1}) = \\ &= \gamma_{2n}\gamma_{2n+1} - (\beta - 2n - 1)\nu = \\ &= m\gamma + n(n + 1) - \beta(n + 1) - n\nu + \beta\nu - \beta\nu + \\ &+ (2n + 1)\nu = m\gamma + (n + 1)(n - \beta) + (n + 1)\nu = \\ &= m\gamma + (n + 1)(n - \beta + \nu),\end{aligned}$$

$$\begin{aligned}\gamma_{2n+2}\gamma_{2n+3} &= m_{2n+2}\gamma_{2n+2} - \beta_{2n+2}(1 - \nu_{2n+2}) = \\ &= \gamma_{2n+1}\gamma_{2n+2} - (\beta - 2n - 2)(1 - \nu) = \\ &= m\gamma + (n + 1)n - (n + 1)\beta + (n + 1)\nu - \beta + \\ &+ 2n + 2 + \beta\nu - (2n + 2)\nu =\end{aligned}$$

$$= m\gamma + (n+1)(n+2) - (n+2)\beta + \beta\nu - (n+1)\nu =$$
$$= m\gamma + (n+2)(n+1-\beta) - (n+1-\beta)\nu =$$
$$= m\gamma + (n+1-\beta)(n+2-\nu).$$

Thus the relationships (1.9) are verified. From this the development (1.5) becomes

$$\gamma Y = -\beta(1-\xi) + \cfrac{[m\gamma - \beta(1-\nu)]\xi}{1-\beta + \cfrac{(m\gamma-\beta+\nu)\xi}{(2-\beta)(1-\xi) + \cfrac{[m\gamma+(1-\beta)(2-\nu)]\xi}{3-\beta + \cfrac{[m\gamma+2(1-\beta+\nu)]\xi}{(4-\beta)(1-\xi) + \dots}}}}$$
$$\dots + \cfrac{[m\gamma + n(n-1-\beta+\nu)]\xi}{(2n-\beta)(1-\xi) + \cfrac{[m\gamma+(n-\beta)(n+1-\nu)]\xi}{2n+1-\beta + \dots}}. \tag{1.10}$$

But (c.f. section 4)

$$x = \frac{\dfrac{1}{\eta'-\eta}\xi}{1 - \dfrac{\eta'\xi}{\eta'-\eta}} = \frac{\xi}{\eta'-\eta-\eta'\xi}, \quad y = \frac{Y}{1-\dfrac{\eta'\xi}{\eta'-\eta}} = \frac{(\eta'-\eta)Y}{\eta'-\eta-\eta'\xi}.$$

From these

$$(\eta'-\eta)x = (1+\eta'x)\xi, \quad \xi = \frac{\eta'-\eta}{1+\eta'x}x,$$

$$1-\xi = \frac{1+\eta'x-\eta'x+\eta x}{1+\eta'x} = \frac{1+\eta x}{1+\eta'x}, \quad Y = \frac{\xi y}{x(\eta'-\eta)} = \frac{y}{1+\eta'x}.$$

Inserting these values for ξ and Y in (1.10) we obtain:

$$\frac{\gamma y}{1+\eta'x} = -\beta\frac{1+\eta x}{1+\eta'x} +$$
$$+ \cfrac{[m\gamma-\beta(1-\nu)]\dfrac{\eta'-\eta}{1+\eta'x}x}{1-\beta + \cfrac{(m\gamma-\beta+\nu)\dfrac{\eta'-\eta}{1+\eta'x}x}{(2-\beta)\dfrac{1+\eta x}{1+\eta'x} + }}$$

$$+\frac{[m\gamma+(1-\beta)(2-\nu)]\dfrac{\eta'-\eta}{1+\eta'x}x}{3-\beta}+\frac{[m\gamma+2(1-\beta+\nu)]\dfrac{\eta'-\eta}{1+\eta'x}x}{(4-\beta)\dfrac{1+\eta x}{1+\eta'x}}+\ldots$$

$$\ldots+\frac{[m\gamma+n(n-1-\beta+\nu)]\dfrac{\eta'-\eta}{1+\eta'x}x}{(2n-\beta)\dfrac{1+\eta x}{1+\eta'x}}+$$

$$+\frac{[m\gamma+(n-\beta)(n+1-\nu)]\dfrac{\eta'-\eta}{1+\eta'x}x}{2n+1-\beta}+\ldots,$$

$$\gamma y=-\beta(1+\eta x)+$$

$$+\frac{[m\gamma-\beta(1-\nu)](\eta'-\eta)x}{1-\beta}+\frac{(m\gamma-\beta+\nu)(\eta'-\eta)x}{(2-\beta)(1+\eta x)}+$$

$$+\frac{[m\gamma+(1-\beta)(2-\nu)](\eta'-\eta)x}{3-\beta}+\frac{[m\gamma+2(1-\beta+\nu)](\eta'-\eta)x}{(4-\beta)(1+\eta x)}+\ldots$$

$$\ldots+\frac{[m\gamma+n(n-1-\beta+\nu)](\eta'-\eta)x}{(2n-\beta)(1+\eta x)}+$$

$$+\frac{[m\gamma+(n-\beta)(n+1-\nu)](\eta'-\eta)x}{2n+1-\beta}+\ldots \tag{1.11}$$

7. In equation (1.3) we replace x by x^k. Then y' becomes y'/kx^{k-1} and the equation transposes into

$$(1+\eta'x^k)(1+\eta x^k)\frac{xy'}{k}+(\beta+\beta'x^k-\eta\eta'x^{2k})y+\gamma y^2=$$
$$=\delta x^k(1+\eta x^k). \tag{1.12}$$

Its solution, obtained from the development (1.11), becomes

$$\gamma y=-\beta(1+\eta x^k)+$$

$$+\frac{[m\gamma-\beta(1-\nu)](\eta'-\eta)x^k}{1-\beta}+\frac{(m\gamma-\beta+\nu)(\eta'-\eta)x^k}{(2-\beta)(1+\eta x^k)}+$$

$$+\frac{[m\gamma+(1-\beta)(2-\nu)](\eta'-\eta)x^k}{3-\beta} + \frac{[m\gamma+2(1-\beta+\nu)](\eta'-\eta)x^k}{(4-\beta)(1+\eta x^k)} + \dots$$

$$\dots + \frac{[m\gamma+n(n-1-\beta+\nu)](\eta'-\eta)x^k}{(2n-\beta)(1+\eta x^k)} +$$

$$+\frac{[m\gamma+(n-\beta)(n+1-\nu)](\eta'-\eta)x^k}{2n+1-\beta} + \dots \ . \tag{1.13}$$

We write $y = u - (\beta/\gamma)$. With this equation (1.12) becomes

$$(1+\eta' x^k)(1+\eta x^k)\frac{xu'}{k} + (\beta+\beta' x^k - \eta\eta' x^{2k})u + \gamma u^2 -$$

$$-\frac{\beta}{\gamma}(\beta+\beta' x^k - \eta\eta' x^{2k}) + 2\gamma\left(-\frac{\beta}{\gamma}\right)u + \frac{\beta^2}{\gamma} = \delta x^k(1+\eta x^k),$$

i.e.

$$(1+\eta' x^k)(1+\eta x^k)\frac{xu'}{k} + (-\beta+\beta' x^k - \eta\eta' x^{2k})u + \gamma u^2 =$$

$$= \left(\frac{\beta\beta'}{\gamma} + \delta\right)x^k + \left(\delta\eta - \frac{\beta}{\gamma}\eta\eta'\right)x^{2k}. \tag{1.14}$$

The solution of this equation is of course obtained from the right hand side of expansion (1.13) by removing the term in β alone.

8. Let $\eta = 0$. Equation (1.12) becomes

$$(1+\eta' x^k)\frac{xy'}{k} + (\beta+\beta' x^k)y + \gamma y^2 = \delta x^k. \tag{1.15}$$

According to (1.13) the solution of (1.15) is

$$\gamma y = -\beta + \frac{[m\gamma-\beta(1-\nu)]\eta' x^k}{1-\beta} + \frac{(m\gamma-\beta+\nu)\eta' x^k}{2-\beta} +$$

$$+\frac{[m\gamma+(1-\beta)(2-\nu)]\eta' x^k}{3-\beta} + \frac{[m\gamma+2(1-\beta+\nu)]\eta' x^k}{4-\beta} + \dots$$

$$\dots + \frac{[m\gamma+n(n-1-\beta+\nu)]\eta' x^k}{2n-\beta} + \frac{[m\gamma+(n-\beta)(n+1-\nu)]\eta' x^k}{2n+1-\beta} + \dots \ .$$

But here (see the latter part of section 4)

$$m\gamma = \frac{\gamma\delta}{\eta'}, \qquad \nu = \frac{\beta' + \eta'}{\eta'} = \frac{\beta'}{\eta'} + 1.$$

Consequently,

$$\gamma y = -\beta + \frac{(\gamma\delta + \beta\beta')x^k}{1-\beta + \dfrac{(\gamma\delta - \beta\eta' + \beta' + \eta')x^k}{2-\beta + \dfrac{[\gamma\delta + (1-\beta)(\eta' - \beta')]x^k}{3-\beta + \dfrac{\{\gamma\delta + 2[(2-\beta)\eta' + \beta']\}x^k}{4-\beta + \dots}}}}$$

$$\dots + \frac{\{\gamma\delta + n[(n-\beta)\eta' + \beta']\}x^k}{2n-\beta + \dfrac{[\gamma\delta + (n-\beta)(n\eta' - \beta')]x^k}{2n+1-\beta + \dots}}. \tag{1.16}$$

In this case, equation (1.14) becomes

$$(1 + \eta' x^k)\frac{xu'}{k} + (-\beta + \beta' x^k)u + \gamma u^2 = \left(\delta + \frac{\beta\beta'}{\gamma}\right)x^k \quad \left(y = u - \frac{\beta}{\gamma}\right). \tag{1.17}$$

It may be obtained from equation (1.15) by replacing β by $-\beta$ and replacing δ by $\delta + (\beta\beta'/\gamma)$. Therefore its solution, based on (1.16), is

$$\gamma u = \beta + \frac{(\gamma\delta + \beta\beta' - \beta\beta')x^k}{1+\beta + \dfrac{(\gamma\delta + \beta\beta' + \beta\eta' + \beta' + \eta')x^k}{2+\beta + \dfrac{(\gamma\delta + \beta\beta' + \eta' + \beta\eta' - \beta' - \beta\beta')x^k}{3+\beta + \dfrac{(\gamma\delta + \beta\beta' + 4\eta' + 2\beta\eta' + 2\beta')x^k}{4+\beta + \dots}}}}$$

$$\dots + \frac{(\gamma\delta + \beta\beta' + n^2\eta' + n\beta\eta' + n\beta')x^k}{2n+\beta + \dfrac{(\gamma\delta + \beta\beta' + n^2\eta' + n\beta\eta' - n\beta' - \beta\beta')x^k}{2n+1+\beta + \dots}}.$$

But $\gamma u = \gamma y + \beta$, where y is the solution of equation (1.15). Therefore that solution of equation (1.15) tending to zero when

$x = 0$, is

$$y = \frac{\delta x^k}{1 + \beta +} \frac{[\gamma\delta + (1 + \beta)(\eta' + \beta')]x^k}{2 + \beta \qquad +} \frac{(\gamma\delta + \eta' + \beta\eta' - \beta')x^k}{3 + \beta \qquad +}$$

$$+ \frac{[\gamma\delta + (2 + \beta)(2\eta' + \beta')]x^k}{4 + \beta \qquad + \dots +} \frac{[\gamma\delta + (n + \beta)(n\eta' + \beta')]x^k}{2n + \beta \qquad +}$$

$$+ \frac{(\gamma\delta + n^2\eta' + n\beta\eta' - n\beta')x^k}{2n + 1 + \beta \qquad + \dots} . \tag{1.18}$$

9. Divide both sides of equation (1.15) by η' and denote (not to be confused with the notation for β_1, γ_1 of section 6)

$$\frac{\beta}{\eta'} = \beta_1, \quad \frac{\beta'}{\eta'} = \beta_1', \quad \frac{\gamma}{\eta'} = \gamma_1, \quad \frac{\delta}{\eta'} = \delta_1.$$

With these, equation (1.15) becomes

$$\left(\frac{1}{\eta'} + x^k\right)\frac{xy'}{k} + (\beta_1 + \beta_1' x^k)y + \gamma_1 y^2 = \delta_1 x^k. \tag{1.19}$$

In equation (1.19) one can consider the quantities η', β_1, β_1', γ_1, δ_1 to be completely independent parameters. Letting η' tend to infinity (and thus removing it) in this equation we obtain

$$\frac{x^{k+1}y'}{k} + (\beta_1 + \beta_1' x^k)y + \gamma_1 y^2 = \delta_1 x^k. \tag{1.20}$$

The continued fraction expansion (1.16) relating to equation (1.19) becomes

$$\gamma_1 y = -\beta_1 + \frac{(\gamma_1\delta_1 + \beta_1\beta_1')x^k}{\dfrac{1}{\eta'} - \beta_1 \qquad +} \frac{\left(\gamma_1\delta_1 - \beta_1 + \dfrac{\beta_1'}{\eta'} + \dfrac{1}{\eta'}\right)x^k}{\dfrac{2}{\eta'} - \beta_1 \qquad +}$$

$$+ \frac{\left[\gamma_1\delta_1 + \left(\dfrac{1}{\eta'} - \beta_1\right)(1 - \beta_1')\right]x^k}{\dfrac{3}{\eta'} - \beta_1 \qquad +} \frac{\left[\gamma_1\delta_1 + 2\left(\dfrac{2}{\eta'} - \beta_1 + \dfrac{\beta_1'}{\eta'}\right)\right]x^k}{\dfrac{4}{\eta_1} - \beta_1 \qquad + \dots}$$

$$\cdots + \frac{\left[\gamma_1\delta_1 + n\left(\frac{n}{\eta'} - \beta_1 + \frac{\beta_1'}{\eta'}\right)\right]x^k}{\frac{2n}{\eta'} - \beta_1} + \frac{\left[\gamma_1\delta_1 + \left(\frac{n}{\eta'} - \beta_1\right)(n - \beta_1')\right]x^k}{\frac{2n+1}{\eta'} - \beta_1} + \cdots.$$

Letting η' tend to ∞ in this expansion we obtain the solution of equation (1.20)

$$\gamma_1 y = -\beta_1 - \frac{(\gamma_1\delta_1 + \beta_1\beta_1')x^k}{\beta_1} + \frac{(\gamma_1\delta_1 - \beta_1)x^k}{\beta_1} + \\ + \frac{[\gamma_1\delta_1 - \beta_1(1 - \beta_1')]x^k}{\beta_1} + \frac{(\gamma_1\delta_1 - 2\beta_1)x^k}{\beta_1} + \cdots \\ \cdots + \frac{(\gamma_1\delta_1 - n\beta_1)x^k}{\beta_1} + \frac{[\gamma_1\delta_1 - \beta_1(n - \beta_1')]x^k}{\beta_1} + \cdots. \tag{1.21}$$

The continued fraction expansion relating to equation (1.19) becomes

$$y = \frac{\delta_1 x^k}{\frac{1}{\eta'} + \beta_1} + \frac{\left[\gamma_1\delta_1 + \left(\frac{1}{\eta'} + \beta_1\right)(1 + \beta_1')\right]x^k}{\frac{2}{\eta'} + \beta_1} + \\ + \frac{\left(\gamma_1\delta_1 + \frac{1}{\eta'} + \beta_1 - \frac{\beta_1'}{\eta'}\right)x^k}{\frac{3}{\eta'} + \beta_1} + \frac{\left[\gamma_1\delta_1 + \left(\frac{2}{\eta'} + \beta_1\right)(2 + \beta_1')\right]x^k}{\frac{4}{\eta'} + \beta_1} + \cdots \\ \cdots + \frac{\left[\gamma_1\delta_1 + \left(\frac{n}{\eta'} + \beta_1\right)(n + \beta_1')\right]x^k}{\frac{2n}{\eta'} + \beta_1} + \\ + \frac{\left(\gamma_1\delta_1 + \frac{n^2}{\eta'} + n\beta_1 - \frac{n\beta_1'}{\eta'}\right)x^k}{\frac{2n+1}{\eta'} + \beta_1} + \cdots.$$

Letting η' tend to infinity in this expression we obtain that solution of equation (1.20) tending to zero when $x = 0$:

$$y = \cfrac{\delta_1 x^k}{\beta_1 + \cfrac{[\gamma_1\delta_1 + \beta_1(1+\beta_1')]x^k}{\beta_1 + \cfrac{(\gamma_1\delta_1+\beta_1)x^k}{\beta_1 + \cfrac{[\gamma_1\delta_1+\beta_1(2+\beta_1')]x^k}{\beta_1 + \dots}}}}$$

$$\dots + \cfrac{[\gamma_1\delta_1+\beta_1(n+\beta_1')]x^k}{\beta_1 + \cfrac{(\gamma_1\delta_1+n\beta_1)x^k}{\beta_1 + \dots}}. \tag{1.22}$$

10. We now consider the case $\gamma s = \beta - \nu$ (c.f. equation (1.6)). The substitution (1.5) becomes

$$\gamma Y = -\beta + (\beta-\nu)\xi + \frac{\gamma\xi(1-\xi)}{z}, \tag{1.5''}$$

however equation (1.6) may be written as

$$z' + \left(\frac{\beta-1}{\xi} + \frac{1+\nu}{1-\xi}\right)z + \frac{1}{\xi(1-\xi)}\left[m - \frac{(\beta-\nu)(1+\beta-\nu)}{\gamma} + \frac{(\beta-\nu)^2}{\gamma}\right]z^2 = \gamma,$$

i.e.

$$z' + \left(\frac{\beta-1}{\xi} + \frac{1+\nu}{1-\xi}\right)z + \frac{1}{\xi(1-\xi)}\left(m + \frac{\nu-\beta}{\gamma}\right)z^2 = \gamma,$$

or finally

$$z' + \left(\frac{\beta_1}{\xi} + \frac{\nu_1}{1-\xi}\right)z + \frac{\gamma_1 z^2}{\xi(1-\xi)} = m_1,$$

where the notation

$$\beta_1 = \beta - 1, \quad \nu_1 = 1+\nu, \quad \gamma_1 = m + \frac{\nu-\beta}{\gamma}, \quad m_1 = \gamma.$$

has been introduced.

From these

$$\gamma\gamma_1 = m\gamma + \nu - \beta.$$

Repeated substitutions in (1.5″) (with appropriate values of the parameters) yields

$$\gamma Y = -\beta + (\beta - \nu)\xi + \frac{\gamma\gamma_1\xi(1-\xi)}{-\beta_1 + (\beta_1 - \nu_1)\xi} + $$

$$+ \frac{\gamma_1\gamma_2\xi(1-\xi)}{-\beta_2 + (\beta_2 - \nu_2)\xi} + \ldots + \frac{\gamma_{n-1}\gamma_n\xi(1-\xi)}{-\beta_n + (\beta_n - \nu_n)\xi} + \ldots$$

Here

$$\beta_2 = \beta_1 - 1 = \beta - 2, \ldots, \beta_n = \beta - n;$$

$$\nu_2 = 1 + \nu_1 = 2 + \nu, \ldots, \nu_n = n + \nu;$$

$$\nu_n - \beta_n = 2n + \nu - \beta;$$

$$\gamma_1\gamma_2 = m_1\gamma_1 + \nu_1 - \beta_1 = \gamma\gamma_1 + 2 + \nu - \beta = $$
$$= m\gamma + 2(1 + \nu - \beta),$$

$$\gamma_2\gamma_3 = m_2\gamma_2 + \nu_2 - \beta_2 = \gamma_1\gamma_2 + 4 + \nu - \beta =$$
$$= m\gamma + 6 + 3(\nu - \beta) = m\gamma + 3(2 + \nu - \beta),$$

$$\gamma_3\gamma_4 = m_3\gamma_3 + \nu_3 - \beta_3 = \gamma_2\gamma_3 + 6 + \nu - \beta =$$
$$= m\gamma + 12 + 4(\nu - \beta) = m\gamma + 4(3 + \nu - \beta).$$

Let

$$\gamma_{n-1}\gamma_n = m\gamma + n(n - 1 + \nu - \beta).$$

Then

$$\gamma_n\gamma_{n+1} = m_n\gamma_n + \nu_n - \beta_n = \gamma_{n-1}\gamma_n + 2n + \nu - \beta =$$
$$= m\gamma + n^2 - n + 2n + (n+1)(\nu - \beta) =$$
$$= m\gamma + n(n+1) + (n+1)(\nu - \beta) =$$
$$= m\gamma + (n+1)(n + \nu - \beta).$$

Consequently,

$$\gamma Y = -\beta + (\beta - \nu)\xi + \frac{(m\gamma + \nu - \beta)\xi(1-\xi)}{1 - \beta - (2 + \nu - \beta)\xi} + $$

$$+ \frac{[m\gamma + 2(1 + \nu - \beta)]\xi(1-\xi)}{2 - \beta - (4 + \nu - \beta)\xi} + \frac{[m\gamma + 3(2 + \nu - \beta)]\xi(1-\xi)}{3 - \beta - (6 + \nu - \beta)\xi} + \ldots$$

$$\ldots + \frac{[m\gamma + n(n - 1 + \nu - \beta)]\xi(1-\xi)}{n - \beta - (2n + \nu - \beta)\xi} + \ldots$$

But from section 6, we know that

$$1 - \xi = \frac{1 + \eta x}{1 + \eta' x}, \quad \xi = \frac{\eta' - \eta}{1 + \eta' x} x, \quad Y = \frac{y}{1 + \eta' x}.$$

Hence

$$\frac{\gamma y}{1 + \eta' x} = -\beta + \frac{(\beta - \nu)(\eta' - \eta)}{1 + \eta' x} x + \cfrac{(m\gamma + \nu - \beta) \dfrac{(\eta' - \eta)x(1 + \eta x)}{(1 + \eta' x)^2}}{1 - \beta - (2 + \nu - \beta) \dfrac{\eta' - \eta}{1 + \eta' x} x + \cfrac{[m\gamma + 2(1 + \nu - \beta)] \dfrac{(\eta' - \eta)x(1 + \eta x)}{(1 + \eta' x)^2}}{2 - \beta - (4 + \nu - \beta) \dfrac{\eta' - \eta}{1 + \eta' x} x + \dots}}$$

$$\dots + \cfrac{[m\gamma + n(n - 1 + \nu - \beta)] \dfrac{(\eta' - \eta)x(1 + \eta x)}{(1 + \eta' x)^2}}{n - \beta - (2n + \nu - \beta) \dfrac{\eta' - \eta}{1 + \eta' x} x + \dots},$$

i.e.

$$\gamma y = -\beta(1 + \eta' x) + (\beta - \nu)(\eta' - \eta)x + \cfrac{(m\gamma + \nu - \beta)(\eta' - \eta)x(1 + \eta x)}{(1 - \beta)(1 + \eta' x) - (2 + \nu - \beta)(\eta' - \eta)x + \cfrac{[m\gamma + 2(1 + \nu - \beta)](\eta' - \eta)x(1 + \eta x)}{(2 - \beta)(1 + \eta' x) - (4 + \nu - \beta)(\eta' - \eta)x + \dots}}$$

$$\dots + \cfrac{[m\gamma + n(n - 1 + \nu - \beta)](\eta' - \eta)x(1 + \eta x)}{(n - \beta)(1 + \eta' x) - (2n + \nu - \beta)(\eta' - \eta)x + \dots}.$$

But since

$$(n - \beta)\eta' - (2n + \nu - \beta)(\eta' - \eta) = (2n + \nu - \beta)\eta - (n + \nu)\eta',$$
$$-\beta\eta' + (\beta - \nu)(\eta' - \eta) = (\nu - \beta)\eta - \nu\eta',$$

then

$$\gamma y = -\beta + [(\nu - \beta)\eta - \nu\eta']x + \frac{(m\gamma + \nu - \beta)(\eta' - \eta)x(1 + \eta x)}{1 - \beta + [(2 + \nu - \beta)\eta - (1 + \nu)\eta']x} + \frac{[m\gamma + 2(1 + \nu - \beta)](\eta' - \eta)x(1 + \eta x)}{2 - \beta + [(4 + \nu - \beta)\eta - (2 + \nu)\eta']x} + \dots + \frac{[m\gamma + n(n - 1 + \nu - \beta)](\eta' - \eta)x(1 + \eta x)}{n - \beta + [(2n + \nu - \beta)\eta - (n + \nu)\eta']x} + \dots \tag{1.23}$$

Replacing x by x^k, we obtain from (1.23) the solution of equation (1.12)

$$\gamma y = -\beta + [(\nu - \beta)\eta - \nu\eta']x^k + \frac{(m\gamma + \nu - \beta)(\eta' - \eta)x^k(1 + \eta x^k)}{1 - \beta + [(2 + \nu - \beta)\eta - (1 + \nu)\eta']x^k} + \frac{[m\gamma + 2(1 + \nu - \beta)](\eta' - \eta)x^k(1 + \eta x^k)}{2 - \beta + [(4 + \nu - \beta)\eta - (2 + \nu)\eta']x^k} + \dots + \frac{[m\gamma + n(n - 1 + \nu - \beta)](\eta' - \eta)x^k(1 + \eta x^k)}{n - \beta + [(2n + \nu - \beta)\eta - (n + \nu)\eta']x^k} + \dots \tag{1.24}$$

Dropping $-\beta$ from the right hand side of (1.24) we obtain the solution of equation (1.14).

From (1.24) with $\eta = 0$ we obtain the solution of equation (1.15)

$$\gamma y = -\beta - \nu\eta' x^k + \frac{(m\gamma + \nu - \beta)\eta' x^k}{1 - \beta - (1 + \nu)\eta' x^k} + \frac{[m\gamma + 2(1 + \nu - \beta)]\eta' x^k}{2 - \beta - (2 + \nu)\eta' x^k} + \dots + \frac{[m\gamma + n(n - 1 + \nu - \beta)]\eta' x^k}{n - \beta - (n + \nu)\eta' x^k} + \dots.$$

Here (c.f. the latter part of section 4)

$$m\gamma = \frac{\gamma\delta}{\eta'}, \quad \nu = \frac{\beta'}{\eta'} + 1.$$

Consequently

$$\gamma y = -\beta - (\beta' + \eta')x^k + \frac{(\gamma\delta + \beta' + \eta' - \beta\eta')x^k}{1 - \beta - (\beta' + 2\eta')x^k} + \frac{[\gamma\delta + 2(\beta' + 2\eta' - \beta\eta')]x^k}{2 - \beta - (\beta' + 3\eta')x^k} + \dots$$

$$\dots + \frac{[\gamma\delta + n(\beta' + n\eta' - \beta\eta')]x^k}{n - \beta - [\beta' + (n+1)\eta']x^k + \dots}. \tag{1.25}$$

The solution of equation (1.15) tending to zero when $x = 0$, is obtained from (1.25) as in section 8, dropping $-\beta$ from the right hand side, replacing β by $-\beta$ and δ by $\delta + (\beta\beta'/\gamma)$. Therefore we have

$$\gamma y = -(\beta' + \eta')x^k + \frac{(\gamma\delta + \beta\beta' + \beta' + \eta' + \beta\eta')x^k}{1 + \beta - (\beta' + 2\eta')x^k} + \frac{(\gamma\delta + \beta\beta' + 4\eta' + 2\beta' + 2\beta\eta')x^k}{2 + \beta - (\beta' + 3\eta')x^k} + \dots$$

$$\dots + \frac{(\gamma\delta + \beta\beta' + n^2\eta' + n\beta' + n\beta\eta')x^k}{n + \beta - [\beta + (n+1)\eta']x^k} + \dots,$$

i.e.

$$\gamma y = -(\beta' + \eta')x^k + \frac{[\gamma\delta + (1+\beta)(\eta' + \beta')]x^k}{1 + \beta - (\beta' + 2\eta')x^k} + \frac{[\gamma\delta + (2+\beta)(2\eta' + \beta')]x^k}{2 + \beta - (\beta' + 3\eta')x^k} + \dots$$

$$\dots + \frac{[\gamma\delta + (n+\beta)(n\eta' + \beta')]x^k}{n + \beta - [\beta' + (n+1)\eta']x^k + \dots}. \tag{1.26}$$

Proceeding as in section 9, we obtain from (1.25) the solution of equation (1.20):

$$\gamma_1 y = -\beta_1 - (\beta_1' + 1)x^k - \frac{(\gamma_1\delta_1 - \beta_1)x^k}{\beta_1 + (\beta_1' + 2)x^k} +$$

$$+ \frac{(\gamma_1\delta_1 - 2\beta_1)x^k}{\beta_1 + (\beta_1' + 3)x^k} + \dots + \frac{(\gamma_1\delta_1 - n\beta_1)x^k}{\beta_1 + (\beta_1' + n - 1)x^k} + \dots, \tag{1.27}$$

and from (1.26) that solution of equation (1.20) tending to zero when $x = 0$:

$$\gamma_1 y = -(\beta_1' + 1)x^k + \cfrac{[\gamma_1\delta_1 + \beta_1(1+\beta_1')]x^k}{\beta_1 - (\beta_1'+2)x^k + \cfrac{[\gamma_1\delta_1 + \beta_1(2+\beta_1')]x^k}{\beta_1 - (\beta_1'+3)x^k + \dots + \cfrac{[\gamma_1\delta_1 + \beta_1(n+\beta_1')]x^k}{\beta_1 - (\beta_1'+n+1)x^k + \dots}}}. \quad (1.28)$$

11. We put in equation (1.12) $\delta = 0$, then $m = 0$ also. Equation (1.12) then evolves to the form

$$(1+\eta' x^k)(1+\eta x^k)\frac{xy'}{k} + (\beta + \beta' x^k - \eta\eta' x^{2k})y + \gamma y^2 = 0. \quad (1.29)$$

Its solution, obtained from (1.13) with $\gamma s = \beta$ is

$$\gamma y = -\beta(1+\eta x^k) - \cfrac{\beta(1-\nu)(\eta'-\eta)x^k}{1-\beta + \cfrac{(\nu-\beta)(\eta'-\eta)x^k}{(2-\beta)(1+\eta x^k) + \cfrac{(1-\beta)(2-\nu)(\eta'-\eta)x^k}{3-\beta + \cfrac{2(1-\beta+\nu)(\eta'-\eta)x^k}{(4-\beta)(1+\eta x^k) + \dots + \cfrac{n(n-1-\beta+\nu)(\eta'-\eta)x^k}{(2n-\beta)(1+\eta x^k) + \cfrac{(n-\beta)(n+1-\nu)(\eta'-\eta)x^k}{2n+1-\beta + \dots}}}}}}. \quad (1.30)$$

But in equation (1.29) η and η' are equally significant. Therefore from (1.30) one can derive another expansion for the solution of equation (1.29):

$$\gamma y = -\beta(1+\eta' x^k) - \cfrac{\beta(1-\mu)(\eta-\eta')x^k}{1-\beta + \cfrac{(\mu-\beta)(\eta-\eta')x^k}{(2-\beta)(1+\eta' x^k) + \cfrac{(1-\beta)(2-\mu)(\eta-\eta')x^k}{3-\beta + \cfrac{2(1-\beta+\mu)(\eta-\eta')x^k}{(4-\beta)(1+\eta' x^k) + \dots + \cfrac{n(n-1-\beta+\mu)(\eta-\eta')x^k}{(2n-\beta)(1+\eta' x^k) + \cfrac{(n-\beta)(n+1-\mu)(\eta-\eta')x^k}{2n+1-\beta + \dots}}}}}}, \quad (1.31)$$

where μ has the same meaning as at the beginning of this section and may be evaluated in terms of ν by interchanging η and η':

$$\mu = \frac{\beta' + \eta - \beta\eta'}{\eta - \eta'}.$$

Besides this the solution of equation (1.29) also has an expansion which may be derived from (1.24) (i.e. with $\gamma s = \beta - \nu$):

$$\gamma y = -\beta + [(\nu - \beta)\eta - \nu\eta']x^k + \cfrac{(\nu-\beta)(\eta'-\eta)x^k(1+\eta x^k)}{1-\beta+[(2+\nu-\beta)\eta-(1+\nu)\eta']x^k + \cfrac{2(1+\nu-\beta)(\eta'-\eta)x^k(1+\eta x^k)}{2-\beta+[(4+\nu-\beta)\eta-(2+\nu)\eta']x^k + \dots}}$$

$$\dots + \cfrac{n(n-1+\nu-\beta)(\eta'-\eta)x^k(1+\eta x^k)}{n-\beta+[(2n+\nu-\beta)\eta-(n+\nu)\eta']x^k+\dots}. \tag{1.32}$$

Exchanging the rôles of η and η' in (1.32), we derive yet another development of a solution of equation (1.29):

$$\gamma y = -\beta + [(\mu - \beta)\eta' - \mu\eta]x^k + \cfrac{(\mu-\beta)(\eta-\eta')x^k(1+\eta' x^k)}{1-\beta+[(2+\mu-\beta)\eta'-(1+\mu)\eta]x^k + \cfrac{2(1+\mu-\beta)(\eta-\eta')x^k(1+\eta' x^k)}{2-\beta+[(4+\mu-\beta)\eta'-(2+\mu)\eta]x^k + \dots}}$$

$$\dots + \cfrac{n(n-1+\mu-\beta)(\eta-\eta')x^k(1+\eta' x^k)}{n-\beta+[(2n+\mu-\beta)\eta'-(n+\mu)\eta]x^k+\dots}. \tag{1.33}$$

12. We now discuss what form the solution of equation (1.29) has if this solution is to be expressed with the aid of a definite integral. In order to accomplish this we put $x^k = t$ in equation (1.29), then

$$\frac{x}{k}\frac{dy}{dx} = \frac{\sqrt[k]{t}}{k}\frac{dy}{d\sqrt[k]{t}} = \sqrt[k]{t}\,\frac{dy}{t^{(1/k)-1}dt} = \frac{t\,dy}{dt},$$

and equation (1.29) becomes

$$(1+\eta' t)(1+\eta t)ty' + (\beta + \beta' t - \eta\eta' t^2)y + \gamma y^2 = 0,$$

i.e.

$$y' = -\frac{\beta + \beta' t - \eta\eta' t^2}{(1+\eta' t)(1+\eta t)t}\,y - \frac{\gamma y^2}{(1+\eta' t)(1+\eta t)t}.$$

We write $1/y = z$. The equation becomes

$$z' = \frac{\beta + \beta' t - \eta\eta' t^2}{(1 + \eta' t)(1 + \eta t)t} z + \frac{\gamma}{(1 + \eta' t)(1 + \eta t)t}.$$

We develop the first term on the right hand side as a proper fraction, and have

$$\frac{\beta + \beta' t - \eta\eta' t^2}{(1 + \eta' t)(1 + \eta t)t} = \frac{\beta}{t} - \frac{\nu\eta}{1 + \eta t} - \frac{\mu\eta'}{1 + \eta' t}.$$

A solution of the equation without the second term on the right hand side is as follows:

$$\ln \frac{z}{C} = \int \left(\frac{\beta}{t} - \frac{\nu\eta}{1 + \eta t} - \frac{\mu\eta'}{1 + \eta' t} \right) dt =$$

$$= \beta \ln t - \nu \ln (1 + \eta t) - \mu \ln (1 + \eta' t),$$

whence

$$z = C t^{\beta} (1 + \eta t)^{-\nu} (1 + \eta' t)^{-\mu}.$$

For a solution of the equation with the complete right hand side we have

$$C' t^{\beta} (1 + \eta t)^{-\nu} (1 + \eta' t)^{-\mu} = \frac{\gamma}{t(1 + \eta t)(1 + \eta' t)},$$

i.e.

$$C' = \gamma t^{-\beta-1} (1 + \eta t)^{\nu-1} (1 + \eta' t)^{\mu-1},$$

from which

$$C = \gamma \int_0^t t^{-\beta-1} (1 + \eta t)^{\nu-1} (1 + \eta' t)^{\mu-1} dt,$$

consequently

$$z = \gamma t^{\beta} (1 + \eta t)^{-\nu} (1 + \eta' t)^{-\mu} \int_0^t t^{-\beta-1} (1 + \eta t)^{\nu-1} (1 + \eta' t)^{\mu-1} dt$$

and

$$\gamma y = \frac{t^{-\beta} (1 + \eta t)^{\nu} (1 + \eta' t)^{\mu}}{\int_0^t t^{-\beta-1} (1 + \eta t)^{\nu-1} (1 + \eta' t)^{\mu-1} dt}.$$

Replacing t by x^k, we have finally:

$$\gamma y = \frac{x^{-k\beta}(1+\eta x^k)^{\nu}(1+\eta' x^k)^{\mu}}{\int\limits_0^x x^{-k\beta-k}(1+\eta x^k)^{\nu-1}(1+\eta' x^k)^{\mu-1} k x^{k-1}\, dx},$$

i.e.

$$\gamma y = \frac{x^{-k\beta}(1+\eta x^k)^{\nu}(1+\eta' x^k)^{\mu}}{k\int\limits_0^x x^{-k\beta-1}(1+\eta x^k)^{\nu-1}(1+\eta' x^k)^{\mu-1}\, dx}. \tag{1.34}$$

13. The expansions of the solutions of equation (1.12) were derived under the assumption that $\eta' \neq \eta$. We assume now that $\eta' = \eta$. Then, since

$$m\gamma = \frac{\gamma\delta}{\eta'-\eta}, \quad \nu = \frac{\beta'+\eta'-\beta\eta}{\eta'-\eta},$$

we have

$$\lim_{\eta'\to\eta}[m\gamma + n(n-1-\beta+\nu)](\eta'-\eta) = \gamma\delta + n(\beta'+\eta-\beta\eta),$$

$$\lim_{\eta'\to\eta}[m\gamma + (n-\beta)(n+1-\nu)](\eta'-\eta) = \gamma\delta - (n-\beta)(\beta'+\eta-\beta\eta).$$

Therefore when $\eta' = \eta$ equation (1.12) and its solution (1.13) (with $\gamma s = \beta$) become

$$(1+\eta x^k)^2\frac{xy'}{k} + (\beta+\beta' x^k - \eta^2 x^{2k})y + \gamma y^2 = \delta x^k(1+\eta x^k) \tag{1.35}$$

and

$$\gamma y = -\beta(1+\eta x^k) +$$

$$+\frac{[\gamma\delta+\beta(\beta'+\eta-\beta\eta)]x^k}{1-\beta} + \frac{(\gamma\delta+\beta'+\eta-\beta\eta)x^k}{(2-\beta)(1+\eta x^k)} +$$

$$+\frac{[\gamma\delta-(1-\beta)(\beta'+\eta-\beta\eta)]x^k}{3-\beta} + \frac{[\gamma\delta+2(\beta'+\eta-\beta\eta)]x^k}{(4-\beta)(1+\eta x^k)} + \dots$$

$$\dots + \frac{[\gamma\delta+n(\beta'+\eta-\beta\eta)]x^k}{(2n-\beta)(1+\eta x^k)} + \frac{[\gamma\delta-(n-\beta)(\beta'+\eta-\beta\eta)]x^k}{2n+1-\beta} + \dots. \tag{1.36}$$

Besides the two limits already found, we consider the further two

$$\lim_{\eta'\to\eta} [(\nu - \beta)\eta - \nu\eta'] = -\beta' - \eta + \beta\eta - \beta\eta = -(\beta' + \eta),$$

$$\lim_{\eta'\to\eta} [(2n + \nu - \beta)\eta - (n + \nu)\eta'] = \\ = n\eta - \beta' - \eta + \beta\eta - \beta\eta = (n - 1)\eta - \beta'.$$

Therefore from (1.24) (with $\gamma s = \beta - \nu$) we obtain the following expansion for the solution of equation (1.35):

$$\gamma y = -\beta - (\beta' + \eta)x^k + \frac{(\gamma\delta + \beta' + \eta - \beta\eta)x^k(1 + \eta x^k)}{1 - \beta - \beta' x^k} + \\ + \frac{[\gamma\delta + 2(\beta' + \eta - \beta\eta)]x^k(1 + \eta x^k)}{2 - \beta + (\eta - \beta')x^k} + \dots \\ \dots + \frac{[\gamma\delta + n(\beta' + \eta - \beta\eta)]x^k(1 + \eta x^k)}{n - \beta + [(n - 1)\eta - \beta']x^k} + \dots . \qquad (1.37)$$

14. We put $\delta = 0$ in equation (1.35). The equation becomes

$$(1 + \eta x^k)^2 \frac{xy'}{k} + (\beta + \beta' x^k - \eta^2 x^{2k})y + \gamma y^2 = 0, \qquad (1.38)$$

and (1.36) and (1.37) transpose into the following expansions of the solutions of equation (1.38):

$$\gamma y = -\beta(1 + \eta x^k) + \\ + \frac{\beta(\beta' + \eta - \beta\eta)x^k}{1 - \beta} + \frac{(\beta' + \eta - \beta\eta)x^k}{(2 - \beta)(1 + \eta x^k)} - \frac{(1 - \beta)(\beta' + \eta - \beta\eta)x^k}{3 - \beta} + \\ + \frac{2(\beta' + \eta - \beta\eta)x^k}{(4 - \beta)(1 + \eta x^k)} - \dots + \frac{n(\beta' + \eta - \beta\eta)x^k}{(2n - \beta)(1 + \eta x^k)} - \\ - \frac{(n - \beta)(\beta' + \eta - \beta\eta)x^k}{2n + 1 - \beta} + \dots \qquad (1.39)$$

and

$$\gamma y = -\beta - (\beta' + \eta)x^k + \\ + \frac{(\beta' + \eta - \beta\eta)x^k(1 + \eta x^k)}{1 - \beta - \beta' x^k} + \frac{2(\beta' + \eta - \beta\eta)x^k(1 + \eta x^k)}{2 - \beta + (\eta - \beta')x^k} + \dots \\ \dots + \frac{n(\beta' + \eta - \beta\eta)x^k(1 + \eta x^k)}{n - \beta + [(n - 1)\eta - \beta']x^k} + \dots . \qquad (1.40)$$

15. We discuss what form the solution of equation (1.38) has when $\eta \neq 0$, if this solution is to be represented with the help of a definite integral. In order to do this we write $x^k = t$ in equation (1.38). Then (c.f. section 12) the equation becomes

$$(1 + \eta t)^2 t y' + (\beta + \beta' t - \eta^2 t^2) y + \gamma y^2 = 0,$$

i.e.

$$y' = -\frac{\beta + \beta' t - \eta^2 t^2}{(1 + \eta t)^2 t} y - \frac{\gamma y^2}{(1 + \eta t)^2 t}.$$

We put $1/y = z$. The equation becomes

$$z' = \frac{\beta + \beta' t - \eta^2 t^2}{(1 + \eta t)^2 t} z + \frac{\gamma}{(1 + \eta t)^2 t}.$$

We expand the first term in the sum on the right hand side as a proper fraction. We have

$$\frac{\beta + \beta' t - \eta^2 t^2}{(1 + \eta t)^2 t} = \frac{\beta}{t} - \frac{\eta(\beta + 1)}{1 + \eta t} + \frac{\beta' + \eta - \beta\eta}{(1 + \eta t)^2}.$$

A solution of the equation without the second term on the right hand side has the following form:

$$\ln \frac{z}{C} = \int \left[\frac{\beta}{t} - \frac{\eta(\beta + 1)}{1 + \eta t} + \frac{\beta' + \eta - \beta\eta}{(1 + \eta t)^2} \right] dt =$$

$$= \beta \ln t - (\beta + 1) \ln (1 + \eta t) - \frac{\beta' + \eta - \beta\eta}{\eta(1 + \eta t)},$$

consequently,

$$z = C t^{\beta} (1 + \eta t)^{-\beta - 1} e^{-\frac{\beta' + \eta - \beta\eta}{\eta(1 + \eta t)}}.$$

For a solution of the equation with the complete right hand side we have

$$C' t^{\beta} (1 + \eta t)^{-\beta - 1} e^{-\frac{\beta' + \eta - \beta\eta}{\eta(1 + \eta t)}} = \frac{\gamma}{(1 + \eta t)^2 t};$$

$$C' = \gamma t^{-\beta - 1} (1 + \eta t)^{\beta - 1} e^{\frac{\beta' + \eta - \beta\eta}{\eta(1 + \eta t)}}.$$

From which

$$C = \gamma \int_0^t t^{-\beta - 1} (1 + \eta t)^{\beta - 1} e^{\frac{\beta' + \eta - \beta\eta}{\eta(1 + \eta t)}} dt,$$

and therefore

$$z = \gamma t^{\beta}(1+\eta t)^{-\beta-1} e^{-\frac{\beta'+\eta-\beta\eta}{\eta(1+\eta t)}} \int\limits_0^t t^{-\beta-1}(1+\eta t)^{\beta-1} e^{\frac{\beta'+\eta-\beta\eta}{\eta(1+\eta t)}}\, dt$$

and

$$\gamma y = \frac{t^{-\beta}(1+\eta t)^{\beta+1} e^{\frac{\beta'+\eta-\beta\eta}{\eta(1+\eta t)}}}{\int\limits_0^t t^{-\beta-1}(1+\eta t)^{\beta-1} e^{\frac{\beta'+\eta-\beta\eta}{\eta(1+\eta t)}}\, dt}.$$

Replacing t by x^k, we have finally

$$\gamma y = \frac{x^{-k\beta}(1+\eta x^k)^{\beta+1} e^{\frac{\beta'+\eta-\beta\eta}{\eta(1+\eta x^k)}}}{\int\limits_0^x x^{-k\beta-k}(1+\eta x^k)^{\beta-1} e^{\frac{\beta'+\eta-\beta\eta}{\eta(1+\eta x^k)}} kx^{k-1}\, dx},$$

i.e.

$$\gamma y = \frac{x^{-k\beta}(1+\eta x^k)^{\beta+1} e^{\frac{\beta'+\eta-\beta\eta}{\eta(1+\eta x^k)}}}{k\int\limits_0^x x^{-k\beta-1}(1+\eta x^k)^{\beta-1} e^{\frac{\beta'+\eta-\beta\eta}{\eta(1+\eta x^k)}}\, dx}. \tag{1.41}$$

§ 2. Continued Fraction Expansions of Binomial Functions

1. We put in (1.34) $k = 1$, $\beta = -1$, $\eta' = 0$, $\eta = 0$. Then

$$\gamma y = \frac{x(1+x)^{\nu}}{\int\limits_0^x (1+x)^{\nu-1} dx} = \frac{\nu x(1+x)^{\nu}}{(1+x)^{\nu}-1}, \qquad \mu = 1+\beta-\nu = -\nu,$$

whence

$$(1+x)^{\nu}(\gamma y - \nu x) = \gamma y, \quad (1+x)^{\nu} = \frac{1}{1-\dfrac{\nu x}{\gamma y}}.$$

Expansion (1.30) gives:

$$(1+x)^\nu = \frac{1}{1} - \frac{\nu x}{1+x} - \frac{(1-\nu)x}{2} - \frac{(1+\nu)x}{3(1+x)} - \frac{2(2-\nu)x}{4} - \dots$$

$$\dots - \frac{n(n-\nu)x}{2n} - \frac{n(n+\nu)x}{(2n+1)(1+x)} - \dots,$$

i.e.

$$(1+x)^\nu = \frac{1}{1} - \frac{\nu x}{1+x} - \frac{(1-\nu)x}{2} - \frac{(1+\nu)x}{3(1+x)} - \frac{(2-\nu)x}{2} - \dots$$

$$\dots - \frac{(n-\nu)x}{2} - \frac{(n+\nu)x}{(2n+1)(1+x)} - \dots. \tag{2.1}$$

Expansion (1.31) gives:

$$(1+x)^\nu = \frac{1}{1} - \frac{\nu x}{1} + \frac{(1+\nu)x}{2} + \frac{(1-\nu)x}{3} + \frac{(2+\nu)x}{2} +$$

$$+ \frac{(2-\nu)x}{5} + \dots + \frac{(n+\nu)x}{2} + \frac{(n-\nu)x}{2n+1} + \dots. \tag{2.2}$$

Here (c.f. formulae (2.5) and (7.1) of chapter I)

$$\lim_{n\to\infty} \frac{n+\nu}{2(2n-1)} = \frac{1}{4}, \qquad \lim_{n\to\infty} \frac{n-\nu}{2(2n+1)} = \frac{1}{4}.$$

Therefore according to the theorem of section 17, § 7, chapter I, the continued fraction (2.2) converges in the finite complex x-plane, cut along the negative real axis from $x = -\infty$ to $x = -1$.

Expansion (1.32) gives:

$$(1+x)^\nu = \frac{1}{1} - \frac{\nu x}{1+(1+\nu)x} - \frac{(1+\nu)x(1+x)}{2+(3+\nu)x} -$$

$$- \frac{2(2+\nu)x(1+x)}{3+(5+\nu)x} - \dots - \frac{n(n+\nu)x(1+x)}{n+1+(2n+1+\nu)x} - \dots. \tag{2.3}$$

Expansion (1.33) gives:

$$(1+x)^\nu = \frac{1}{1} - \frac{\nu x}{1+\nu x} + \frac{(1-\nu)x}{2-(1-\nu)x} +$$

$$+ \frac{2(2-\nu)x}{3-(2-\nu)x} + \dots + \frac{n(n-\nu)x}{n+1-(n-\nu)x} + \dots. \tag{2.4}$$

Replacing ν by $-\nu$, we obtain from (2.1), (2.2):

$$(1+x)^\nu = 1 + \frac{\nu x}{1+x} - \frac{(1+\nu)x}{2} - \frac{(1-\nu)x}{3(1+x)} - \frac{(2+\nu)x}{2} - \dots$$

$$\dots - \frac{(n+\nu)x}{2} - \frac{(n-\nu)x}{(2n+1)(1+x)} - \dots, \tag{2.5}$$

$$(1+x)^\nu = 1 + \frac{\nu x}{1} + \frac{(1-\nu)x}{2} + \frac{(1+\nu)x}{3} + \frac{(2-\nu)x}{2} + \dots$$

$$\dots + \frac{(n-\nu)x}{2} + \frac{(n+\nu)x}{2n+1} + \dots \tag{2.6}$$

$$\frac{P_{2n}}{Q_{2n}} \qquad \frac{P_{2n+1}}{Q_{2n+1}}$$

(Lagrange [43]). The domain of convergence of the continued fraction (2.6) coincides with that of (2.2). In exactly the same way we obtain from (2.3), (2.4):

$$(1+x)^\nu = 1 + \frac{\nu x}{1+(1-\nu)x} - \frac{(1-\nu)x(1+x)}{2+(3-\nu)x} - \dots$$

$$\dots - \frac{n(n-\nu)x(1+x)}{n+1+(2n+1-\nu)x} - \dots, \tag{2.7}$$

$$(1+x)^\nu = 1 + \frac{\nu x}{1-\nu x} + \frac{(1+\nu)x}{2-(1+\nu)x} +$$

$$+ \frac{2(2+\nu)x}{3-(2+\nu)x} + \dots + \frac{n(n+\nu)x}{n+1-(n+\nu)x} + \dots. \tag{2.8}$$

2. We consider for instance the continued fraction expansion for $\sqrt[3]{2}$. For this we put in expansions (2.1)–(2.8) $x = 1$, $\nu = \frac{1}{3}$:

$$1)\ \sqrt[3]{2} = \frac{1}{1} - \frac{1}{6} - \frac{2}{2} - \frac{4}{18} - \frac{5}{2} - \dots$$

$$\frac{0}{1} \quad \frac{1}{1} \quad \frac{6}{5} \quad \frac{10}{8} \quad \frac{156}{124} \quad \frac{262}{208}$$

$$1{\cdot}2 \quad 1{\cdot}25 \quad 1{\cdot}258 \quad 1{\cdot}2596$$

$$\dots - \frac{3n-1}{2} - \frac{3n+1}{6(2n+1)} - \dots$$

$$2)\quad \sqrt[3]{2} = \frac{1}{1} - \frac{1}{3} + \frac{4}{2} + \frac{2}{9} + \frac{7}{2} + \frac{5}{15} + \dots$$

$$\frac{0}{1}\quad \frac{1}{1}\quad \frac{3}{2}\quad \frac{10}{8}\quad \frac{96}{76}\quad \frac{262}{208}$$

$$1{\cdot}5\quad 1{\cdot}25\quad 1{\cdot}263\quad 1{\cdot}2596$$

$$\dots + \frac{3n+1}{2} + \frac{3n-1}{3(2n+1)} + \dots$$

$$3)\quad \sqrt[3]{2} = \frac{1}{1} - \frac{1}{7} - \frac{24}{16} - \frac{84}{25} - \frac{180}{34} - \dots$$

$$\dots - \frac{6n(3n+1)}{9n+7} - \dots =$$

$$= \frac{1}{1} - \frac{1}{7} - \frac{12}{8} - \frac{42}{25} - \frac{90}{17} - \dots$$

$$\frac{0}{1}\quad \frac{1}{1}\quad \frac{7}{6}\quad \frac{44}{36}\quad \frac{806}{648}$$

$$1{\cdot}17\quad 1{\cdot}22\quad 1{\cdot}244$$

$$4)\quad \sqrt[3]{2} = \frac{1}{1} - \frac{1}{4} + \frac{6}{4} + \frac{30}{4} + \dots + \frac{3n(3n-1)}{4} + \dots;$$

$$\frac{0}{1}\quad \frac{1}{1}\quad \frac{4}{3}\quad \frac{22}{18}\quad \frac{208}{162}$$

$$1{\cdot}33\quad 1{\cdot}22\quad 1{\cdot}284$$

$$5)\quad \sqrt[3]{2} = 1 + \frac{1}{6} - \frac{4}{2} - \frac{2}{18} - \frac{7}{2} - \frac{5}{30} - \dots$$

$$\frac{1}{1}\quad \frac{7}{6}\quad \frac{10}{8}\quad \frac{166}{132}\quad \frac{262}{208}$$

$$1{\cdot}17\quad 1{\cdot}25\quad 1{\cdot}258\quad 1{\cdot}2596$$

$$\dots - \frac{3n+1}{2} - \frac{3n-1}{6(2n+1)} - \dots;$$

$$6)\quad \sqrt[3]{2} = 1 + \frac{1}{3} \underset{+}{} \frac{2}{2} \underset{+}{} \frac{4}{9} \underset{+}{} \frac{5}{2} + \ldots + \frac{3n-1}{2} + \frac{3n+1}{3(2n+1)} + \ldots;$$

$$\begin{array}{ccccc} \frac{1}{1} & \frac{4}{3} & \frac{10}{8} & \frac{106}{84} & \frac{262}{208} \\ & 1{\cdot}33 & 1{\cdot}25 & 1{\cdot}262 & 1{\cdot}2596 \end{array}$$

$$7)\quad \sqrt[3]{2} = 1 + \frac{1}{5} \underset{-}{} \frac{12}{14} \underset{-}{} \frac{60}{23} - \ldots - \frac{6n(3n-1)}{9n+5} - \ldots;$$

$$\begin{array}{cccc} \frac{1}{1} & \frac{6}{5} & \frac{72}{58} & \frac{1296}{1034} \\ & 1{\cdot}2 & 1{\cdot}241 & 1{\cdot}253 \end{array}$$

$$8)\quad \sqrt[3]{2} = 1 + \frac{1}{2} \underset{+}{} \frac{12}{2} \underset{+}{} \frac{42}{2} + \ldots + \frac{3n(3n+1)}{2} + \ldots$$

$$\begin{array}{cccc} \frac{1}{1} & \frac{3}{2} & \frac{18}{16} & \frac{162}{116} \\ & 1{\cdot}5 & 1{\cdot}125 & 1{\cdot}395 \end{array}$$

3. We wish to derive the even part of expansion (2.6). For this it is necessary to apply formula (2.8) of chapter I to expansion (2.6) and use on the other hand identity (2.1). But it is simpler here to reproduce all the calculations independently, as in the derivation of formula (2.8) chapter I. In the notation of formula (1.2) section 2 § 1 chapter I we have the equations

$$\begin{aligned} P_{2n} &= 2P_{2n-1} + (n-\nu)xP_{2n-2}, \\ P_{2n+1} &= (2n+1)P_{2n} + (n+\nu)xP_{2n-1}, \\ P_{2n+2} &= 2P_{2n+1} + (n+1-\nu)xP_{2n}. \end{aligned}$$

Multiplying the first of these equations by $-(n+\nu)x$, the second by 2 and adding the resulting equations to the third, we obtain

$$P_{2n+2} = [(n+\nu+n+1-\nu)x + 2(2n+1)]P_{2n} - (n^2-\nu^2)x^2P_{2n-2},$$

i.e.

$$P_{2n+2} = (2n+1)(2+x)P_{2n} - (n^2 - \nu^2)P_{2n-2}.$$

Similar relationships connect Q_{2n-2}, Q_{2n}, Q_{2n+2}. Consequently (Euler [21])

$$(1+x)^\nu = 1 + \frac{2\nu x}{2+(1-\nu)x} - \frac{(1-\nu^2)x^2}{3(2+x)} - \\ - \frac{(4-\nu^2)x^2}{5(2+x)} - \ldots - \frac{(n^2-\nu^2)x^2}{(2n+1)(2+x)} - \ldots. \tag{2.9}$$

4. From (2.9) we derive

$$\frac{2\nu x}{(1+x)^\nu - 1} = 2 + (1-\nu)x + \\ + \frac{(\nu^2-1)x^2}{3(2+x)} + \frac{(\nu^2-4)x^2}{5(2+x)} + \ldots + \frac{(\nu^2-n^2)x^2}{(2n+1)(2+x)} + \ldots$$

and further

$$\nu x \frac{(1+x)^\nu + 1}{(1+x)^\nu - 1} = 2 + x + \\ + \frac{(\nu^2-1)x^2}{3(2+x)} + \frac{(\nu^2-4)x^2}{5(2+x)} + \ldots + \frac{(\nu^2-n^2)x^2}{(2n+1)(2+x)} + \ldots.$$

We put in this expression $x/(2+x) = z$, i.e. put

$$x = 2z + xz, \quad x = \frac{2z}{1-z}, \quad 1 + x = \frac{1+z}{1-z},$$

$$2 + x = \frac{2}{1-z},$$

and obtain a certain continued fraction. After this continued fraction has been derived we shall write x instead of z. The continued fraction then becomes

$$\nu x \frac{(1+x)^\nu + (1-x)^\nu}{(1+x)^\nu - (1-x)^\nu} = \\ = 1 + \frac{(\nu^2-1)x^2}{3} + \frac{(\nu^2-4)x^2}{5} + \ldots + \frac{(\nu^2-n^2)x^2}{2n+1} + \ldots. \tag{2.10}$$

Here (c.f. formulae (2.5) and (7.1) of chapter I)

$$c_n = \frac{(\nu^2 - n^2)}{(4n^2 - 1)},$$

therefore

$$\lim_{n\to\infty} c_n = \lim_{n\to\infty} \frac{\nu^2 - n^2}{4n^2 - 1} = -\frac{1}{4}.$$

Consequently (according to the theorem of section 17, § 7, chapter I) the continued fraction (2.10) converges throughout the whole finite complex x^2-plane, with the exception of that segment of the real axis satisfying the inequality $1 \leqslant x^2 \leqslant \infty$. Hence the continued fraction (2.10) converges throughout the whole of the finite complex x-plane with the exception of those sections of the real axis satisfying the inequalities $-\infty \leqslant x \leqslant -1$ and $1 \leqslant x \leqslant \infty$.

5. One can transcribe the continued fraction (2.10) as

$$\frac{(1+x)^\nu - (1-x)^\nu}{(1+x)^\nu + (1-x)^\nu} =$$

$$= \frac{\nu x}{1} \; \genfrac{}{}{0pt}{}{}{+} \; \frac{(\nu^2-1)x^2}{3} \; \genfrac{}{}{0pt}{}{}{+} \; \frac{(\nu^2-4)x^2}{5} \; \genfrac{}{}{0pt}{}{}{+ \dots +} \; \frac{(\nu^2-n^2)x^2}{2n+1} \; \genfrac{}{}{0pt}{}{}{+ \dots}. \tag{2.11}$$

Replacing x by $1/x$ in (2.10), we obtain

$$\nu \frac{(x+1)^\nu + (x-1)^\nu}{(x+1)^\nu - (x-1)^\nu} =$$

$$= x + \frac{\nu^2 - 1}{3x} \; \genfrac{}{}{0pt}{}{}{+} \; \frac{\nu^2 - 4}{5x} \; \genfrac{}{}{0pt}{}{}{+ \dots +} \; \frac{\nu^2 - n^2}{(2n+1)x} \; \genfrac{}{}{0pt}{}{}{+ \dots}. \tag{2.12}$$

From this we successively derive the following continued fractions:

$$2\nu \frac{(x-1)^\nu}{(x+1)^\nu - (x-1)^\nu} =$$

$$= x - \nu + \frac{\nu^2 - 1}{3x} \; \genfrac{}{}{0pt}{}{}{+} \; \frac{\nu^2 - 4}{5x} \; \genfrac{}{}{0pt}{}{}{+ \dots +} \; \frac{\nu^2 - n^2}{(2n+1)x} \; \genfrac{}{}{0pt}{}{}{+ \dots},$$

$$\frac{(x+1)^\nu - (x-1)^\nu}{(x-1)^\nu} =$$

$$= \frac{2\nu}{x - \nu} \; \genfrac{}{}{0pt}{}{}{+} \; \frac{\nu^2 - 1}{3x} \; \genfrac{}{}{0pt}{}{}{+} \; \frac{\nu^2 - 4}{5x} \; \genfrac{}{}{0pt}{}{}{+ \dots +} \; \frac{\nu^2 - n^2}{(2n+1)x} \; \genfrac{}{}{0pt}{}{}{+ \dots},$$

$$\left(\frac{x+1}{x-1}\right)^\nu = 1 + \frac{2\nu}{x-\nu+} \frac{\nu^2-1}{3x} + \frac{\nu^2-4}{5x} + \dots$$

$$\dots + \frac{\nu^2-n^2}{(2n+1)x} + \dots. \tag{2.13}$$

Expansion (2.13) was derived by Laguerre [47].

6. When $|x| > 1$ we have

$$\left(\frac{x+1}{x-1}\right)^\nu = e^{\nu \ln \frac{x+1}{x-1}},$$

replacing x, ν in this relation by ix, $i\nu$, we obtain

$$\left(\frac{ix+1}{ix-1}\right)^{\nu i} = e^{2\nu \arctan \frac{1}{x}}.$$

Consequently from (2.13) we have:

$$e^{2\nu \arctan x} = 1 + \frac{2\nu}{x-\nu+} \frac{\nu^2+1}{3x} + \frac{\nu^2+4}{5x} + \dots$$

$$\dots + \frac{\nu^2+n^2}{(2n+1)x} + \dots. \tag{2.14}$$

For $\nu = \frac{1}{2}$ this expansion was derived by Laguerre [47], for arbitrary ν it was derived by Perron [73]. Since

$$\lim_{\nu \to 0} \frac{e^{2\nu \arctan x} - 1}{2\nu} = \arctan x,$$

then the expansion

$$\arctan x = \frac{1}{x} + \frac{1}{3x} + \frac{4}{5x} + \dots + \frac{n^2}{(2n+1)x} + \dots$$

can be derived from (2.14) with $\nu = 0$ (c.f. § 6 of this chapter).

7. Euler [21] replaced x by $i \tan \varphi$ in (2.11). Then

$$(1 \pm x)^\nu = \frac{(\cos\varphi \pm i \sin\varphi)^\nu}{\cos^\nu \varphi} = \frac{\cos \nu\varphi \pm i \sin \nu\varphi}{\cos^\nu \varphi},$$

$$\frac{(1+x)^\nu - (1-x)^\nu}{(1+x)^\nu + (1-x)^\nu} = \frac{2i \sin \nu\varphi}{2 \cos \nu\varphi} = i \tan \nu\varphi$$

and (2.11) becomes

$$\tan \nu\varphi = \frac{\nu \tan \varphi}{1} - \frac{(\nu^2 - 1) \tan^2 \varphi}{3} - \frac{(\nu^2 - 4) \tan^2 \varphi}{5} - \ldots$$

$$\ldots - \frac{(\nu^2 - n^2) \tan^2 \varphi}{2n + 1} - \ldots . \qquad (2.15)$$

In particular,

$$\tan 2\varphi = \frac{2 \tan \varphi}{1 - \tan^2 \varphi},$$

$$\tan 3\varphi = \frac{3 \tan \varphi}{1} - \frac{8 \tan^2 \varphi}{3} - \frac{\tan^2 \varphi}{1},$$

$$\frac{0}{1} \quad \frac{3 \tan \varphi}{1} \quad \frac{9 \tan \varphi}{3 - 8 \tan^2 \varphi} \quad \frac{(9 - 3 \tan^2 \varphi) \tan \varphi}{3 - 9 \tan^2 \varphi} =$$

$$= \frac{3 - \tan^2 \varphi}{1 - 3 \tan^2 \varphi} \tan \varphi.$$

8. In conclusion we show the expansion of quadratic irrational numbers in continued fractions by elementary methods. Let $\sqrt{x} \doteq a$. Then

$$\sqrt{x} = a + (\sqrt{x} - a) = a + \frac{x - a^2}{a + \sqrt{x}}.$$

Consequently,

$$\sqrt{x} = a + \frac{x - a^2}{2a} + \frac{x - a^2}{2a} + \ldots . \qquad (2.16)$$

One can rewrite this continued fraction as

$$\sqrt{x} = a + \frac{\frac{x - a^2}{2a}}{1} + \frac{\frac{x - a^2}{4a^2}}{1} + \ldots + \frac{\frac{x - a^2}{4a^2}}{1} + \ldots .$$

Write $(x - a^2)/(4a^2) = z$. Then according to section 4, § 7 of chapter I the continued fraction (2.16) converges in the complex z-plane with the exception of that segment of the real axis satisfying the inequality $-\infty < z \leqslant -\frac{1}{4}$. Consequently the continued fraction (2.16) converges in the complex x-plane, with the exception of those segments of the real axis satisfying the inequalities

$$-\infty < \frac{x-a^2}{4a^2} \leqslant -\frac{1}{4},$$

i.e.

$$-\infty < x - a^2 \leqslant -a^2; \qquad -\infty < x \leqslant 0.$$

Putting in (2.16) $a = 1$, we have

$$\sqrt{x} = 1 + \frac{x-1}{2}\,{+}\,\frac{x-1}{2}\,{+}\,\frac{x-1}{2}\,{+}\,\frac{x-1}{2}\,{+}\dots.$$

$$\frac{1}{1} \quad \frac{x+1}{2} \quad \frac{3x+1}{x+3} \quad \frac{x^2+6x+1}{4x+4} \quad \frac{5x^2+10x+1}{x^2+10x+5}$$

§ 3. The Continued Fraction Expansion of $\sqrt[x]{x}$

1. The expression $\sqrt[n]{n}$ is often encountered in the theory of series and for this reason n is usually taken to be a positive whole number. We consider the expression $\sqrt[x]{x}$, assuming that $x \geqslant 1$.

Replacing $1 + x$ by x and putting $\nu = 1/x$ in (2.6) we have

$$x^{1/x} = 1 + \frac{x-1}{x}\,{+}\,\frac{(x-1)^2}{2}\,{+}\,\frac{x^2-1}{3x}\,{+}$$

$$\frac{1}{1} \quad \frac{2x-1}{x} \quad \frac{x^2+2x-1}{x^2+1} \quad \frac{5x^3+5x^2-5x+1}{4x^3+2x}$$

$$+\,\frac{(2x-1)(x-1)}{2}\,{+}\dots{+}\,\frac{(nx-1)(x-1)}{2}\,{+}\,\frac{(nx+1)(x-1)}{(2n+1)x}\,{+}\dots. \tag{3.1}$$

$$\frac{2x^4+11x^3+3x^2-5x+1}{2x^4+5x^3+3x^2+x+1}$$

From this

$$1 \leqslant \frac{x^2+2x-1}{x^2+1} \leqslant \frac{2x^4+11x^3+3x^2-5x+1}{2x^4+5x^3+3x^2+x+1} \leqslant \dots \leqslant \sqrt[x]{x} \leqslant \dots$$

$$\dots \leqslant \frac{5x^3+5x^2-5x+1}{4x^3+2x} \leqslant \frac{2x-1}{x}. \tag{3.2}$$

2. Replacing $1 + x$ by x and writing $\nu = 1/x$ in (2.9), we have

$$\sqrt[x]{x} = 1 + \frac{2(x-1)}{x^2+1} - \frac{(x^2-1)(x-1)^2}{3x(x+1)} - \frac{(4x^2-1)(x-1)^2}{5x(x+1)} - \dots$$
$$\dots - \frac{(n^2x^2-1)(x-1)^2}{(2n+1)(x+1)} - \dots . \quad (3.3)$$

This continued fraction is the even part of expansion (3.1).

§ 4. Continued Fraction Expansions of the Natural Logarithm

1. We write in (1.34) $k = 1$, $\beta = -1$, $\eta' = 0$, $\eta = 1$ and let ν tend to zero. Then

$$\gamma y = \lim_{\nu \to 0} \frac{x(1+x)^\nu}{\int_0^x (1+x)^{\nu-1} dx} = \lim_{\nu \to 0} \frac{\nu x(1+x)^\nu}{(1+x)^\nu - 1} =$$
$$= \lim_{\nu \to 0} \frac{x(1+x)^\nu + \nu x(1+x)^\nu \ln(1+x)}{(1+x)^\nu \ln(1+x)} = \frac{x}{\ln(1+x)}.$$

With the same substitutions, expansion (1.30) gives the continued fraction expansion of the natural logarithm

$$\ln(1+x) = \frac{x}{1+x} - \frac{x}{2} - \frac{x}{3(1+x)} - \frac{2x}{2} - \frac{2x}{5(1+x)} - \dots$$
$$\dots - \frac{nx}{2} - \frac{nx}{(2n+1)(1+x)} - \dots . \quad (4.1)$$

With the supplementary condition $\mu = 0$, expansion (1.31) gives yet another expansion for the natural logarithm:

$$\ln(1+x) = \frac{x}{1} + \frac{x}{2} + \frac{x}{3} + \frac{2x}{2} + \frac{2x}{5} + \dots + \frac{nx}{2} + \frac{nx}{2n+1} + \dots \quad (4.2)$$

(Lagrange [43]). Here

$$\lim_{n \to \infty} \frac{n}{2(2n-1)} = \lim_{n \to \infty} \frac{n}{2(2n+1)} = \frac{1}{4}.$$

According to the theorem of section 17, § 7, chapter I, therefore, the continued fraction (4.2) converges throughout the complex

x-plane, cut along the negative real axis from $x = -\infty$ to $x = -1$.

Expansion (1.32) gives

$$\ln(1+x) = \frac{x}{1+x} - \frac{x(1+x)}{2+3x} - \frac{4x(1+x)}{3+5x} - \dots$$
$$\dots - \frac{n^2x(1+x)}{n+1+(2n+1)x} - \dots. \tag{4.3}$$

In expansion (1.33), and also in expansion (1.31), we shall make the auxiliary stipulation $\mu = 0$, then we have

$$\ln(1+x) = \frac{x}{1} + \frac{x}{2-x} + \frac{4x}{3-2x} + \dots + \frac{n^2x}{n+1-nx} + \dots. \tag{4.4}$$

The continued fraction (4.4) is the equivalent continued fraction for $\ln(1+x)$.

2. Contracting the continued fraction (4.2) according to formula (2.8) of chapter I, we obtain

$$\ln(1+x) = \frac{2x}{2+x} - \frac{2x^2}{(6+x)2+4x} - \frac{4.4x^2}{(2.5+2x)2+2.3x} - \dots$$
$$\dots - \frac{4n^2x^2}{[2(2n+1)+nx]2+2(n+1)x} - \dots,$$

i.e.

$$\ln(1+x) = \frac{2x}{2+x} - \frac{x^2}{3(2+x)} - \frac{4x^2}{5(2+x)} - \dots$$
$$\dots - \frac{n^2x^2}{(2n+1)(2+x)} - \dots. \tag{4.5}$$

Replacing $1+x$ by x in (4.5) we have (Euler [21])

$$\ln x = \frac{2(x-1)}{x+1} - \frac{(x-1)^2}{3(x+1)} - \frac{4(x-1)^2}{5(x+1)} -$$
$$\frac{0}{1} \quad \frac{2(x-1)}{x+1} \quad \frac{6(x^2-1)}{2x^2+8x+2} \quad \frac{2(x-1)(11x^2+38x+11)}{6(x+1)(x^2+8x+1)}$$
$$- \frac{9(x-1)^2}{7(x+1)} - \dots - \frac{n^2(x-1)^2}{(2n+1)(x+1)} - \dots. \tag{4.6}$$
$$\frac{20(x^2-1)(5x^2+32x+5)}{24(x^4+16x^3+36x^2+16x+1)}$$

The convergents of expansion (46) are obtained from the even order convergents of expansion (4.2) (replacing in the latter $1 + x$ by x). Consequently, when $x \geqslant 1$, we have the sequence of inequalities

$$\ln x \geqslant \ldots \geqslant \frac{5(x^2-1)(5x^2+32x+5)}{6(x^4+16x^3+36x^2+16x+1)} \geqslant$$

$$\geqslant \frac{(x-1)(11x^2+38x+11)}{3(x+1)(x^2+8x+1)} \geqslant \frac{3(x^2-1)}{x^2+4x+1} \geqslant 2\frac{x-1}{x+1}. \tag{4.7}$$

For example,

$$\ln 2 > \ldots > 0{,}6931464 > 0{,}69312 > 0{,}6923 > 0{,}67$$

$$(\ln 2 \approx 0{,}6931472).$$

§ 5. Continued Fraction Expansions of e^x

1. Replace x by x/ν in expansions (2.1)–(2.8), and let ν tend to infinity.

Then expansions (2.1) and (2.2) give one and the same expansion

$$e^x = \frac{1}{1} - \frac{x}{1} + \frac{x}{2} - \frac{x}{3} + \frac{x}{2} - \frac{x}{5} + \ldots + \frac{x}{2} - \frac{x}{2n+1} + \ldots. \tag{5.1}$$

$$\frac{1}{1} \quad \frac{1}{1-x} \quad \frac{2+x}{2-x} \quad \frac{6+2x}{6-4x+x^2} \quad \frac{12+6x+x^2}{12-6x+x^2} \quad \frac{60+24x+3x^2}{60-36x+9x^2-x^3}$$

Here

$$\lim_{n\to\infty} \frac{1}{2(2n-1)} = \lim_{n\to\infty} \frac{-1}{2(2n+1)} = 0.$$

According to the theorem of section 3, § 7, chapter I, therefore, the continued fraction (5.1) converges throughout the whole of the finite complex x-plane.

Expansions (2.3) and (2.4) also yield the same expansion:

$$e^x = \frac{1}{1} - \frac{x}{1 + x} - \frac{x}{2 + x} - \frac{2x}{3 + x} - \dots - \frac{nx}{n + 1 + x} - \dots. \tag{5.2}$$

This is the equivalent continued fraction for e^x.

After the transformations denoted, expansions (2.5) and (2.6) reduce to the following:

$$\begin{array}{ccccccccccccc} e^x = 1 + & \frac{x}{1} & - & \frac{x}{2} & + & \frac{x}{3} & - & \frac{x}{2} & + & \frac{x}{5} & - \dots - & \frac{x}{2} + \frac{x}{2n+1} - \dots \\ & \frac{1}{1} & & \frac{1+x}{1} & & \frac{2+x}{2-x} & & \frac{6+4x+x^2}{6-2x} & & \frac{12+6x+x^2}{12-6x+x^2} & & \\ & & & & & & & & & \frac{60+36x+9x^2+x^3}{60-24x+3x^2} & & \end{array} \tag{5.3}$$

Here

$$\lim_{n\to\infty} \frac{-1}{(2n-1)2} = \lim_{n\to\infty} \frac{1}{(2n+1)2} = 0.$$

According to the theorem of section 3, § 7, chapter I, therefore, the continued fraction (5.3) converges throughout the whole finite complex x-plane. The expansion (5.3) is due to Lagrange [43].

From expansions (2.7) and (2.8) we obtain the following:

$$e^x = 1 + \frac{x}{1 - x} + \frac{x}{2 - x} + \frac{2x}{3 - x} + \dots + \frac{nx}{n + 1 - x} + \dots. \tag{5.4}$$

The right hand side of this continued fraction is obtained from (5.2) by replacing x by $-x$. Therefore the reciprocal of the continued fraction (5.4) is the equivalent continued fraction for e^{-x}.

2. Contracting (5.3) according to formula (2.8) of chapter I, we have

$$e^x = 1 - \frac{2x}{-2 + x} - \frac{2x^2}{6.2} + \frac{4x^2}{10.2} + \dots + \frac{4x^2}{4(2x + 1)} + \dots$$

(Euler [21]), i.e.

$$e^x = 1 + \frac{2x}{2 - x +} \quad \frac{x^2}{6} \quad + \quad \frac{x^2}{10} \quad +$$

$$\frac{1}{1} \quad \frac{2+x}{2-x} \quad \frac{12 + 6x + x^2}{12 - 6x + x^2} \quad \frac{120 + 60x + 12x^2 + x^3}{120 - 60x + 12x^2 - x^3}$$

$$+ \quad \frac{x^2}{14} \quad +$$

$$\frac{1680 + 840x + 180x^2 + 20x^3 + x^4}{1680 - 840x + 180x^2 - 20x^3 + x^4}$$

$$+ \quad \frac{x^2}{18} \quad + \dots$$

$$\frac{30240 + 15120x + 3360x^2 + 420x^3 + 30x^4 + x^5}{30240 - 15120x + 3360x^2 - 420x^3 + 30x^4 - x^5}$$

$$\dots + \frac{x^2}{2(2n+1)} + \dots \tag{5.5}$$

Replacing x by $-x$ in (5.5), we obtain:

$$e^x = \frac{1}{1} - \frac{2x}{2+x} + \frac{x^2}{6} + \frac{x^2}{10} + \dots + \frac{x^2}{2(2n+1)} \dots + .$$

This expansion has the same convergents as (5.5).

§ 6. Continued Fraction Expansions of the Inverse Trigonometric and Hyperbolic Functions

1. We recall the following relations:

$$\left.\begin{aligned} \arcsin x &= -i \ln (ix + \sqrt{1 - x^2}), \\ \arccos x &= -i \ln (x + i\sqrt{1 - x^2}), \\ \arctan x &= -\frac{i}{2} \ln \frac{1 + ix}{1 - ix}, \\ \operatorname{arccot} x &= +\frac{i}{2} \ln \frac{ix + 1}{ix - 1}, \end{aligned}\right\} \tag{6.1}$$

$$\left.\begin{aligned}\operatorname{arcsinh} x &= \ln\left(x + \sqrt{x^2+1}\right),\\ \operatorname{arccosh} x &= \ln\left(x + \sqrt{x^2-1}\right),\\ \operatorname{arctanh} x &= \frac{1}{2}\ln\frac{1+x}{1-x},\\ \operatorname{arccotanh} x &= \frac{1}{2}\ln\frac{x+1}{x-1}.\end{aligned}\right\} \tag{6.1}$$

From these

$$\left.\begin{aligned}&\operatorname{arcsinh} x = i \arcsin\frac{x}{i}, \quad \operatorname{arctanh} x = i \arctan\frac{x}{i},\\ &\operatorname{arccosh} x = i \arccos x, \quad \operatorname{arccotanh} x = -i \operatorname{arccotan}\frac{x}{i},\\ &\frac{\operatorname{arccosh} x}{\sqrt{x^2-1}} = \frac{\arccos x}{\sqrt{1-x^2}}.\end{aligned}\right\} \tag{6.2}$$

2. The differential equation for $y = \arctan x$ has the form

$$y' = \frac{1}{1+x^2}, \quad y(0) = 0.$$

Write $y = x/(1+z)$, then the equation transposes into

$$\frac{1+z-xz'}{(1+z)^2} = \frac{1}{1+x^2},$$

i.e.

$$x^2 + (1+x^2)z - (1+x^2)xz' = 2z + z^2,$$

or

$$(1+x^2)xz' + (1-x^2)z + z^2 = x^2. \tag{6.3}$$

Comparing equations (6.3) and (1.5), we see that here $k = 2$, $\eta' = 1$, $\beta = \gamma = \delta = \frac{1}{2}$, $\beta' = -\frac{1}{2}$. Therefore (1.18) gives the following solution for (6.3)

$$z = \cfrac{\frac{1}{2}x^2}{\frac{3}{2} + \cfrac{\left(\frac{1}{4} + \frac{3.1}{4}\right)x^2}{\frac{5}{2} + \cfrac{\left(\frac{1}{4} + 1 + \frac{1}{2} + \frac{1}{2}\right)x^2}{\frac{7}{2} + \cdots}}}$$

$$+ \frac{\left(\frac{1}{4} + \frac{5}{2} \cdot \frac{3}{2}\right) x^2}{\frac{9}{2}} + \ldots + \frac{\left[\frac{1}{4} + \frac{(2n+1)(2n-1)}{4}\right] x^2}{\frac{4n+1}{2}} +$$

$$+ \frac{\left(\frac{1}{4} + n^2 + \frac{n}{2} + \frac{n}{2}\right) x^2}{\frac{4n+3}{2}} + \ldots =$$

$$= \frac{x^2}{3} + \frac{4x^2}{5} + \frac{9x^2}{7} + \frac{16x^2}{9} + \ldots + \frac{4n^2x^2}{4n+1} + \frac{(2n+1)^2x^2}{4n+3} + \ldots .$$

From this (Lambert [48]),

$$\arctan x = \frac{x}{1+} \frac{x^2}{3} + \frac{4x^2}{5} + \frac{9x^2}{7} +$$

$$\frac{0}{1} \quad \frac{x}{1} \quad \frac{3x}{3+x^2} \quad \frac{15x+4x^3}{15+9x^2} \quad \frac{105x+55x^3}{105+90x^2+9x^4}$$

$$+ \frac{16x^2}{9} + \ldots + \frac{n^2x^2}{2n+1} + \ldots . \tag{6.4}$$

$$\frac{945x+735x^3+64x^5}{945+1050x^2+225x^4}$$

Here $\lim_{n\to\infty} n^2/(4n^2-1) = \frac{1}{4}$. According to the theorem of section 17, § 7, chapter I, therefore, the continued fraction (6.4) converges throughout the whole of the finite complex x^2-plane, with the exception of those segments of the imaginary axis $(-i\infty, -i]$, $[i, i\infty)$.

Since, when x is real, all coefficients (except the leading partial numerator) of the continued fraction (6.4) are positive, then we have the sequence of inequalities for positive real x

$$\frac{3x}{3+x^2} \leqslant \frac{105x+55x^3}{105+90x^2+9x^4} \leqslant \ldots \leqslant \arctan x \leqslant \ldots$$

$$\ldots \leqslant \frac{945x+735x^3+64x^5}{945+1050x^2+225x^4} \leqslant \frac{15x+4x^3}{15+9x^2} \leqslant x. \tag{6.5}$$

With the assistance of (6.2) we have from (6.4), replacing x by x/i:

$$\operatorname{arctanh} x = \frac{x}{1} \, \frac{}{-} \, \frac{x^2}{3} \, \frac{}{-} \, \frac{4x^2}{5} \, \frac{}{-} \cdots \frac{}{-} \, \frac{n^2x^2}{2n+1} \, \frac{}{-} \cdots . \tag{6.6}$$

Knowing the convergence domain of the continued fraction (6.4), we see that the continued fraction (6.6) converges throughout the whole of the finite complex x-plane with the exception of those segments of the real axis $(-\infty, -1], [1, \infty)$.

3. Noting that

$$[(2n+1)^2 - 4n^2]x^2(4n-3) \equiv [(2n-1)^2 - (2n-2)^2]x^2(4n+1),$$

it follows that

$$x^2 = \frac{9x^2 - 4x^2}{5} = \frac{16x^2 - 9x^2}{7} = \ldots = \frac{(2n+1)^2x^2 - 4n^2x^2}{4n+1} = \ldots,$$

i.e. condition (2.22) of chapter I is satisfied, and therefore it follows from identity (2.23) of chapter I that one can write the continued fraction (6.4) in the form

$$\arctan x = x - \frac{\frac{x^3}{3}}{\frac{x}{1}\;\frac{3x-x^3}{3}} \, \frac{}{+} \, \frac{\frac{9x^2}{5}}{\frac{15x+4x^3}{15+9x^2}} \, \frac{}{+} \, \frac{\frac{4x^2}{7}}{\frac{105x+40x^3-4x^5}{105+75x^2}} \, \frac{}{+}$$

$$\frac{}{+} \, \frac{25x^2}{9} \, \frac{}{+} \cdots \frac{}{+} \, \frac{(2n+1)^2x^2}{4n+1} \, \frac{}{+} \, \frac{4n^2x^2}{4n+3} \, \frac{}{+} \cdots . \tag{6.7}$$

From this

$$\operatorname{arctanh} x = x +$$

$$+ \frac{x^3}{3} \, \frac{}{-} \, \frac{9x^2}{5} \, \frac{}{-} \, \frac{4x^2}{7} \, \frac{}{-} \, \frac{25x^2}{9} \, \frac{}{-} \cdots \frac{}{-} \, \frac{(2n+1)^2x^2}{4n+1} \, \frac{}{-} \, \frac{4n^2x^2}{4n+3} \, \frac{}{-} \cdots . \tag{6.8}$$

The convergence domains of the continued fractions (6.7) and (6.8) coincide with the convergence domains of the continued fractions (6.4) and (6.6) respectively.

4. Noting that $\arctan(x/\sqrt{1-x^2}) = \arcsin x$, we derive from (6.4) the expansion for $\arcsin x$. Replacing x by $x/\sqrt{1-x^2}$ in (6.4)

$$\arcsin x = \frac{\dfrac{x}{\sqrt{1-x^2}}}{1} + \frac{\dfrac{x^2}{1-x^2}}{3} +$$

$$+ \frac{\dfrac{4x^2}{1-x^2}}{5} + \ldots + \frac{\dfrac{n^2x^2}{1-x^2}}{2n+1} + \ldots,$$

i.e.

$$\frac{\arcsin x}{\sqrt{1-x^2}} = \frac{x}{1-x^2} + \frac{x^2}{3} + \frac{4x^2}{5(1-x^2)} + \frac{9x^2}{7} + \ldots + \frac{4n^2x^2}{(4n+1)(1-x^2)} + \frac{(2n+1)^2x^2}{4n+3} + \ldots \quad (6.9)$$

$$\frac{0}{1} \quad \frac{x}{1-x^2} \quad \frac{3x}{3-2x^2} \quad \frac{15x-11x^3}{15-21x^2+6x^4} \quad \frac{105x-50x^3}{105-120x^2+24x^4}$$

According to (6.4) the continued fraction expansion of the function $\arcsin x = \arctan (x/\sqrt{1-x^2})$ converges throughout the whole of the finite complex x-plane with the exception of those segments of the real axis satisfying the inequality

$$-\infty < \frac{x^2}{1-x^2} \leqslant -1.$$

This inequality is equivalent to the inequality $1 \leqslant x^2 < \infty$. Therefore the continued fraction (6.9) converges throughout the whole of the finite complex x-plane with the exception of those segments of the real axis $(-\infty, -1]$ and $[1, \infty)$.

With the help of (6.2), we have from (6.9)

$$\frac{\operatorname{arcsinh} x}{\sqrt{1+x^2}} = \frac{x}{1+x^2} - \frac{x^2}{3} - \frac{4x^2}{5(1+x^2)} - \frac{9x^2}{7} - \ldots$$

$$\ldots - \frac{4n^2x^2}{(4n+1)(1+x^2)} - \frac{(2n+1)^2x^2}{4n+3} \ldots - . \quad (6.10)$$

5. Replacing x by $x/\sqrt{1-x^2}$ in (6.7) we obtain a second expansion for $\arcsin x$, and have

$$\arcsin x = \frac{\dfrac{x}{\sqrt{1-x^2}}}{1} - \frac{\dfrac{x^3}{(1-x^2)^{\frac{3}{2}}}}{3\;+}\;\frac{\dfrac{9x^2}{1-x^2}}{5\;+}\;\frac{\dfrac{4x^2}{1-x^2}}{7\;+}\cdots$$

$$\cdots\;+\frac{\dfrac{(2n+1)^2x^2}{1-x^2}}{4n+1}\;+\;\frac{\dfrac{4n^2x^2}{1-x^2}}{4n+3\;+}\cdots,$$

i.e.

$$\sqrt{1-x^2}\arcsin x = x - \frac{x^3}{3(1-x^2)\;+}\;\frac{9x^2}{5\;+}\;\frac{4x^2}{7(1-x^2)\;+}\cdots$$

$$\cdots\;+\frac{(2n+1)^2x^2}{4n+1}\;+\;\frac{4n^2x^2}{(4n+3)(1-x^2)\;+}\cdots. \qquad (6.11)$$

Replacing x by x/i in (6.11) and multiplying throughout by i, we obtain

$$\sqrt{1+x^2}\operatorname{arcsinh} x = x + \frac{x^3}{3(1+x^2)\;-}\;\frac{9x^2}{5\;-}\;\frac{4x^2}{7(1+x^2)\;-}\cdots$$

$$\cdots\;-\frac{(2n+1)^2x^2}{4n+1}\;-\;\frac{4n^2x^2}{(4n+3)(1+x^2)\;-}\cdots. \qquad (6.12)$$

6. Noting that $\arccos x = \arctan(\sqrt{1-x^2}/x)$, we replace x by $\sqrt{1-x^2}/x$ in (6.4) and obtain

$$\arccos x = \frac{\dfrac{\sqrt{1-x^2}}{x}}{1\;+}\;\frac{\dfrac{1-x^2}{x^2}}{3\;+}\;\frac{4\dfrac{1-x^2}{x^2}}{5\;+}$$

$$+\;\frac{9\dfrac{1-x^2}{x^2}}{7}\;+\cdots+\;\frac{n^2\dfrac{1-x^2}{x^2}}{2n+1\;+}\cdots,$$

i.e.

$$\frac{\arccos x}{\sqrt{1-x^2}} = \frac{1}{x\;+}\;\frac{1-x^2}{3x\;+}\;\frac{4(1-x^2)}{5x\;+}\;\frac{9(1-x^2)}{7x\;+}\cdots$$

$$\frac{0}{1}\quad \frac{1}{x}\quad \frac{3x}{1+2x^2}\quad \frac{4+11x^2}{9x+6x^3}\quad \frac{55x+50x^3}{9+72x^2+24x^4}$$

$$\cdots\;+\frac{n^2(1-x^2)}{(2n+1)x\;+}\cdots. \qquad (6.13)$$

From this, using identity (6.2), we obtain

$$\frac{\operatorname{arccosh} x}{\sqrt{x^2-1}} = \frac{1}{x} - \frac{x^2-1}{3x} - \dots - \frac{n^2(x^2-1)}{(2n+1)x} - \dots. \tag{6.14}$$

7. We shall derive yet another expansion for functions of the type being considered. In order to do this we write

$$y = \frac{x \arcsin x}{\sqrt{1-x^2}}.$$

Then

$$y' = \frac{y}{x} + \frac{x}{1-x^2} + \frac{x^2 \arcsin x}{(1-x^2)^{\frac{3}{2}}},$$

i.e.

$$y' = \frac{y}{x} + \frac{x}{1-x^2} + \frac{x}{1-x^2}\, y$$

or

$$(1-x^2)xy' - y = x^2, \quad y(0) = 0. \tag{6.15}$$

Comparing this equation with (1.15) we see that here $k = 2$, $\eta' = -1$, $\beta = -\frac{1}{2}$, $\beta' = \gamma = 0$, $\delta = \frac{1}{2}$. Therefore from (1.18) we obtain the expansion of the solution of (6.15) which tends to zero as $x = 0$.

$$y = \frac{\frac{1}{2}x^2}{\frac{1}{2}} + \frac{-\frac{1}{2}x^2}{\frac{3}{2}} + \frac{-\frac{1}{2}x^2}{\frac{5}{2}} + \dots$$

$$\dots + \frac{-\frac{2n-1}{2}nx^2}{\frac{4n-1}{2}} + \frac{\left(-n^2 + \frac{n}{2}\right)x^2}{\frac{4n+1}{2}} + \dots,$$

i.e.

$$\frac{\arcsin x}{\sqrt{1-x^2}} = \frac{x}{1} - \frac{1 \, . \, 2x^2}{3} - \frac{1 \, . \, 2x^2}{5} - \dots$$

$$\dots - \frac{(2n-1)2nx^2}{4n-1} - \frac{(2n-1)2nx^2}{4n+1} - \dots. \tag{6.16}$$

From this

$$\frac{\operatorname{arcsinh} x}{\sqrt{1+x^2}} = \frac{x}{1+}\,\frac{1.2x^2}{3+}\,\frac{1.2x^2}{5+}\ldots$$
$$\ldots+\frac{(2n-1)2nx^2}{4n-1+}\,\frac{(2n-1)2nx^2}{4n+1+}\ldots. \qquad (6.17)$$

Putting $x = t/\sqrt{1+t^2}$ in (6.16), we obtain

$$\frac{\arcsin\dfrac{t}{\sqrt{1+t^2}}}{\sqrt{1-\dfrac{t^2}{1+t^2}}} = \sqrt{1+t^2}\arctan t =$$
$$= \frac{\dfrac{t}{\sqrt{1+t^2}}}{1-}\,\frac{\dfrac{1.2t^2}{1+t^2}}{3-}\,\frac{\dfrac{1.2t^2}{1+t^2}}{5-}\ldots-\frac{\dfrac{(2n-1)2nt^2}{1+t^2}}{4n-1-}\,\frac{\dfrac{(2n-1)2nt^2}{1+t^2}}{4n+1-}\ldots,$$

i.e.

$$\arctan x = \frac{x}{1+x^2-}\,\frac{1.2x^2}{3-}\,\frac{1.2x^2}{5(1+x^2)-}\ldots$$
$$\ldots-\frac{(2n-1)2nx^2}{4n-1-}\,\frac{(2n-1)2nx^2}{(4n+1)(1+x^2)-}\ldots. \qquad (6.18)$$

From this

$$\operatorname{arctanh} x = \frac{x}{1-x^2+}\,\frac{1.2x^2}{3+}\,\frac{1.2x^2}{5(1-x^2)+}\ldots$$
$$\ldots+\frac{(2n-1)2nx^2}{4n-1+}\,\frac{(2n-1)2nx^2}{(4n+1)(1-x^2)+}\ldots. \qquad (6.19)$$

Replacing x by $\sqrt{1-x^2}$ in (6.16), we obtain

$$\frac{\arccos x}{\sqrt{1-x^2}} = \frac{x}{1-}\,\frac{1.2(1-x^2)}{3-}\,\frac{1.2(1-x^2)}{5-}\ldots$$
$$\ldots-\frac{(2n-1)2n(1-x^2)}{4n-1-}\,\frac{(2n-1)2n(1-x^2)}{4n+1-}\ldots, \qquad (6.20)$$

whence

$$\frac{\operatorname{arccosh} x}{\sqrt{x^2-1}} = \frac{x}{1\ +}\ \frac{1.2(x^2-1)}{3\qquad +}\ \frac{1.2(x^2-1)}{5\qquad + \dots}$$

$$\dots + \frac{(2n-1)2n(x^2-1)}{4n-1\qquad +}\ \frac{(2n-1)2n(x^2-1)}{4n+1\qquad + \dots}. \tag{6.21}$$

§ 7. Continued Fraction Expansions for tan *x* and tanh *x*

1. The differential equation for $y = \tan x$ has the form

$$y' = 1 + y^2, \quad y(0) = 0.$$

Write $y = x/(1+z)$. The equation transposes into

$$1 + z - xz' = 1 + 2z + z^2 + x^2,$$

i.e.

$$xz' + z + z^2 = -x^2, \quad z(0) = 0.$$

Comparing this equation with (1.15), we see that here $k = 2$, $\eta' = \beta' = 0$, $\beta = \gamma = \frac{1}{2}$, $\delta = -\frac{1}{2}$. Therefore using expansion (1.18) with the denoted values of the parameters, we obtain the expansion for z

$$z = \frac{-\dfrac{x^2}{2}}{\dfrac{3}{2}\ -}\ \frac{\dfrac{x^2}{4}}{\dfrac{5}{2}\ -}\ \frac{\dfrac{x^2}{4}}{\dfrac{7}{2}\ - \dots -}\ \frac{\dfrac{x^2}{4}}{\dfrac{2n+1}{2}\ - \dots} =$$

$$= -\frac{x^2}{3\ -}\ \frac{x^2}{5\ - \dots -}\ \frac{x^2}{2n+1\ - \dots},$$

i.e.

$$\tan x = \frac{x}{1\ -}\ \frac{x^2}{3\qquad -}\ \frac{x^2}{5\qquad -}\ \frac{x^2}{7\qquad -}$$

$$\frac{0}{1}\quad \frac{x}{1}\quad \frac{3x}{3-x^2}\quad \frac{15x-x^3}{15-6x^2}\quad \frac{105x-10x^3}{105-45x^2+x^4}$$

$$-\ \frac{x^2}{9\qquad - \dots -}\ \frac{x^2}{2n+1\ - \dots}. \tag{7.1}$$

$$\frac{945x-105x^3+x^5}{945-420x^2+15x^4}$$

This expansion was first discovered by Lambert [48] and derived subsequently by Lagrange [43] and Euler [21].

Here

$$\lim_{n\to\infty} \frac{1}{(2n-1)(2n+1)} = 0.$$

According to the theorem of section 3, § 7, chapter I, therefore, the continued fraction converges throughout the whole of the finite complex x-plane with the exception of certain points of inessential divergence.

2. Replacing x by x/i in (7.1), and multiplying (7.1) throughout by i, we obtain [1]

$$\tanh x = \frac{x}{1} + \frac{x^2}{3} + \frac{x^2}{5} + \dots + \frac{x^2}{2n+1} + \dots \quad (7.2)$$

The convergence domain of the continued fraction (7.2) coincides with the convergence domain of the continued fraction (7.1). For positive real x we obtain from (7.2) the sequence of inequalities

$$\frac{3x}{3+x^2} \leqslant \frac{105x+10x^3}{105+45x^2+x^4} \leqslant \dots \leqslant \tanh x \leqslant \dots \leqslant$$

$$\leqslant \frac{945x+105x^3+x^5}{945+420x^2+15x^4} \leqslant \frac{15x+x^3}{15+6x^2} \leqslant x. \quad (7.3)$$

3. Schlömilch [84] proposed the following direct derivation of the continued fraction for $\tan x$.

Denote $\cos \sqrt{x}$ by y. Then

$$2\sqrt{x}y' = -\sin\sqrt{x}, \quad \frac{y'}{\sqrt{x}} + 2\sqrt{x}y'' = -\frac{y}{2\sqrt{x}},$$

$$4xy'' + 2y' + y = 0,$$

$$4xy''' + 6y'' + y' = 0,$$

$$\dots\dots\dots\dots\dots\dots$$

$$4xy^{(n+2)} + (4n+2)y^{(n+1)} + y^{(n)} = 0.$$

[1] $\tanh x = i \tan (x/i)$.

Denote $y^{(m+1)}/y^{(m)}$ by u_{m+1}. Then

$$u_1 = -\frac{\tan\sqrt{x}}{2\sqrt{x}}, \quad 4xu_{n+2} + 4n + 2 = -\frac{1}{u_{n+1}},$$

$$u_{n+1} = \frac{-\frac{1}{2}}{2n + 1 + 2xu_{n+2}}.$$

Consequently,

$$-\frac{\tan\sqrt{x}}{2\sqrt{x}} = \frac{-\frac{1}{2}}{1} - \frac{x}{3} - \frac{x}{5} - \dots - \frac{x}{2n+1} - \dots,$$

whence we again arrive at (7.1).

4. Applying the transformation (2.24) of chapter I to (7.2):

$$\frac{\tanh x}{x} = 1 - \frac{5x^2}{5x^2 + 3.5 + 2x^2} - \frac{x^2}{1} - \frac{9x^2}{5.7.9 + 2(5+9)x^2} -$$

$$- \frac{5x^2}{1} - \frac{13x^2}{9.11.13 + 2(9+13)x^2} - \dots$$

$$\dots - \frac{(4n+1)x^2}{(4n-3)(4n-1)(4n+1) + 2(4n-3+4n+1)x^2} - \frac{(4n-3)x^2}{1} - \dots.$$

From this

$$\tanh x = x - \frac{5x^3}{15 + 7x^2} - \frac{x^2}{1} - \frac{9x^2}{315 + 28x^2} -$$

$$\frac{x}{1} \quad \frac{15x + 2x^3}{15 + 7x^2} \quad \frac{15x + x^3}{15 + 6x^2} \quad \frac{4725x + 600x^3 + 10x^5}{4725 + 2175x^2 + 105x^4}$$

$$\frac{945 + 120x^3 + 2x^5}{945 + 435x^2 + 21x^4}$$

$$- \frac{5x^2}{1} - \frac{13x^2}{1287 - 44x^2} - \dots$$

$$\frac{4725x + 525x^3 + 5x^5}{4725 + 2100x^2 + 75x^4}$$

$$\frac{945x + 105x^3 + x^5}{945 + 420x^2 + 15x^4}$$

$$\dots - \frac{(4n+1)x^2}{(4n-3)(4n-1)(4n+1) + 4(4n-1)x^2} - \frac{(4n-3)x^2}{1} - \dots. \quad (7.4)$$

Replacing x by ix in this expression and dividing throughout by i, we obtain

$\tan x =$

$$= x + \frac{5x^3}{15 - 7x^2 +} \frac{x^2}{1} + \frac{9x^2}{315 - 28x^2 +} \frac{5x^2}{1} + \frac{13x^2}{1287 - 44x^2 +} \cdots$$

$$\cdots + \frac{(4n+1)x^2}{(4n-3)(4n-1)(4n+1) - 4(4n-1)x^2 +} \frac{(4n-3)x^2}{1} + \cdots. \quad (7.5)$$

§ 8. The Continued Fraction Expansion of the Integral $\int_0^x \frac{dx}{1+x^k}$

1. Differentiating this integral, we obtain the equation

$$(1 + x^k)y' = 1, \quad y(0) = 0. \quad (8.1)$$

Let $y \approx ax$. Then inserting this value in (8.1) we obtain $a = 1$. Next we write $y = x/(1 + z)$. The equation becomes

$$(1 + x^k)(1 + z - xz') = (1 + z)^2,$$

i.e.

$$(1 + x^k)xz' + (1 - x^k)z + z^2 = x^k.$$

This is a special case of equation (1.15), in which $\eta' = 1$, $\beta = \gamma = \delta = 1/k$, $\beta' = -(1/k)$. Therefore, for the case under consideration, (1.18) gives

$$z = \frac{\frac{1}{k}x^k}{\frac{k+1}{k} +} \frac{\left(\frac{1}{k^2} + \frac{k+1}{k}\cdot\frac{k-1}{k}\right)x^k}{\frac{2k+1}{k} +} \frac{\left(\frac{1}{k^2} + 1 + \frac{1}{k} + \frac{1}{k}\right)x^k}{\frac{3k+1}{k} +}$$

$$+ \frac{\left(\frac{1}{k^2} + \frac{2k+1}{k}\cdot\frac{2k-1}{k}\right)x^k}{\frac{4k+1}{k} +} \cdots + \frac{\left(\frac{1}{k^2} + \frac{nk+1}{k}\cdot\frac{nk-1}{k}\right)x^k}{\frac{2nk+1}{k} +}$$

$$+ \frac{\left(\frac{1}{k^2} + n^2 + \frac{n}{k} + \frac{n}{k}\right)x^k}{\frac{(2n+1)k+1}{k} +} \cdots,$$

i.e.

$$z = \frac{x^k}{k+1} + \frac{k^2 x^k}{2k+1} + \frac{(k+1)^2 x^k}{3k+1} + \frac{4k^2 x^k}{4k+1} + \dots$$
$$\dots + \frac{n^2 k^2 x^k}{2nk+1} + \frac{(nk+1)^2 x^k}{(2n+1)k+1} + \dots .$$

From this (Laguerre [43])

$$\int_0^x \frac{dx}{1+x^k} = \frac{x}{1} + \frac{x^k}{k+1} + \frac{k^2 x^k}{2k+1} + \frac{(k+1)^2 x^k}{3k+1} + \dots$$
$$\dots + \frac{n^2 k^2 x^k}{2nk+1} + \frac{(nk+1)^2 x^k}{(2n+1)k+1} + \dots . \qquad (8.2)$$

Here

$$\lim_{n\to\infty} \frac{n^2 k^2}{[(2n-1)k+1](2nk+1)} = \frac{1}{4}.$$

From the theorem of section 17, § 7, chapter I, therefore, the continued fraction (8.2) converges throughout the whole of the finite complex x^k-plane, cut along the negative real axis from -1 to $-\infty$.

When $k = 1$ and $k = 2$, (8.2) transposes into (4.2) and (6.4) respectively.

2. In the integral $\int_0^x dx/(1 + x^k)$ we take as a new variable $x = t^{p+1}$. The integral then becomes

$$(p+1) \int_0^t \frac{t^p\, dt}{1 + t^{k(p+1)}}.$$

Replace t by x and denote $k(p + 1)$ by q. Then $k = q/(p + 1)$. Therefore expansion (8.2) (in which we also substitute x^{p+1} for x) gives

$$\int_0^x \frac{x^p\, dx}{1+x^q} = \frac{x^{p+1}}{p+1} + \frac{(p+1)^2 x^q}{q+1+p} + \frac{q^2 x^q}{2q+1+p} + \dots$$
$$\dots + \frac{n^2 q^2 x^q}{2nq+1+p} + \frac{(nq+1+p)^2 x^q}{(2n+1)q+1+p} + \dots . \qquad (8.3)$$

For example,

$$\int_0^1 \frac{x^2\,dx}{1+x^4} = \frac{1}{3+}\;\frac{9}{7}\;+\;\frac{16}{11}\;+\;\frac{49}{15}\;+\dots$$

$$\frac{0}{1}\quad\frac{1}{3}\quad\frac{7}{30}\quad\frac{93}{378}\quad\frac{1738}{7140}$$

$$0{,}3\quad 0{,}233\quad 0{,}2460\quad 0{,}2434$$

$$\dots+\frac{16n^2}{8n+3}+\frac{(4n+3)^2}{8n+7}+\dots.$$

The exact value of this integral is 0·243748....

3. We note in connection with (8.3) the following relationships

$$\frac{(p+1+nq)^2-n^2q^2}{p+1+2nq} = p+1 \qquad (n=1,2,\dots),$$

consequently, if (8.3) is presented in the form

$$\frac{1}{\dfrac{p+1}{x^{p+1}}\displaystyle\int_0^x \frac{x^p\,dx}{1+x^q}} = 1+\frac{(p+1)x^q}{q+1+p}+\frac{q^2x^q}{2q+1+p}+\dots$$

$$\dots+\frac{n^2q^2x^q}{2nq+1+p}+\frac{(nq+1+p)^2x^q}{(2n+1)q+1+p}+\dots,$$

then the conditions (2.22) of chapter I are fulfilled. One can, therefore, transcribe the continued fraction (8.3) by means of equation (2.23) of chapter I in the following way:

$$\int_0^x \frac{x^p\,dx}{1+x^q} =$$

$$=\frac{x^{p+1}}{p+1}-\frac{x^{p+1+q}}{q+1+p}+\frac{(q+1+p)^2x^q}{2q+1+p}+\frac{q^2x^q}{3q+1+p}+\dots$$

$$\dots+\frac{(nq+1+p)^2x^q}{2nq+1+p}+\frac{n^2q^2x^q}{(2n+1)q+1+p}+\dots. \tag{8.4}$$

In particular

$$\int_0^1 \frac{x^2\,dx}{1+x^4} = \frac{1}{3} - \frac{1}{7} + \frac{49}{11} + \frac{16}{15} + \dots$$

$$\frac{1}{3} \quad \frac{4}{21} \quad \frac{93}{378} \quad \frac{1459}{6006}$$

$$0{\cdot}190 \quad 0{\cdot}2460 \quad 0{\cdot}2429$$

4. We make the substitution $x^q = t$ in the integral

$$\int_0^1 \frac{x^{p-1}}{1+x^q}\,dx.$$

Then $qx^{q-1}\,dx = dt$, $dx = (1/q)t^{(1-q)/q}$, and hence

$$\int_0^1 \frac{x^{p-1}\,dx}{1+x^q} = \frac{1}{q}\int_0^1 \frac{t^{\frac{p-1}{q}}\,t^{\frac{1-q}{q}}\,dt}{1+t} = \frac{1}{q}\int_0^1 \frac{t^{\frac{p}{q}-1}}{1+t}\,dt.$$

In order that this integral may be developed as a continued fraction, it is necessary to put $x = 1$ and replace p by $p - 1$ in (8.3), which then becomes

$$\int_0^1 \frac{t^{\frac{p}{q}-1}}{1+t}\,dt = \frac{q}{p} + \frac{p^2}{q+p} + \frac{q^2}{2q+p} + \frac{(q+p)^2}{3q+p} + \dots$$

$$\dots + \frac{n^2q^2}{2nq+p} + \frac{(nq+p)^2}{(2n+1)q+p} + \dots =$$

$$= \frac{1}{\frac{p}{q}} + \frac{\frac{p^2}{q^2}}{1+\frac{p}{q}} + \frac{1}{2+\frac{p}{q}} + \frac{\left(1+\frac{p}{q}\right)^2}{3+\frac{p}{q}} + \dots$$

$$\dots + \frac{n^2}{2n+\frac{p}{q}} + \frac{\left(n+\frac{p}{q}\right)^2}{2n+1+\frac{p}{q}} + \dots.$$

Denoting p/q by x, we have

$$\int_0^1 \frac{t^{x-1}}{1+t}\,dt = \frac{1}{x+}\,\frac{x^2}{1+x+}\,\frac{1}{2+x+}\,\frac{(1+x)^2}{3+x}\,+ \dots$$

$$\dots + \frac{n^2}{2n+x+}\,\frac{(n+x)^2}{2n+1+x+\dots}. \tag{8.5}$$

Writing $t = e^{-2u}$, then

$$\int_0^1 \frac{t^{x-1}}{1+t}\,dt = -2\int_\infty^0 \frac{e^{-2u(x-1)}\,e^{-2u}}{1+e^{-2u}}\,du =$$

$$= 2\int_0^\infty \frac{e^{-2ux}\,e^{u}}{e^{u}+e^{-u}}\,du = \int_0^\infty \frac{e^{(1-2x)u}}{\cosh u}\,du.$$

Therefore, replacing x by $(1+x)/2$ in (8.5), we obtain

$$\int_0^\infty \frac{e^{-xt}}{\cosh t}\,dt = \frac{1}{\frac{1+x}{2}}+\frac{\left(\frac{1+x}{2}\right)^2}{\frac{3+x}{2}}+\frac{1}{\frac{5+x}{2}}+\frac{\left(\frac{3+x}{2}\right)^2}{\frac{7+x}{2}}+\dots$$

$$\dots + \frac{n^2}{\frac{4n+1+x}{2}}+\frac{\left(\frac{2n+1+x}{2}\right)^2}{\frac{4n+2+x}{2}}+\dots,$$

i.e.

$$\int_0^\infty \frac{e^{-xt}}{\cosh t}\,dt = \frac{2}{1+x+}\,\frac{(1+x)^2}{3+x+}\,\frac{4}{5+x+}\,\frac{(3+x)^2}{7+x}\,+\dots$$

$$\dots + \frac{4n^2}{4n+1+x+}\,\frac{(2n+1+x)^2}{4n+2+x}\,+\dots. \tag{8.6}$$

It is known that $\int_0^\infty dt/\cosh t = \pi/2$. In particular, therefore, there follows from (8.6):

$$\frac{\pi}{4} = \frac{1}{1+}\,\frac{1^2}{3+}\,\frac{2^2}{5+}\dots+\frac{n^2}{2n+1+}\dots.$$

This equation also follows from (6.4).

§ 9. The Solution of the Equations of Boole and Riccati with the help of Continued Fractions

1. We consider Boole's equation

$$\alpha x y' + \beta y + \gamma y^2 = \delta x^k. \tag{9.1}$$

This is a special case of equation (1.15) in which $\eta' = \beta' = 0$, and β, γ, δ are replaced by $\beta/k\alpha$, $\gamma/k\alpha$, $\delta/k\alpha$ respectively. Therefore the expansion of the form (1.18) relating to equation (9.1) becomes

$$y = \frac{\delta x^k}{k\alpha + \beta +} \frac{\gamma\delta x^k}{2k\alpha + \beta +} \frac{\gamma\delta x^k}{3k\alpha + \beta + \ldots +} \frac{\gamma\delta x^k}{nk\alpha + \beta + \ldots}, \tag{9.2}$$

and (1.16) gives

$$y = -\frac{\beta}{\gamma} + \frac{\delta x^k}{k\alpha - \beta +} \frac{\gamma\delta x^k}{2k\alpha - \beta + \ldots +} \frac{\gamma\delta x^k}{nk\alpha - \beta + \ldots}. \tag{9.3}$$

When $\alpha = 0$ these continued fractions degenerate into the expansions of the roots of the quadratic equation $\gamma y^2 + \beta y - \delta x^k = 0$.

With the help of the method of Lagrange, Euler [22] found the expansion (9.3) for the case $\gamma = \delta = 1$.

2. We write $y = zx$ in (9.1), which then becomes

$$\alpha x(z'x + z) + \beta z x + \gamma z^2 x^2 = \delta x^k,$$

i.e. replacing z by y

$$\alpha y' + \frac{\alpha + \beta}{x} y + \gamma y^2 = \delta x^{k-2}. \tag{9.4}$$

When $\beta = -\alpha$, $\delta = 1$ we obtain the equation of Riccati

$$\alpha y' + \gamma y^2 = x^{k-2}. \tag{9.5}$$

For (9.4) the expansions (9.2) and (9.3) become respectively

$$y = \frac{\delta x^{k-1}}{k\alpha + \beta +} \frac{\gamma\delta x^k}{2k\alpha + \beta +} \frac{\gamma\delta x^k}{3k\alpha + \beta + \ldots +} \frac{\gamma\delta x^k}{nk\alpha + \beta + \ldots}. \tag{9.6}$$

and

$$y = -\frac{\beta}{\gamma x} + \frac{\delta x^{k-1}}{k\alpha - \beta +} \frac{\gamma\delta x^k}{2k\alpha - \beta + \ldots +} \frac{\gamma\delta x^k}{nk\alpha - \beta + \ldots}. \tag{9.7}$$

In particular, for (9.5) we obtain

$$y = \frac{x^{k-1}}{(k-1)\alpha +} \frac{\gamma x^k}{(2k-1)\alpha +} \frac{\gamma x^k}{(3k-1)\alpha + \ldots}$$

$$\ldots + \frac{\gamma x^k}{(nk-1)\alpha + \ldots} \tag{9.8}$$

and

$$y = \frac{\alpha}{\gamma x +} \frac{x^{k-1}}{(k+1)\alpha +} \frac{\gamma x^k}{(2k+1)\alpha + \ldots +} \frac{\gamma x^k}{(nk+1)\alpha + \ldots}. \tag{9.9}$$

The connection between continued fractions and Riccati's equation was also considered in the earlier works of Euler [20].

3. We now recapitulate the connection between linear differential equations of the second order and the general Riccati equation

$$y' = \varphi_0(x) + y\varphi_1(x) + y^2\varphi_2(x).$$

We write in the equation

$$f_2(x)z'' + f_1(x)z' + f_0(x)z = 0,$$

$z = e^{\int y\, dx}$, and have:

$$z' = yz, \quad z'' = (y' + y^2)z,$$

consequently

$$f_2(x)(y' + y^2) + f_1(x)y + f_0(x) = 0,$$

i.e.

$$y' = -\frac{f_0(x)}{f_2(x)} - \frac{f_1(x)}{f_2(x)}y - y^2.$$

In this way, by means of the substitution $z = e^{\int y\, dx}$ (i.e. $y = z'/z$) one is lead from a differential equation of the second order to the general Riccati equation.

4. We now determine which linear equation of the second order leads to the equation

$$y' = \frac{\delta}{\alpha}x^{k-2} - \frac{\alpha + \beta}{\alpha x}y - y^2,$$

which may be derived from (9.4) by putting $\gamma = \alpha$. Here

$$\frac{f_0(x)}{f_2(x)} = -\frac{\delta}{\alpha}x^{k-2}, \quad \frac{f_1(x)}{f_2(x)} = \frac{\alpha + \beta}{\alpha x}.$$

Writing $f_2(x) = 1$, we have

$$f_0(x) = -\frac{\delta}{\alpha} x^{k-2}, \quad f_1(x) = \frac{\alpha+\beta}{\alpha x}.$$

Thus the required equation is

$$z'' + \frac{\alpha+\beta}{\alpha x} z' - \frac{\delta}{\alpha} x^{k-2} z = 0. \tag{9.10}$$

We compare this equation with the equation for $Z_p(ix)$ (where $Z_p(ix)$ is the *cylinder function* of imaginary argument):

$$z'' + \frac{z'}{x} - \left(1 + \frac{p^2}{x^2}\right) z = 0.$$

These equations correspond if $\beta = p = 0$, $k = 2$, $\delta = \alpha$; whence, in particular, (9.7) gives

$$\frac{J_0'(ix)}{J_0(ix)} = \frac{x}{2} + \frac{x^2}{4} + \frac{x^2}{6} + \ldots + \frac{x^2}{2n} + \ldots, \tag{9.11}$$

where $J_0(ix)$ is the Bessel function of zero order and argument ix. From this

$$-\frac{J_0'(x)}{J_0(x)} \equiv \frac{J_1(x)}{J_0(x)} = \frac{x}{2} - \frac{x^2}{4} - \frac{x^2}{6} - \ldots - \frac{x^2}{2n} - \ldots, \tag{9.12}$$

where $J_1(x)$ is the Bessel function of the first order.

5. We derive here the continued fraction expansion of $J_m(x)/J_{m-1}(x)$ where $J_m(x)$ is the *Bessel function* of the mth order. This expansion was derived by Bessel [11].

Knowing the relation between the Bessel functions

$$xJ_{m-1}(x) - 2mJ_m(x) + xJ_{m+1}(x) = 0$$

one can proceed to the formula

$$\frac{J_{m-1}(x)}{J_m(x)} = \frac{2m}{x} - \frac{J_{m+1}(x)}{J_m(x)},$$

i.e.

$$\frac{J_m(x)}{J_{m-1}(x)} = \frac{1}{\dfrac{2m}{x} - \dfrac{J_{m+1}(x)}{J_m(x)}}.$$

From this

$$\frac{J_m(x)}{J_{m-1}(x)} = \cfrac{\frac{x}{2m}}{1 - \frac{x}{2m}\frac{J_{m+1}(x)}{J_m(x)}} = \cfrac{\frac{x}{2m}}{1 - \cfrac{\frac{x^2}{2m(2m+2)}}{1 - \dots - \cfrac{\frac{x^2}{(2m+2n)(2m+2n-2)}}{1 - \dots}}} .$$

Hence

$$\frac{J_m(x)}{J_{m-1}(x)} = \frac{x}{2m -}\,\frac{x^2}{2m+2 -}\,\frac{x^2}{2m+4 - \dots -}\,\frac{x^2}{2m+2n - \dots} . \tag{9.13}$$

With $m = 1$ we come again to equation (9.12).

The work of several distinguished mathematicians has been devoted to expansion (9.13) and its convergence behaviour (Schlömilch [83], Lommel [52], Günther [26], Herz [32], Graf [25], Perron [71], Nielsen [61]).

§ 10. Continued Fractions and the Hypergeometric Series

1. The series

$$F(a, b, c, x) = 1 + \frac{ab}{1!c}x + \frac{a(a+1)b(b+1)}{2!c(c+1)}x^2 + $$
$$+ \frac{a(a+1)(a+2)b(b+1(b+2)}{3!c(c+1)(c+2)}x^3 + \dots \tag{10.1}$$

is called the *hypergeometric series*. It converges for $|x| < 1$ and diverges for $|x| > 1$. When $x = 1$ it converges if $c > a + b$; when $x = -1$ it converges if $c + 1 > a + b$.

From the definition of the series it is evident that $F(a, b, c, x) = F(b, a, c, x)$.

2. We note that

$$F(a+1, b, c+1, x) =$$
$$= 1 + \frac{(a+1)b}{1!(c+1)}x + \frac{(a+1)(a+2)b(b+1)}{2!(c+1)(c+2)}x^2 + \dots$$

Then

$$F(a+1, b, c+1, x) - F(a, b, c, x) =$$

$$= \frac{(c-a)b}{1!\,c(c+1)}\,x + \frac{(a+1)b(b+1)}{2!\,(c+1)}\left(\frac{a+2}{c+2} - \frac{a}{c}\right)x^2 +$$

$$+ \frac{(a+1)(a+2)b(b+1)(b+2)}{3!\,(c+1)(c+2)}\left(\frac{a+3}{c+3} - \frac{a}{c}\right)x^3 + \dots =$$

$$= \frac{(c-a)b}{c(c+1)}\,x\left[1 + \frac{(a+1)(b+1)}{1!\,(c+2)}\,x +\right.$$

$$\left.+ \frac{(a+1)(a+2)(b+1)(b+2)}{2!\,(c+2)(c+3)}\,x^2 + \dots\right],$$

i.e.

$$F(a+1, b, c+1, x) - F(a, b, c, x) =$$

$$= \frac{(c-a)b}{c(c+1)}\,xF(a+1, b+1, c+2, x).$$

From this

$$F(b+1, a, c+1, x) - F(b, a, c, x) =$$

$$= \frac{(c-b)a}{c(c+1)}\,xF(b+1, a+1, c+2, x)$$

and

$$F(a, b+1, c+1, x) - F(a, b, c, x) =$$

$$= \frac{(c-b)a}{c(c+1)}\,xF(a+1, b+1, c+2, x). \qquad (10.2)$$

3. Using the notation

$$\frac{F(a, b+1, c+1, x)}{F(a, b, c, x)} = G(a, b, c, x),$$

then

$$\frac{F(a+1, b, c+1, x)}{F(a, b, c, x)} = G(b, a, c, x).$$

Dividing (10.2) by $F(a, b+1, c+1, x)$, we obtain

$$1-\frac{1}{G(a, b, c, x)}=\frac{a(c-b)}{c(c+1)} xG(b+1, a, c+1, x).$$

From this

$$G(a, b, c, x)=\frac{1}{1-\dfrac{a(c-b)}{c(c+1)} xG(b+1, a, c+1, x)}.$$

Further

$$G(b+1, a, c+1, x)=$$

$$=\frac{1}{1-\dfrac{(b+1)(c+1-a)}{(c+1)(c+2)} xG(a+1, b+1, c+2, x)}.$$

Consequently [1],

$$\frac{F(a, b+1, c+1, x)}{F(a, b, c, x)}=$$

$$=\frac{1}{1-}\,\frac{\dfrac{a(c-b)x}{c(c+1)}}{1}\,-\,\frac{\dfrac{(b+1)(c+1-a)}{(c+1)(c+2)}x}{1}\,-\,\frac{\dfrac{(a+1)(c+1-b)}{(c+2)(c+3)}x}{1}\,-\ldots$$

$$\ldots-\frac{\dfrac{(b+n)(c-a+n)}{(c+2n-1)(c+2n)}x}{1}\,-\,\frac{\dfrac{(a+n)(c-b+n)}{(c+2n)(c+2n+1)}x}{1}\,-\ldots,$$

i.e.

$$\frac{F(a, b, c, x)}{F(a, b+1, c+1, x)}=$$

$$=1-\frac{\dfrac{a}{c}(c-b)x}{c+1}\,-\,\frac{(b+1)(c-a+1)x}{c+2}\,-\ldots$$

$$\ldots-\frac{(b+n)(c-a+n)x}{c+2n}\,-\,\frac{(a+n)(c-b+n)x}{c+2n+1}\,-\ldots. \qquad (10.3)$$

[1] One can demonstrate the validity of this formula by the method of mathematical induction.

Here

$$\lim_{n\to\infty}\left[-\frac{(b+n)(c-a+n)}{(c+2n-1)(c+2n)}\right]=$$

$$=\lim_{n\to\infty}\left[-\frac{(a+n)(c-b+n)}{(c+2n)(c+2n+1)}\right]=-\frac{1}{4}.$$

According to the theorem of section 17, § 7, chapter I, therefore, the continued fraction (10.3) converges throughout the finite complex x-plane, cut along the positive real axis from $x = 1$ to $x = \infty$.

Expansion (10.3) was derived by Gauss [24]. Its convergence behaviour was investigated for the first time by Riemann [80] and independently of him by Thomé [96], [97].

If a or b are negative integers, then $F(a, b, c, x)$ and $F(a, b+1, c+1, x)$ are polynomials in x, i.e. in this case the continued fraction (10.3) terminates.

4. We show that the expansion (10.3) is a special case of expansion (1.16). For this we transcribe (1.16) as

$$y=-\frac{\beta}{\gamma}+$$

$$+\frac{\left(\frac{\beta\beta'}{\gamma}+\delta\right)x^k}{1-\beta}+\frac{(\gamma\delta-\beta\eta'+\beta'+\eta')x^k}{2-\beta}+$$

$$+\frac{[\gamma\delta+(1-\beta)(\eta'-\beta')]x^k}{3-\beta}+\ldots+\frac{\{\gamma\delta+n[(n-\beta)\eta'+\beta']\}x^k}{2n-\beta}+$$

$$+\frac{[\gamma\delta+(n-\beta)(n\eta'-\beta')]x^k}{2n+1-\beta}+\ldots.$$

Comparing this continued fraction with (10.3), we have:

$$k=1,\quad \beta=-c,\quad \gamma=c.$$

Further,

$$\eta'n^2+(\beta'-\eta'\beta)n+\gamma\delta\equiv-n^2-(b+c-a)n-b(c-a),$$

$$\eta'n^2-(\beta'+\eta'\beta)n+\beta\beta'+\gamma\delta\equiv$$

$$\equiv-n^2-(a+c-b)n-a(c-b).$$

Hence

$$\eta' = -1, \quad \beta' = a - b, \quad \delta = \frac{b(a-c)}{c}.$$

Equation (1.15) itself becomes in this case

$$\left.\begin{aligned} (1-x)xy' + [-c + (a-b)x]y + cy^2 &= \frac{b(a-c)}{c}\,x, \\ y(0) &= 1. \end{aligned}\right\} \tag{10.4}$$

5. If $b = 0$, then (10.4) becomes

$$(1-x)xy' + (-c + ax)y + cy^2 = 0, \quad y(0) = 1,$$

and expansion (10.3) goes over into

$$\frac{1}{F(a, 1, c+1, x)} = 1 - \frac{ax}{c+1} - \frac{(c-a+1)x}{c+2} - \dots$$

$$\dots - \frac{n(c-a+n)x}{c+2n} - \frac{(a+n)(c+n)x}{c+2n+1} - \dots.$$

From this, denoting $F(a, 1, c, x)$ by $\psi(a, c, x)$, we obtain (having previously replaced $c+1$ by c)

$$\psi(a, c, x) = \frac{1}{1} - \frac{ax}{c} - \frac{(c-a)x}{c+1} - \dots$$

$$\dots - \frac{n(c-a+n-1)x}{c+2n-1} - \frac{(a+n)(c+n-1)x}{c+2n} - \dots. \tag{10.5}$$

From (10.1) it follows that

$$\psi(a, c, x) =$$

$$= 1 + \frac{a}{c}x + \frac{a(a+1)}{c(c+1)}x^2 + \frac{a(a+1)(a+2)}{c(c+1)(c+2)}x^3 + \dots. \tag{10.6}$$

Expansion (10.5) was used by A. A. Markoff [3] for the solution of a problem in the theory of probability.

6. Replacing x by x/a in (10.1), we have:

$$F\left(a, b, c, \frac{x}{a}\right) = 1 + \frac{b}{1!c}x + \frac{\left(1 + \frac{1}{a}\right)b(b+1)}{2!c(c+1)}x^2 +$$

$$+\frac{\left(1+\frac{1}{a}\right)\left(1+\frac{2}{a}\right)b(b+1)(b+2)}{3!c(c+1)(c+2)}x^3+\ldots$$

From this

$$\lim_{a\to\infty} F\left(a, b, c, \frac{x}{a}\right) \equiv \Phi(b, c, x) =$$

$$= 1 + \frac{b}{c}\,\frac{x}{1!} + \frac{b(b+1)}{c(c+1)}\,\frac{x^2}{2!} + \ldots$$

$$\ldots + \frac{b(b+1)\ldots(b+n)}{c(c+1)\ldots(c+n)}\,\frac{x^{n+1}}{(n+1)!} + \ldots \tag{10.7}$$

Then expansion (10.3) becomes

$$\frac{\Phi(b, c, x)}{\Phi(b+1, c+1, x)} = 1 - \frac{\frac{1}{c}(c-b)x}{c+1} +$$

$$+ \frac{(b+1)x}{c+2} - \frac{(c-b+1)x}{c+3} + \ldots + \frac{(b+n)}{c+2n} - \frac{(c-b+n)x}{c+2n+1} + \ldots \tag{10.8}$$

Here

$$\lim_{n\to\infty} \frac{b+n}{(c+2n-1)(c+2n)} = -\lim_{n\to\infty} \frac{c-b+n}{(c+2n)(c+2n+1)} = 0.$$

According to the theorem of section 3, § 7, chapter I, therefore, the continued fraction (10.8) converges throughout the whole of the finite complex x-plane, with the exception of certain points of inessential divergence.

Correspondingly, replacing x by x/a, the transformation of equation (10.4) gives (the product xy' of course remains unaltered)

$$\left(1-\frac{x}{a}\right)xy' + \left(-c + \frac{a-b}{a}x\right)y + cy^2 = \frac{b}{c}(a-c)\frac{x}{a},$$

i.e. when $a \to \infty$

$$xy' + (-c+x)y + cy^2 = \frac{b}{c}x, \quad y(0) = 1. \tag{10.9}$$

7. If $b = 0$ then (10.9) becomes

$$xy' + (-c + x)y + cy^2 = 0, \quad y(0) = 1, \tag{10.10}$$

and expansion (10.4) goes over into

$$\frac{1}{\Phi(1, c+1, x)} = 1 - \frac{x}{c+1} + \frac{x}{c+2} - \frac{(c+1)x}{c+3} + \ldots + \frac{nx}{c+2n} - \frac{(c+n)x}{c+2n+1} + \ldots.$$

From this

$$\Phi(1, c, x) = 1 + \frac{x}{c} + \frac{x^2}{c(c+1)} + \ldots$$

$$\ldots + \frac{x^n}{c(c+1)\ldots(c+n-1)} + \ldots = \frac{1}{1} - \frac{x}{c} + \frac{x}{c+1} - \frac{cx}{c+2} + \frac{2x}{c+3} - \ldots + \ldots + \frac{nx}{c+2n-1} - \frac{(c-1+n)x}{c+2n} + \ldots. \tag{10.11}$$

8. Replacing x by x/b in (10.1) we have

$$F\left(a, b, c, \frac{x}{b}\right) = 1 + \frac{a}{1!c}x + \frac{a(a+1)\left(1+\frac{1}{b}\right)x^2}{2!c(c+1)} + \frac{a(a+1)(a+2)\left(1+\frac{1}{b}\right)\left(1+\frac{2}{b}\right)x^3}{3!c(c+1)(c+2)} + \ldots.$$

From this

$$\lim_{b\to\infty} F\left(a, b, c, \frac{x}{b}\right) \equiv \Phi(a, c, x) = 1 + \frac{a}{c}\frac{x}{1!} + \frac{a(a+1)}{c(c+1)}\frac{x^2}{2!} + \ldots \tag{10.12}$$

Then expansion (10.3) becomes

$$\frac{\Phi(a, c, x)}{\Phi(a, c+1, x)} = 1 + \frac{\frac{a}{c}x}{c+1} - \frac{(c-a+1)x}{c+2} + \dots$$

$$\dots - \frac{(c-a+n)x}{c+2n} + \frac{(a+n)x}{c+2n+1} - \dots . \tag{10.13}$$

Here

$$-\lim_{n\to\infty} \frac{c-a+n}{(c+2n-1)(c+2n)} = \lim_{n\to\infty} \frac{a+n}{(c+2n)(c+2n+1)} = 0.$$

According to the theorem of section 3, § 7, chapter I, therefore, the continued fraction (10.3) converges throughout the whole of the finite complex x-plane, with the exception of certain points of inessential divergence.

Correspondingly the transformation of equation (10.4) gives

$$\left(1 - \frac{x}{b}\right) xy' + \left(-c + \frac{a-b}{b}x\right) y + cy^2 = \frac{a-c}{c}x,$$

i.e. when $b \to \infty$

$$xy' - (c+x)y + cy^2 = \frac{a-c}{c}x, \quad y(0) = 1. \tag{10.14}$$

9. Replacing x by x/a in (10.12), we have

$$\lim_{a\to\infty} \Phi\left(a, c, \frac{x}{a}\right) \equiv \Psi(c, x) = 1 + \frac{x}{1!c} +$$

$$+ \frac{x^2}{2!c(c+1)} + \dots + \frac{x^n}{n!c(c+1)\dots(c+n-1)} + \dots . \tag{10.15}$$

Then from (10.13) we obtain, for any finite x,

$$\frac{\Psi(c, x)}{\Psi(c+1, x)} = 1 + \frac{\frac{x}{c}}{c+1} + \frac{x}{c+2} + \dots + \frac{x}{c+n} + \dots . \tag{10.16}$$

Correspondingly, the transformation of equation (10.14) gives

$$xy' - cy + cy^2 = \frac{x}{c}, \quad y(0) = 1. \tag{10.17}$$

10. Replacing x by $-cx$ in (10.1), we obtain

$$\lim_{c\to\infty} F(a, b, c, -cx) = \Omega(a, b, x) =$$

$$= 1 - ab\frac{x}{1!} + a(a+1)b(b+1)\frac{x^2}{2!} - \ldots \cdot \qquad (10.18)$$

Then (10.3) becomes

$$\frac{\Omega(a, b, x)}{\Omega(a, b+1, x)} = 1 + \frac{ax}{1} + \frac{(b+1)x}{1} + \frac{(a+1)x}{1} + \ldots$$

$$\ldots + \frac{(b+n)x}{1} + \frac{(a+n)x}{1} + \ldots. \qquad (10.19)$$

According to § 7 of chapter I the continued fraction (10.19) converges throughout the whole of the finite complex x-plane, cut along the negative real axis.

Correspondingly, the transformation of equation (10.4) gives:

$$(1 + cx)xy' - c[1 + (a - b)x]y + cy^2 = -b(a - c)x,$$

i.e. when $c \to \infty$

$$x^2y' - [1 + (a - b)x]y + y^2 = bx, \quad y(0) = 1. \qquad (10.20)$$

11. If $b = 0$, then (10.20) becomes

$$x^2y' - (1 + ax)y + y^2 = 0, \quad y(0) = 1, \qquad (10.21)$$

and expansion (10.19) goes over into

$$\frac{1}{\Omega(a, 1, x)} = 1 + \frac{ax}{1} + \frac{x}{1} + \frac{(a+1)x}{1} +$$

$$+ \frac{2x}{1} + \ldots + \frac{nx}{1} + \frac{(a+n)x}{1} + \ldots.$$

From this

$$\Omega(a, 1, x) = 1 - ax + a(a+1)x^2 - a(a+1)(a+2)x^3 + \ldots =$$

$$= \frac{1}{1} + \frac{ax}{1} + \frac{x}{1} + \frac{(a+1)x}{1} + \ldots + \frac{nx}{1} + \frac{(a+n)x}{1} + \ldots. \qquad (10.22)$$

This expansion was derived by Euler [18], and then investigated by Trembley [98] and Soldner [89].

From (10.21) it follows that $\Omega(a, 1, x)$ satisfies [1] the equation

$$x^2y' + (1 + ax)y = 1.$$

The power series associated with $\Omega(a, 1, x)$ diverges everywhere except at the point $x = 0$. The continued fraction (10.22) relating to $\Omega(a, 1, x)$ is uniformly convergent in any finite domain in the complex x-plane, which does not include any point on the negative real axis.

§ 11. Continued Fraction Expansions of Prym's Function

1. The following expression:

$$\Gamma(a) = \int_0^\infty x^{a-1}e^{-x}\,dx \qquad (a > 0)$$

is called the *Gamma function*. One of the generalizations of the Gamma function is *Prym's function* $\int_x^\infty x^{a-1}e^{-x}\,dx$. We introduce the function

$$y = x^{1-a}e^x \int_x^\infty x^{a-1}e^{-x}\,dx, \tag{11.1}$$

the continued fraction expansion of which was considered for the first time by Legendre [50]. We shall assume that $x > 0$ and that a is a real number. Differentiating (11.1) with respect to x, we have:

$$y' = \frac{1-a}{x}y + y - 1,$$

i.e.

$$xy' - (1 - a + x)y = -x. \tag{11.2}$$

2. Legendre [56] considered a more general equation which is easily developed in the form

$$xy' - (1 - a + x)y - \delta_1 y^2 = -x, \quad y(\infty) = 1. \tag{11.3}$$

In order to reduce this equation to the form (1.20), we write

[1]) In order to verify this it is necessary to write $y = 1/z$ in (10.21), and then to denote z by y.

$x = 1/t$. Then we have

$$x \frac{dy}{dx} = \frac{1}{t} \frac{dy}{d\frac{1}{t}} = -t \frac{dy}{dt}.$$

Therefore equation (11.3) becomes

$$-ty' - \left(1 - a + \frac{1}{t}\right) y - \delta_1 y^2 = -\frac{1}{t},$$

i.e.

$$t^2 y' + [1 + (1 - a)t] y + \delta_1 t y^2 = 1, \quad y(0) = 1.$$

Writing $y = 1/z$ in this equation, we have

$$-\frac{t^2 z'}{z^2} + [1 + (1 - a)t] \frac{1}{z} + \frac{\delta_1 t}{z^2} = 1,$$

i.e.

$$t^2 z' - [1 + (1 - a)t] z + z^2 = \delta_1 t. \tag{11.4}$$

Comparing (11.4) and (1.20), we see that here $k = 1$, $\beta_1 = -1$, $\beta_1' = -(1 - a)$, $\gamma_1 = 1$. Therefore expansion (1.21) becomes

$$z = 1 - \frac{(\delta_1 + 1 - a)t}{-1} + \frac{(\delta_1 + 1)t}{-1} + \frac{(\delta_1 + 2 - a)t}{-1} + \ldots$$
$$\ldots + \frac{(\delta_1 + n)t}{-1} + \frac{(\delta_1 + n + 1 - a)t}{-1} + \ldots,$$

i.e.

$$z = 1 + \frac{(\delta_1 + 1 - a)t}{1} + \frac{(\delta_1 + 1)t}{1} + \frac{(\delta_1 + 2 - a)t}{1} + \ldots$$
$$\ldots + \frac{\delta_1 + n}{1} + \frac{(\delta_1 + n + 1 - a)t}{1} + \ldots.$$

From this

$$y = \frac{x}{x} + \frac{\delta_1 + 1 - a}{1} + \frac{\delta_1 + 1}{x} + \frac{\delta_1 + 2 - a}{1} + \ldots$$
$$\ldots + \frac{\delta_1 + n}{x} + \frac{\delta_1 + n + 1 - a}{1} + \ldots.$$

In particular,

$$x^{1-a} e^x \int_x^\infty x^{a-1} e^{-x} dx =$$

$$= \frac{x}{x+} \frac{1-a}{1+} \frac{1}{x+} \frac{2-a}{1+} \cdots + \frac{n}{x+} \frac{n+1-a}{1+} \cdots .$$

Consequently ($x > 0$, a real),

$$e^x \int_x^\infty x^{a-1} e^{-x} dx =$$

$$= \frac{x^a}{x+} \frac{1-a}{1+} \frac{1}{x+} \frac{2-a}{1+} \cdots + \frac{n}{x+} \frac{n+1-a}{1+} \cdots . \tag{11.5}$$

Contracting the continued fraction (11.5) with the help of relations (2.8) of chapter I, we have

$$e^x \int_x^\infty x^{a-1} e^{-x} dx = \frac{x^a}{x+1-a-} \frac{1-a}{x+3-a-}$$

$$- \frac{2(2-a)}{x+5-a-} \cdots - \frac{n(n-a)}{x+2n+1-a-} \cdots . \tag{11.6}$$

Expansion (11.6) was derived by Tannery [95] for $x = 1$, and by Laguerre [47] for general x. Expansion (11.5) and (with $x = 1$) (11.6) are given by Nielsen [59]. A more detailed exposition is to be found in Nielsen [60].

3. Putting $a = 0$ in expansions (11.5) and (11.6) we obtain

$$\int_x^\infty \frac{e^{-x}}{x} dx = e^{-x} \left(\frac{1}{x+} \frac{1}{1+} \frac{1}{x+} \right.$$

$$\left. + \frac{2}{1+} \frac{2}{x+} \cdots + \frac{n}{1+} \frac{n}{x+} \cdots \right) \tag{11.7}$$

and

$$\int_x^\infty \frac{e^{-x}}{x}\,dx = e^{-x}\left(\frac{1}{x+1} - \frac{1}{x+3} - \right.$$

$$\left. - \frac{4}{x+5} - \ldots - \frac{n^2}{x+2n+1} - \ldots\right). \qquad (11.8)$$

respectively.

The integral $\int_{-\infty}^{x} (e^x/x)\,dx$ is called the *exponential integral* and is denoted by $Ei(x)$. Therefore the continued fractions (11.7) and (11.8) are the expansions of the function $Ei(x)$. Consequently, replacing x by $-x$ in (11.7), and changing the sign of both sides of the expansion, we obtain for $x < 0$:

$$\text{Ei}(x) = e^x\left(\frac{1}{x-}\ \frac{1}{1}\ -\ \frac{1}{x}\ -\ldots-\frac{n}{1}-\frac{n}{x}-\ldots\right). \qquad (11.9)$$

$$\frac{0}{1}\quad \frac{1}{x}\quad \frac{1}{x-1}\quad \frac{x-1}{x^2-2x}$$

4. The function

$$\text{Ei}(\ln x) = \int_{-\infty}^{\ln x} \frac{e^z}{z}\,dz = \int_0^x \frac{e^{\ln t}}{\ln t}\,d\ln t = \int_0^x \frac{t}{\ln t}\,\frac{dt}{t} = \int_0^x \frac{dx}{\ln x}$$

is called the *logarithmic integral*, and is denoted by li (x). Hence, from (11.9) we obtain

$$\text{li}(x) = \frac{x}{\ln x}\ -\ \frac{1}{1}\ -\ \frac{1}{\ln x}\ -\ldots-\ \frac{n}{1}\ -\ \frac{n}{\ln x}\ -\ldots. \qquad (11.10)$$

5. Putting $a = \frac{1}{2}$ in (11.5), we have when $x > 0$

$$e^x\int_x^\infty \frac{e^{-x}}{\sqrt{x}}\,dx = \frac{\sqrt{x}}{x}\ +\ \frac{1}{2}\ +\ \frac{2}{x}\ +\ \frac{3}{2}\ +\ \frac{4}{x}\ +\ldots$$

$$\ldots+\ \frac{2n}{x}\ +\ \frac{2n+1}{2}\ +\ldots. \qquad (11.11)$$

Putting $a = -1$ in (11.5), we have when $x > 0$

$$e^x \int_x^\infty \frac{e^{-x}}{x^2}\, dx = \frac{1}{x^2 +}\, \frac{2x}{1 +}\, \frac{1}{x +}\, \frac{3}{1 +}\, \frac{2}{x +} \cdots \frac{n}{x +}\, \frac{n+2}{1} + \cdots. \tag{11.12}$$

Expansion (11.12) was derived in another form by Laplace [49].

6. Replacing x by x^2 in (11.5), we obtain for $x > 0$:

$$e^{x^2} \int_x^\infty x^{2a-1} e^{-x^2}\, dx =$$

$$= \frac{x^{2a}}{2x^2 +}\, \frac{2(1-a)}{1}\, + \frac{1}{x^2 +}\, \frac{2-a}{1}\, + \frac{2}{x^2 +} \cdots + \frac{n}{x^2 +}\, \frac{n+1-a}{1} + \cdots. \tag{11.13}$$

In particular, when $a = \frac{1}{2}$, expansion (11.13) becomes

$$e^{x^2} \int_x^\infty e^{-x^2}\, dx =$$

$$= \frac{x}{2x^2 +}\, \frac{1}{1 +}\, \frac{2}{2x^2 +}\, \frac{3}{1 +}\, \frac{4}{2x^2 +} \cdots + \frac{2n}{2x^2 +}\, \frac{2n+1}{1} + \cdots. \tag{11.14}$$

Expansion (11.14) was derived in another form by Laplace [49]. Jacobi [33] and Seidel [87] also concerned themselves with it.

7. We now discuss further integral representations which may be derived for the continued fraction expansion (11.5). In order to do this we consider the double integral

$$I = \frac{1}{\Gamma(\alpha)\Gamma(\beta)} \int_0^\infty \int_0^\infty e^{-u-v-xuv} u^{\beta-1} v^{\alpha-1}\, du\, dv$$

$$(\alpha > 0,\ \beta > 0,\ x > 0).$$

We have, integrating with respect to u,

$$I = \frac{1}{\Gamma(\alpha)\Gamma(\beta)} \int_0^\infty e^{-v} v^{\alpha-1}\, dv \int_0^\infty e^{-u-xuv} u^{\beta-1}\, du =$$

$$= \frac{1}{\Gamma(\alpha)} \int_0^\infty \frac{e^{-v} v^{\alpha-1}\, dv}{(1+xv)^\beta}.$$

Integrating with respect to v, we obtain:

$$I = \frac{1}{\Gamma(\alpha)\Gamma(\beta)} \int_0^\infty e^{-u} u^{\beta-1}\, du \int_0^\infty e^{-v-xuv} v^{\alpha-1}\, dv =$$

$$= \frac{1}{\Gamma(\beta)} \int_0^\infty \frac{e^{-u} u^{\beta-1}\, du}{(1+xu)^\alpha}.$$

Hence

$$\frac{1}{\Gamma(\beta)} \int_0^\infty \frac{e^{-u} u^{\beta-1}\, du}{(1+xu)^\alpha} = \frac{1}{\Gamma(\alpha)} \int_0^\infty \frac{e^{-v} v^{\alpha-1}\, dv}{(1+xv)^\beta} \tag{11.15}$$

$$(\alpha > 0,\ \beta > 0,\ x > 0).$$

The validity of this transformation is demonstrated in any course of mathematical analysis which considers double integrals with infinite limits.

We put, in particular, $\beta = 1$, $x = 1/z$. Then (11.15) becomes

$$z^\alpha \int_0^\infty \frac{e^{-u}\, du}{(z+u)^\alpha} = \frac{z}{\Gamma(\alpha)} \int_0^\infty \frac{e^{-v} v^{\alpha-1}}{z+v}\, dv,$$

i.e., taking $z + u = t$,

$$z^{\alpha-1} e^z \int_z^\infty \frac{e^{-t}\, dt}{t^\alpha} = \frac{1}{\Gamma(\alpha)} \int_0^\infty \frac{e^{-v} v^{\alpha-1}}{z+v}\, dv.$$

From this formula, putting $a = 1 - \alpha$ $(\alpha > 0,\ x > 0)$, one can deduce the following expression for expansion (11.5):

$$\frac{1}{\Gamma(\alpha)}\int_0^\infty \frac{e^{-v}v^{\alpha-1}\,dv}{x+v} =$$

$$= \frac{1}{x+}\,\frac{\alpha}{1+}\,\frac{1}{x+}\,\frac{\alpha+1}{1+}\,\frac{2}{x+}\cdots\frac{n}{x+}\,\frac{\alpha+n}{1+}\cdots. \tag{11.16}$$

This expansion was obtained and investigated by Stieltjes [92]. With the help of (11.6), we derive from this:

$$\frac{1}{\Gamma(\alpha)}\int_0^\infty \frac{e^{-v}v^{\alpha-1}}{x+v}\,dv =$$

$$= \frac{1}{x+\alpha-}\,\frac{\alpha}{x+\alpha+2-}\,\frac{2(\alpha+1)}{x+\alpha+4-}\,\frac{3(\alpha+2)}{x+\alpha+6-}\cdots$$

$$\cdots - \frac{n(\alpha+n-1)}{x+\alpha+2n-}\cdots. \tag{11.17}$$

This expansion was derived for $\alpha = 1$ by Tschebyscheff [100] and then by Laguerre [45]. For any $\alpha > 1$ it was obtained by Perron [73].

§ 12. The Continued Fraction Expansion of the Incomplete Gamma-Function

1. The expression $\int_0^x x^{a-1}e^{-x}\,dx$ $(a > 0)$ is called the *incomplete gamma function.*

We introduce the function $(x > 0)$

$$y = x^{-a}e^{x}\int_0^x x^{a-1}e^{-x}\,dx. \tag{12.1}$$

Differentiating (12.1) with respect to x, we obtain

$$y' = -\frac{a}{x}y + y + \frac{1}{x}.$$

Thus y satisfies the differential equation

$$xy' + (a - x)y - 1 = 0, \quad y(0) = \frac{1}{a}. \tag{12.2}$$

We put $y = 1/(a + y_1)$. Equation (12.2) becomes

$$-xy_1' + (a - x)(a + y_1) - (a + y_1)^2 = 0,$$

or, removing brackets,

$$-xy_1' + ay_1 - ax - xy_1 - 2ay_1 - y_1^2 = 0;$$

finally we write it as

$$xy_1' + (a + x)y_1 + y_1^2 = -ax. \tag{12.3}$$

Comparing this equation with (1.15) we see that here $k = 1$, $\eta' = 0$, $\beta = a$, $\beta' = 1$, $\gamma = 1$, $\delta = -a$. Therefore (1.18) becomes

$$y_1 = \frac{-ax}{1 + a +} \frac{(-a + 1 + a)x}{2 + a} \genfrac{}{}{0pt}{}{}{+} \frac{(-a - 1)x}{3 + a} \genfrac{}{}{0pt}{}{}{+} \frac{(-a + 2 + a)x}{4 + a} + \dots$$

$$\dots + \frac{(-a + n + a)x}{2n + a} + \frac{(-a - n)x}{2n + 1 + a + \dots}.$$

From this

$$x^{-a}e^x \int_0^x x^{a-1}e^{-x}\,dx = \frac{1}{a -} \frac{ax}{1 + a +} \frac{x}{2 + a -} \frac{(1 + a)x}{3 + a} + \frac{2x}{4 + a +} \dots$$

$$\dots + \frac{nx}{2n + a -} \frac{(a + n)x}{2n + 1 + a + \dots}. \tag{12.4}$$

2. We develop y as a series. We write

$$y = A_0 + A_1x + A_2x^2 + A_3x^3 + \dots + A_nx^n + \dots.$$

Inserting this expansion into (12.2) we obtain:

$$\sum_{n=1}^{\infty} nA_nx^n + a\sum_{n=0}^{\infty} A_nx^n - \sum_{n=1}^{\infty} A_{n-1}x^n - 1 = 0,$$

$$A_0 = \frac{1}{a}, \qquad (n + a)A_n = A_{n-1}.$$

Hence

$$A_n = \frac{1}{a(1+a)\dots(n+a)},$$

i.e.

$$y = \frac{1}{a} + \frac{x}{a(1+a)} + \frac{x^2}{a(1+a)(2+a)} + \dots$$

$$\dots + \frac{x^n}{a(1+a)\dots(n+a)} + \dots$$

Using identity (3.1) of chapter I we form the continued fraction equivalent to this series. We have

$$y = \frac{\frac{1}{a}}{1} - \frac{\frac{x}{1+a}}{1 + \frac{x}{1+a}} - \frac{\frac{x}{2+a}}{1 + \frac{x}{2+a}} - \dots - \frac{\frac{x}{n+a}}{1 + \frac{x}{n+a}} - \dots,$$

i.e.

$$x^{-a}e^{x}\int_0^x x^{a-1}e^{-x}dx =$$

$$= \frac{1}{a} - \frac{ax}{1+a+x} - \frac{(1+a)x}{2+a+x} - \dots - \frac{(n-1+a)x}{n+a+x} - \dots. \quad (12.5)$$

This expansion was derived by Nachreiner [58], Lerch [51] and Perron [72], the latter (Perron [73]) does not indicate that this is an equivalent and not an associated fraction.

CHAPTER III

FURTHER METHODS FOR OBTAINING RATIONAL FUNCTION APPROXIMATIONS

§ 1. Obreschkoff's Formula

1. If we know the general form of the coefficients of a continued fraction which is the expansion of a given function, it is in general not possible to determine the general form of the convergents of this expansion. Only in certain cases is it possible to determine the general form of the convergents. The most general mode of treatment of this problem is attained with the help of a formula of Obreschkoff [62], which is one of the generalizations of Taylor's Theorem. We proceed to the derivation of this formula.

2. Let the function $f(x)$ be $m + k + 1$ times differentiable in the interval $[x_0, x]$. We introduce the following notation:

$$S_m^{(0)} = f(x_0) + \frac{x - x_0}{1!} f'(x_0) + \dots + \frac{(x - x_0)^m}{m!} f^{(m)}(x_0),$$

$$S_m^{(1)} = S_0^{(0)} + S_1^{(0)} + \dots + S_m^{(0)},$$

$$\dots\dots\dots\dots\dots\dots\dots\dots\dots\dots$$

$$S_m^{(k)} = S_0^{(k-1)} + S_1^{(k-1)} + \dots + S_m^{(k-1)}.$$

Then [1]

$$S_m^{(1)} = (m + 1)f(x_0) + m\frac{x - x_0}{1!} f'(x_0) + \\ + (m - 1)\frac{(x - x_0)^2}{2!} f''(x_0) + \dots + \frac{(x - x_0)^m}{m!} f^{(m)}(x_0),$$

$$S_m^{(2)} = C_{m+2}^2 f(x_0) + C_{m+1}^2 \frac{x - x_0}{1!} f'(x_0) + \\ + C_m^2 \frac{(x - x_0)^2}{2!} f''(x_0) + \dots + \frac{(x - x_0)^m}{m!} f^{(m)}(x_0).$$

[1] C_{m+k}^r is the binomial coefficient $\dfrac{(m + k)(m + k - 1)\dots(m + k - r + 1)}{r!}$

Assuming that

$$S_m^{(k)} = C_{m+k}^k f(x_0) + C_{m+k-1}^k \frac{x - x_0}{1!} f'(x_0) + \dots$$
$$\dots + \frac{(x - x_0)^m}{m!} f^{(m)}(x_0), \qquad (1.1)$$

then

$$S_m^{(k+1)} = \sum_{\nu=0}^{m} C_{m+k-\nu}^k f(x_0) + \sum_{\nu=0}^{m-1} C_{m+k-1-\nu}^k \frac{x - x_0}{1!} f'(x_0) +$$
$$+ \sum_{\nu=0}^{m-2} C_{m+k-2-\nu}^k \frac{(x - x_0)^2}{2!} f''(x_0) + \dots$$
$$\dots + \frac{(x - x_0)^m}{m!} f^{(m)}(x_0) = C_{m+k+1}^{k+1} f(x_0) + C_{m+k}^{k+1} \frac{x - x_0}{1!} f'(x_0) +$$
$$+ C_{m+k-1}^{k+1} \frac{(x - x_0)^2}{2!} f''(x_0) + \dots + \frac{(x - x_0)^m}{m!} f^m(x_0).$$

By means of this formula, (1.1) is proved for all non-negative integers m and k.

3. With the help of our notation, one can transcribe Taylor's formula with the remainder term in the form of a definite integral:

$$f(x) = f(x_0) + \frac{x - x_0}{1!} f'(x_0) + \dots + \frac{(x - x_0)^m}{m!} f^{(m)}(x_0) +$$
$$+ \frac{1}{m!} \int_{x_0}^{x} (x - t)^m f^{(m+1)}(t)\, dt \qquad (1.2)$$

as

$$S_m^{(0)} = f(x) - \frac{1}{m!} \int_{x_0}^{x} (x - t)^m f^{(m+1)}(t)\, dt. \qquad (1.3)$$

We demonstrate the validity of the following formula of Obreschkoff:

$$S_m^{(k)} = \sum_{\nu=0}^{k} (-1)^\nu C_{m+k-\nu}^m \frac{(x - x_0)^\nu}{\nu!} f^{(\nu)}(x) -$$
$$- \frac{1}{k!\,m!} \int_{x_0}^{x} (x - t)^m (x_0 - t)^k f^{(m+k+1)}(t)\, dt. \qquad (1.4)$$

When $k = 0$ this formula is correct since, when $k = 0$, it reduces to (1.3).

Introducing the function

$$g_k(x_0, f) = \sum_{\nu=0}^{m} C_{m+k-\nu}^{k} \frac{(x - x_0)^\nu}{\nu!} f^{(\nu)}(x_0) - \sum_{\nu=0}^{k} (-1)^\nu C_{m+k-\nu}^{m} \frac{(x - x_0)^\nu}{\nu!} f^{(\nu)}(x),$$

then

$$\frac{\partial}{\partial x_0} g_k(x_0, f) = - \sum_{\nu=1}^{m} C_{m+k-\nu}^{k} \frac{(x - x_0)^{\nu-1}}{(\nu - 1)!} f^{(\nu)}(x_0) +$$

$$+ \sum_{\nu=0}^{m} C_{m+k-\nu}^{k} \frac{(x - x_0)^\nu}{\nu!} f^{(\nu+1)}(x_0) -$$

$$- \sum_{\nu=1}^{k} (-1)^{\nu-1} C_{m+k-\nu}^{m} \frac{(x - x_0)^{\nu-1}}{(\nu - 1)!} f^{(\nu)}(x) =$$

$$= \sum_{\nu=0}^{m-1} (C_{m+k-\nu}^{k} - C_{m+k-\nu-1}^{k}) \frac{(x - x_0)^\nu}{\nu!} f^{(\nu+1)}(x_0) +$$

$$+ \frac{(x - x_0)^m}{m!} f^{(m+1)}(x_0) - \sum_{\nu=0}^{k-1} (-1)^\nu C_{m+k-\nu-1}^{m} \frac{(x - x_0)^\nu}{\nu!} f^{(\nu+1)}(x) =$$

$$= \sum_{\nu=0}^{m} C_{m+k-\nu-1}^{k-1} \frac{(x - x_0)^\nu}{\nu!} f^{(\nu+1)}(x_0) -$$

$$- \sum_{\nu=0}^{k-1} (-1)^\nu C_{m+k-\nu-1}^{m} \frac{(x - x_0)^\nu}{\nu!} f^{(\nu+1)}(x) \equiv g_{k-1}(x_0, f').$$

But according to (1.3)

$$g_0(x_0, f) = - \frac{1}{m!} \int_{x_0}^{x} (x - t)^m f^{(m+1)}(t)\, dt.$$

Then

$$g_0(x_0, f') = - \frac{1}{m!} \int_{x_0}^{x} (x - t)^m f^{(m+2)}(t)\, dt,$$

i.e.

$$g_1(x_0, f) = -\frac{1}{1!m!}\int_{x_0}^{x}(x-t)^m(x_0-t)f^{(m+2)}(t)\,dt.$$

Repeating this process, we obtain

$$g_k(x_0, f) = -\frac{1}{k!m!}\int_{x_0}^{x}(x-t)^m(x_0-t)^k f^{(m+k+1)}(t)\,dt.$$

Thus formula (1.4) is proved.

A generalization of Taylor's Theorem similar to Obreschkoff's formula was proposed by Hermite [31]. Kowalewski [40] derived Obreschkoff's formula with the help of generalized Cesaro summation, and also from Kowalewski's derivation one has the general integral formula. Tschakaloff [99] applied Obreschkoff's formula to obtain a formula for approximate integration, and Pflans [74] for the solution of certain differential equations. We apply this formula to obtain the approximation of certain functions by means of rational fractions.

4. We derive a further form of formula (1.4). For this we divide both sides by C^m_{m+k}:

$$\sum_{\nu=0}^{k}(-1)^\nu\frac{C^m_{m+k-\nu}}{C^m_{m+k}}\frac{(x-x_0)^\nu}{\nu!}f^{(\nu)}(x) =$$

$$= \sum_{\nu=0}^{m}\frac{C^k_{m+k-\nu}}{C^m_{m+k}}\frac{(x-x_0)^\nu}{\nu!}f^{(\nu)}(x) +$$

$$+\frac{1}{(k+m)!}\int_{x_0}^{x}(x-t)^m(x_0-t)^k f^{(m+k+1)}(t)\,dt.$$

But

$$\frac{C^m_{m+k-\nu}}{C^m_{m+k}} = \frac{C^\nu_k}{C^\nu_{m+k}}, \tag{1.5}$$

since this relation is equivalent to the identity

$$\frac{(m+k-\nu)(m+k-\nu-1)\dots(k-\nu+1)}{(m+k)(m+k-1)\dots(k+1)} =$$

$$= \frac{k(k-1)\dots(k-\nu+1)}{(m+k)(m+k-1)\dots(m+k-\nu+1)}.$$

The left hand side of this identity is obtained from the right hand side by multiplying the numerator and denominator of the right hand side by $(m + k - \nu)(m + k - \nu - 1) \dots (k + 1)$.

Exchanging the rôles of m and k in (1.5), we obtain:

$$\frac{C^k_{m+k-\nu}}{C^k_{m+k}} = \frac{C^k_{m+k-\nu}}{C^m_{m+k}} = \frac{C^\nu_m}{C^\nu_{m+k}}.$$

One can, therefore, derive the following form of Obreschkoff's formula, used by Beck [9]:

$$\sum_{\nu=0}^{k} (-1)^\nu \frac{C^\nu_k}{C^\nu_{m+k}} \frac{(x - x_0)^\nu}{\nu!} f^{(\nu)}(x) =$$

$$= \sum_{\nu=0}^{m} \frac{C^\nu_m}{C^\nu_{m+k}} \frac{(x - x_0)^\nu}{\nu!} f^{(\nu)}(x_0) +$$

$$+ \frac{1}{(k + m)!} \int_{x_0}^{x} (x - t)^m (x_0 - t)^k f^{(m+k+1)}(t)\, dt. \tag{1.6}$$

In such a form, Obreschkoff's formula permits the derivation of the general form of the convergents of the continued fraction expansions of certain functions.

§ 2. The Derivation of Rational Function Approximations to Certain Functions with the Help of Obreschkoff's Formula

1. In (1.6) we put $x_0 = 0$, $f(x) = e^x$. Then

$$e^x = \frac{\displaystyle\sum_{\nu=0}^{m} \frac{C^\nu_m}{C^\nu_{m+k}} \frac{x^\nu}{\nu!}}{\displaystyle\sum_{\nu=0}^{k} (-1)^\nu \frac{C^\nu_k}{C^\nu_{m+k}} \frac{x^\nu}{\nu!}} + \frac{\displaystyle\frac{(-1)^{m+k}}{(k+m)!} \int_0^x t^k (t - x)^m e^t\, dt}{\displaystyle\sum_{\nu=0}^{k} (-1)^\nu \frac{C^\nu_k}{C^\nu_{m+k}} \frac{x^\nu}{\nu!}}. \tag{2.1}$$

In this expression are included all convergents of expansions (5.1) and (5.3) of chapter II. The existence of the remainder term allows an estimation of the accuracy of the approximation to be made.

In particular, when $m = k$

$$e^k \sim \frac{\sum\limits_{\nu=0}^{k} \frac{C_k^\nu}{C_{2k}^\nu} \frac{x^\nu}{\nu!}}{\sum\limits_{\nu=0}^{k} (-1)^\nu \frac{C_k^\nu}{C_{2k}^\nu} \frac{x^\nu}{\nu!}} =$$

$$= \frac{1 + \frac{C_k^1}{2k} x + \frac{C_k^2}{2k(2k-1)} x^2 + \ldots + \frac{C_k^k}{2k(2k-1)\ldots(k+1)} x^k}{1 - \frac{C_k^1}{2k} x + \frac{C_k^2}{2k(2k-1)} x^2 - \ldots + (-1)^k \frac{C_k^k}{2k(2k-1)\ldots(k+1)} x^k},$$

i.e.

$$e^x \sim \frac{2k(2k-1)\ldots(k+1) + C_k^1(2k-1)(2k-2)\ldots(k+1)x + \ldots + x^k}{2k(2k-1)\ldots(k+1) - C_k^1(2k-1)(2k-2)\ldots(k+1)x + \ldots + (-1)^k x^k}. \tag{2.2}$$

In this expression are included all the convergents of expansion (5.5) of chapter II.

Darboux [12] was the first to concern himself with the rational fraction approximation of e^x, and this problem was considered systematically by Padé [64]–[70], in the context of a whole series of relations between rational fraction approximations and continued fractions.

2. From the relation

$$\tanh x = \frac{e^{2x} - 1}{e^{2x} + 1}$$

and from (2.2), we have

$$\tanh x \sim$$

$$\sim \frac{C_k^1(2k-1)(2k-2)\ldots(k+1)2x + C_k^3(2k-3)(2k-4)\ldots(k+1)8x^3 + \ldots}{2k(2k-1)\ldots(k+1) + C_k^2(2k-2)(2k-3)\ldots(k+1)4x^2 + C_k^4(2k-4)(2k-5)\ldots(k+1)16x^4 + \ldots},$$

i.e.

$$\tanh x \sim$$

$$\sim \frac{C_k^1(2k-1)(2k-2)\ldots(k+1)x - C_k^3(2k-3)(2k-4)\ldots(k+1)4x^3 + \ldots}{k(2k-1)\ldots(k+1) + C_k^2(2k-2)(2k-3)\ldots(k+1)2x^2 + C_k^4(2k-4)(2k-5)\ldots(k+1)8x^4 + \ldots}. \tag{2.3}$$

This is the general expression for all the convergents of expansion (7.2) of chapter II. Replacing x by ix in (2.3) and dividing the right and left hand sides by i, we obtain the general expression for all the convergents of expansion (7.1) of chapter II.

We note that the approximations deriving from (2.4) and (2.2) for $\cos x$, $\cosh x$, $\sin x$ and $\sinh x$ are not very accurate. We do not therefore write them out.

3. In (1.6) we put $x_0 = 1$, $f(x) = x^n$, where n is an arbitrary real number. Then

$$\sum_{\nu=0}^{k} (-1)^\nu \frac{C_k^\nu}{C_{m+k}^\nu} \frac{(x-1)^\nu}{\nu!} n(n-1) \dots (n-\nu+1) x^{n-\nu} \sim$$

$$\sim \sum_{\nu=0}^{n} \frac{C_m^\nu}{C_{m+k}^\nu} \frac{(x-1)^\nu}{\nu!} n(n-1) \dots (n-\nu+1),$$

whence

$$x^n \sim \frac{\sum_{\nu=0}^{m} \frac{C_m^\nu C_n^\nu}{C_{m+k}^\nu} (x-1)^\nu}{\sum_{\nu=0}^{k} (-1)^\nu \frac{C_k^\nu C_n^\nu}{C_{m+k}^\nu} \frac{(x-1)^\nu}{x^\nu}}. \tag{2.4}$$

When $m = k$ equation (2.4) becomes

$$x^n \sim \frac{\sum_{\nu=0}^{k} \frac{C_k^\nu C_n^\nu}{C_{2k}^\nu} (x-1)^\nu}{\sum_{\nu=0}^{k} (-1)^\nu \frac{C_k^\nu C_n^\nu}{C_{2k}^\nu} \frac{(x-1)^\nu}{x^\nu}}. \tag{2.5}$$

In particular, with $k = 1$

$$x^n \sim \frac{1 + \frac{n}{2}(x-1)}{1 - \frac{n}{2} \frac{x-1}{x}} = \frac{2 - n + nx}{n + (2-n)x} x.$$

For example, when $x = 2$, $n = \frac{1}{3}$ we have:

$$\sqrt[3]{2} \doteqdot \frac{\left(2 - \frac{1}{3} + \frac{2}{3}\right)2}{\frac{1}{3} + \frac{5}{3} .2} = \frac{14}{11} \doteqdot 1{\cdot}273.$$

The exact value of $\sqrt[3]{2}$ is 1·2599210...

When $k = 2$

$$x^n \sim \frac{1 + \frac{n}{2}(x-1) + \frac{n(n-1)}{12}(x-1)^2}{1 - \frac{n}{2}\frac{x-1}{x} + \frac{n(n-1)}{12}\frac{(x-1)^2}{x^2}} =$$

$$= \frac{12 + 6n(x-1) + n(n-1)(x-1)^2}{12x^2 - 6nx(x-1) + n(n-1)(x-1)^2}\, x^2.$$

For example, when $x = 2$, $n = \frac{1}{3}$ we have:

$$\sqrt[3]{2} \doteqdot \frac{\left(12 + 2 - \frac{2}{9}\right)4}{12.4 - 2.2 - \frac{2}{9}} = \frac{248}{197} \doteqdot 1{\cdot}2589.$$

This approximation is not among those which may be derived from expansions (2.1)–(2.8) of chapter II.

4. In (1.6) we put $x_0 = 1$, $f(x) = \ln(x)$. Then

$$\ln x + \sum_{\nu=1}^{k} (-1)^\nu \frac{C_k^\nu}{C_{m+k}^\nu} \frac{(x-1)^\nu}{\nu} \frac{(-1)^{\nu-1}}{x^\nu} \sim$$

$$\sim \sum_{\nu=1}^{m} \frac{C_m^\nu}{C_{m+k}^\nu} \frac{(x-1)^\nu}{\nu} (-1)^{\nu-1},$$

whence

$$\ln x \sim \sum_{\nu=1}^{m} \frac{C_m^\nu}{C_{m+k}^\nu} \frac{(x-1)^\nu}{\nu} (-1)^{\nu-1} + \sum_{\nu=1}^{k} \frac{C_k^\nu}{C_{m+k}^\nu} \frac{(x-1)^\nu}{\nu x^\nu}. \tag{2.6}$$

With $m = k$, this relation becomes

$$\ln x \sim \sum_{\nu=1}^{k} \frac{C_k^\nu}{\nu C_{2k}^\nu} \left[(-1)^{\nu-1} + \frac{1}{x^\nu}\right](x-1)^\nu. \tag{2.7}$$

In particular, when $k = 1$

$$\ln x \sim \frac{1}{2}\left(1 + \frac{1}{x}\right)(x-1) = \frac{1}{2}\left(x - \frac{1}{x}\right).$$

When $k = 2$

$$\ln x \sim \frac{2}{4}\left(1 + \frac{1}{x}\right)(x - 1) + \frac{1}{6.2}\left(-1 + \frac{1}{x^2}\right)(x - 1)^2 =$$

$$= \frac{x^2 - 1}{2x} - \frac{(x^2 - 1)(x - 1)^2}{12x^2},$$

i.e.

$$\ln x = \frac{x^2 - 1}{12x^2}(8x - x^2 - 1). \tag{2.8}$$

Approximation (2.8) is not contained among those which may be derived from § 4 of chapter II.

§ 3. The Solution of Certain Difference Equations with the help of Continued Fractions

1. In section 5, § 9 of chapter II we have already encountered the solution of difference equations with the help of continued fractions. We now consider examples of more complicated difference equations and derive from then continued fraction expansions of certain integrals involving elliptic functions. We consider the Jacobian elliptic functions which are defined by the following formulae:

$$x = \int_0^y \frac{dt}{\sqrt{(1 - t^2)(1 - k^2t^2)}}, \quad y = \operatorname{sn}(x, k) = \operatorname{sn} x,$$

$$x = \int_y^1 \frac{dt}{\sqrt{(1 - t^2)(1 - k^2 + k^2t^2)}}, \quad y = \operatorname{cn}(x, k) = \operatorname{cn} x,$$

$$x = \int_y^1 \frac{dt}{\sqrt{(1 - t^2)(t^2 + k^2 - 1)}}, \quad y = \operatorname{dn}(x, k) = \operatorname{dn} x.$$

These functions satisfy the following relationships, which we shall subsequently use:

$$\left.\begin{aligned} &\operatorname{sn}^2 x + \operatorname{cn}^2 x = 1, && (\operatorname{sn} x)' = \operatorname{cn} x \operatorname{dn} x, \\ &\operatorname{dn}^2 x = 1 - k^2 \operatorname{sn}^2 x, && (\operatorname{cn} x)' = -\operatorname{sn} x \operatorname{dn} x, \\ & && (\operatorname{dn} x)' = -k^2 \operatorname{sn} x \operatorname{cn} x. \end{aligned}\right\} \tag{3.1}$$

We remark that $\operatorname{sn} 0 = 0$, $\operatorname{cn} 0 = 1$ and $\operatorname{dn} 0 = 1$.

When $k = 1$

$$\operatorname{sn} x = \tanh x, \quad \operatorname{cn} x = \operatorname{dn} x = \frac{1}{\cosh x}. \tag{3.2}$$

When $k = 0$

$$\operatorname{sn} x = \sin x, \quad \operatorname{cn} x = \cos x, \quad \operatorname{dn} x = 1. \tag{3.3}$$

2. Let

$$u_n = \int_0^\infty e^{-xt} \operatorname{sn}^n t \, dt.$$

Then when $n > 2$ we obtain, by integrating by parts (with $x > 0$):

$$u_n = \frac{1}{x} \int_0^\infty e^{-xt} \frac{d}{dt} (\operatorname{sn}^n t) \, dt = \frac{1}{x^2} \int_0^\infty e^{-xt} \frac{d^2}{dt^2} (\operatorname{sn}^n t) \, dt.$$

But according to (3.1)

$$\frac{d}{dt} \operatorname{sn}^n t = n \operatorname{sn}^{n-1} t \operatorname{cn} t \operatorname{dn} t,$$

$$\frac{d^2}{dt^2} \operatorname{sn}^n t = n(n-1) \operatorname{sn}^{n-2} t \operatorname{cn}^2 t \operatorname{dn}^2 t - n \operatorname{sn}^n t \operatorname{dn}^2 t - k^2 n \operatorname{sn}^n t \operatorname{cn}^2 t =$$

$$= n(n-1) \operatorname{sn}^{n-2} t (1 - \operatorname{sn}^2 t)(1 - k^2 \operatorname{sn}^2 t) -$$

$$- n \operatorname{sn}^n t (1 - k^2 \operatorname{sn}^2 t + k^2 - k^2 \operatorname{sn}^2 t) =$$

$$= n(n-1) \operatorname{sn}^{n-2} t - n(k^2 n - k^2 + n - 1 + 1 + k^2) \operatorname{sn}^n t +$$

$$+ (k^2 n^2 - k^2 n + 2k^2 n) \operatorname{sn}^{n+2} t.$$

Hence we have the difference equation

$$x^2 u_n = n(n-1) u_{n-2} - n^2 (1 + k^2) u_n + n(n+1) k^2 u_{n+2}. \tag{3.4}$$

3. When $n = 1$

$$u_1 = \frac{1}{x} \int_0^\infty e^{-xt} \frac{d}{dt} \operatorname{sn} t \, dt = \frac{1}{x} \int_0^\infty e^{-xt} \operatorname{cn} t \operatorname{dn} t \, dt =$$

$$= \left[-\frac{1}{x^2} \operatorname{cn} t \operatorname{dn} t e^{-xt} \right]_0^\infty +$$

$$+\frac{1}{x^2}\int_0^\infty [-\operatorname{sn} t \operatorname{dn}^2 t - k^2 \operatorname{sn} t \operatorname{cn}^2 t] e^{-xt}\, dt =$$

$$= \frac{1}{x^2} - \frac{1}{x^2}\int_0^\infty \operatorname{sn} t(1 + k^2 - 2k^2 \operatorname{sn}^2 t) e^{-xt}\, dt =$$

$$= \frac{1}{x^2} - (1 + k^2)\frac{u_1}{x^2} + \frac{2k^2}{x^2} u_3.$$

From this

$$u_1 = \cfrac{1}{x^2 + 1 + k^2 - 2k^2 \cfrac{u_3}{u_1}}.$$

But from (3.4) we have:

$$\frac{u_n}{u_{n-2}} = \cfrac{(n-1)n}{n^2(1 + k^2) + x^2 - n(n+1)k^2 \cfrac{u_{n+2}}{u_n}}.$$

Hence (Rogers [81]),

$$\int_0^\infty e^{-xt} \operatorname{sn} t\, dt = \frac{1}{1 + k^2 + x^2 -}\, \frac{1.2^2.3k^2}{3^2(1 + k^2) + x^2 -}\, \frac{3.4^2.5k^2}{5^2(1 + k^2) + x^2 - \dots}$$

$$\dots - \frac{(2n-1)4n^2(2n+1)k}{(2n+1)^2(1 + k^2) + x^2} - \dots. \tag{3.5}$$

In particular, with $k = 1$ (bearing (3.2) in mind)

$$\int_0^\infty e^{-xt} \tanh t\, dt = \frac{1}{2 + x^2 -}\, \frac{1.2^2.3}{2.3^2 + x^2 -}\, \frac{3.4^2.5}{2.5^2 + x^2} - \dots$$

$$\dots - \frac{(2n-1)4n^2(2n+1)}{2(2n+1)^2 + x^2} - \dots. \tag{3.6}$$

4. We note that (3.6) may be written as:

$$x\int_0^\infty e^{-xt} \tanh t\, dt = \frac{x}{1.2 + x^2 -}\, \frac{1.2^2.3}{2.3 + 3.4 + x^2 -}\, \frac{3.4^2.5}{4.5 + 5.6 + x^2 - \dots}$$

$$\dots - \frac{(2n-1)4n^2(2n+1)}{2n(2n+1) + (2n+1)(2n+2) + x^2} - \dots.$$

From this, using relations (2.9) of chapter I, we obtain the extensional of this continued fraction

$$x\int_0^\infty e^{-xt}\tanh t\,dt = \frac{1}{x+}\,\frac{1.2}{x+}\,\frac{2.3}{x+}\cdots+\frac{n(n+1)}{x}\,{}_{+\cdots}. \tag{3.7}$$

This was given without derivation by Stieltjes [93]. Integrating the left hand side of (3.7) by parts we obtain the relationship

$$\int_0^\infty \frac{e^{-xt}}{\cosh^2 t}\,dt = \frac{1}{x+}\,\frac{1.2}{x+}\,\frac{2.3}{x+}\cdots+\frac{n(n+1)}{x}\,{}_{+\cdots}, \tag{3.8}$$

also given without derivation by Stieltjes [93].

5. When $n = 2$ we have

$$u_2 = \frac{1}{x^2}\int_0^\infty e^{-xt}\frac{d^2}{dt^2}\,\mathrm{sn}^2\,t\,dt = \frac{2}{x^3} - \frac{4(1+k^2)}{x^2}\,u_2 + \frac{6k^2}{x^2}\,u_4,$$

$$xu_2 = \frac{2}{2^2(1+k^2)+x^2-6k^2\dfrac{u_4}{u_2}},$$

i.e. (Rogers [81])

$$x\int_0^\infty e^{-xt}\,\mathrm{sn}^2\,t\,dt = \frac{2}{2^2(1+k^2)+x^2-}\,\frac{2.3^2.4k^2}{4^2(1+k^2)+x^2-}\cdots$$
$$\cdots-\frac{2n(2n+1)^2(2n+2)k^2}{(2n+2)^2(1+k^2)+x^2-\cdots}. \tag{3.9}$$

In particular, when $k = 1$, (taking note of (3.2))

$$x\int_0^\infty e^{-xt}\tanh^2 t\,dt =$$

$$= \frac{2}{2.2^2+x^2-}\,\frac{2.3^2.4}{2.4^2+x^2-}\cdots-\frac{2n(2n+1)^2(2n+2)}{2(2n+2)^2+x^2}\,{}_{-\cdots}. \tag{3.10}$$

From (3.8), with the help of the equation $1/\cosh^2 t = 1 - \tanh^2 t$, we obtain:

$$x \int_0^\infty e^{-xt} \tanh^2 t\, dt = 1 - \frac{x}{x+} \frac{1.2}{x+} \frac{2.3}{x+} \dots + \frac{n(n+1)}{x} + \dots \tag{3.11}$$

§ 4. The Derivation of Rational Function Approximations by means of Iteration

1. Knowing [1] that when $x > 0$

$$x = 1 + \ln x + \frac{\ln^2 x}{2!} + \frac{\ln^3 x}{3!} + \dots + \frac{\ln^n x}{n!} + \dots,$$

$$\frac{1}{x} = 1 - \ln x + \frac{\ln^2 x}{2!} - \frac{\ln^3 x}{3!} + \dots + (-1)^n \frac{\ln^n x}{n!} + \dots,$$

we have

$$\left.\begin{aligned} x + \frac{1}{x} &= 2 + \ln^2 x + \frac{\ln^4 x}{12} + \frac{\ln^6 x}{360} + \\ &\quad + \frac{\ln^8 x}{20\,160} + \dots + \frac{2 \ln^{2n} x}{(2n)!} + \dots, \\ x - \frac{1}{x} &= 2 \ln x + \frac{\ln^3 x}{3} + \frac{\ln^5 x}{60} + \\ &\quad + \frac{\ln^7 x}{2520} + \dots + \frac{2 \ln^{2n-1} x}{(2n-1)!} + \dots \end{aligned}\right\} \tag{4.1}$$

Consequently,

$$x + \frac{1}{x} - \left(x - \frac{1}{x}\right)\frac{\ln x}{4} = 2 + \frac{\ln^2 x}{2} + \left(\frac{1}{360} - \frac{1}{240}\right) \ln^6 x + \dots,$$

[1]) Derived from the series

$$e^x = 1 + \frac{x}{1!} + \frac{x^2}{2!} + \frac{x^3}{3!} + \dots + \frac{x^n}{n!} + \dots,$$

replacing x by $\ln x$ and $-\ln x$ respectively.

i.e.

$$x \ln^2 x + \frac{x^2 - 1}{2} \ln x \sim 2(x^2 - 2x + 1),$$

$$\ln x \sim \frac{2(x-1)^2}{\dfrac{x^2-1}{2} + x \ln x}. \tag{4.2}$$

Inserting one of the approximations (4.7) of chapter II in (4.2), we have

$$\ln x \approx \frac{2(x-1)^2}{\dfrac{x^2-1}{2} + \dfrac{3x(x^2-1)}{x^2+4x-1}},$$

i.e.

$$\ln x \approx \frac{4(x-1)(x^2+4x+1)}{(x+1)(x^2+10x+1)}. \tag{4.3}$$

Approximation (4.3) is suitable over a wider range of values of x than approximation (4.7) of Chapter II (c.f. § 6 of this chapter).

2. From expansions (4.1) we have:

$$\left(x + \frac{1}{x}\right)\frac{\ln x}{3} - x + \frac{1}{x} = -\frac{4}{3}\ln x + \frac{\ln^5 x}{90} + \frac{\ln^7 x}{1890} + \dots.$$

and

$$\left(x + \frac{1}{x}\right) - \left(x - \frac{1}{x}\right)\frac{\ln x}{4} = 2 + \frac{\ln^2 x}{2} - \frac{\ln^6 x}{720} - \frac{\ln^8 x}{20\,160} + \dots.$$

From these

$$\left(x + \frac{1}{x}\right)\frac{\ln^2 x}{24} - \left(x - \frac{1}{x}\right)\frac{\ln x}{8} - \left(x - \frac{1}{x}\right)\frac{\ln x}{4} + \left(x + \frac{1}{x}\right) =$$

$$= -\frac{1}{6}\ln^2 x + 2 + \frac{\ln^2 x}{2} + \frac{\ln^8 x}{60\,480} + \dots,$$

i.e.

$$\left(x + \frac{1}{x} - 8\right)\frac{\ln^2 x}{24} - \frac{3}{8}\left(x - \frac{1}{x}\right)\ln x + x + \frac{1}{x} - 2 =$$

$$= \frac{\ln^8 x}{60\,480} + \dots.$$

As can be seen, one can, to a very high degree of accuracy, put:

$$(x^2 - 8x + 1)\ln^2 x - 9(x^2 - 1)\ln x + 24(x - 1)^2 \sim 0.$$

From this

$$\ln x \sim \frac{24(x-1)^2}{9(x^2-1) - (x^2 - 8x + 1)\ln x}. \tag{4.4}$$

Inserting approximation (4.3) in (4.4) we have

$$\ln x \sim \frac{24(x-1)}{9(x+1) - \dfrac{4(x^2-8x+1)(x^2+4x+1)}{(x+1)(x^2+10x+1)}},$$

i.e.

$$\ln x \sim \frac{24(x^2-1)(x^2+10x+1)}{5x^4 + 124x^3 + 318x^2 + 124x + 5}.$$

Factorising the denominator, we have finally:

$$\ln x \sim \frac{24(x^2-1)(x^2+10x+1)}{(x^2+22x+1)(5x^2+14x+5)}. \tag{4.5}$$

Approximation (4.5) is suitable for a still wider range of values of x than (4.3) (c.f. § 6 of this chapter).

§ 5. Table of Approximate Values of e^x

1. Using expansions (5.1), (5.3) and (5.5) of chapter II we obtain the following approximations to e^x:

1) $\dfrac{2+x}{2-x}$, 2) $\dfrac{6+4x+x^2}{6-2x}$, 3) $\dfrac{12+6x+x^2}{12-6x+x^2}$,

4) $\dfrac{60+36x+9x^2+x^3}{60-24x+3x^2}$, 5) $\dfrac{120+60x+12x^2+x^3}{120-60x+12x^2-x^3}$,

6) $\dfrac{1680+840x+180x^2+20x^3+x^4}{1680-840x+180x^2-20x^3+x^4}$,

7) $\dfrac{30\,240+15\,120x+3360x^2+420x^3+30x^4+x^5}{30\,240-15\,120x+3360x^2-420x^3+30x^4-x^5}$.

From these we derive the following table:

TABLE 1

x	e^x	1)	2)	3)	4)	5)
1	2·71828	3·0	2·75	2·714	2·71795	2·71831
2	7·38906		9·0	7·00	7·33	7·400
3	20·08554			13·00	18·4	20·7

x	e^x	6)	7)
1	2·7182818285	2·71828172	2·7182818287
2	7·389056	7·38889	7·3890578
3	20·08554	20·065	20·08597
4	54·59815	53·73	54·63
5	148·41316		149·7

§ 6. Table of Approximate Values of ln x

1. From relations (4.7) of chapter II and (4.3) and (4.5) of chapter III, we have the following approximations for $\ln x$:

$$1)\ 2\frac{x-1}{x+1},\quad 2)\ \frac{3(x^2-1)}{x^2+4x+1},\quad 3)\ \frac{(x-1)(11x^2+38x+11)}{3(x+1)(x^2+8x+1)},$$

$$4)\ \frac{5(x^2-1)(5x^2+32x+5)}{6(x^4+16x^3+36x^2+16x+1)},\quad 5)\ \frac{4(x-1)(x^2+4x+1)}{(x+1)(x^2+10x+1)},$$

$$6)\ \frac{24(x^2-1)(x^2+10x+1)}{(x^2+22x+1)(5x^2+14x+5)}.$$

From these we obtain the following table:

TABLE 2

x	$\ln x$	1)	2)	3)	5)	5)	6)
2	0·6931472	0·67	1·6923	0·69312	0·6931464	0·69333	0·69311
4	1·38629	1·20	1·364	1·3837	1·3860	1·389	1·3860
6	1·79176	1·43	1·72	1·779	1·7894	1·797	1·7923
8	2·07944		1·99	2·008	2·072	2·081	2·082
10	2·30259			2·25	2·287	2·296	2·307
12	2·48491					2·465	2·490
14	2·63906						2·644

§ 7. Table of Approximate Values of tan x and tanh x

1. From expansion (7.1) of chapter II, we have the following approximations for $\tan x$:

$$1)\ \frac{3x}{3-x^2},\quad 2)\ \frac{15x-x^3}{15-6x^2},\quad 3)\ \frac{105x-10x^3}{105-45x^2+x^4},$$

$$4)\ \frac{945x-105x^3+x^5}{945-420x^2+15x^4}.$$

From these we obtain the following table:

TABLE 3

x	$\tan x$	1)	2)	3)	4)
1	1·5574077	1·50	1·55	1·55738	1·5774074
2	−2·1850		−2·44	−2·203	−2·1859
3	−0·143		−0·46		−0·150

From expansion (7.3) of chapter II, we have the following approximations for $\tanh x$:

$$1)\ \frac{3x}{3+x^2},\quad 2)\ \frac{15x+x^3}{15+6x^2},\quad 3)\ \frac{105x+10x^3}{105+45x^2+x^4},$$

$$4)\ \frac{945x+105x^3+x^5}{945+420x^2+15x^4}.$$

From these we obtain the following table:

TABLE 4

x	$\tanh x$	1)	2)	3)	4)
1	0·76159416	0·750	0·7619	0·761589	0·76159420
2	0·96403	0·86	0·974	0·9635	0·96405
3	0·9951		1·04	0·990	0·9955
4	0·999			0·981	1·002

§ 8. Rational Function Approximations for sinh x and sin x

1. In this and the following sections of this chapter we give some rational function approximations for functions for which the general form of the continued fraction expansion is unknown.

We shall use the method of Viskovatoff (section 6, § 3, chapter I) to derive the continued fraction expansions of such functions.

2. Applying the method of Viskovatoff to the expansion

$$\sinh x = x + \frac{x^3}{3!} + \frac{x^5}{5!} + \frac{x^7}{7!} + \dots,$$

we obtain

$$\begin{array}{ccccc}
1 & & & & \\
1 & \frac{1}{6} & \frac{1}{120} & \frac{1}{5040} & \frac{1}{9!} \\
-\frac{1}{6} & -\frac{1}{120} & -\frac{1}{5040} & -\frac{1}{9!} & \\
-\frac{7}{360} & -\frac{1}{840} & -\frac{11}{9!} & & \\
-\frac{11}{720.420} & -\frac{13}{30.9!} & & & \\
\frac{551}{10!7.1080} & & & &
\end{array}$$

Thus,

$$\sinh x = \frac{x}{1} - \frac{\frac{x^2}{6}}{1} - \frac{\frac{7}{360}x^2}{-\frac{1}{6}} - \frac{\frac{11}{720.420}x^2}{-\frac{7}{360}} + \frac{\frac{551x^2}{10!7.1080}}{-\frac{11}{720.420}} + \dots =$$

$$= \frac{x}{1} - \frac{x^2}{6} + \frac{7x^2}{10} - \frac{11x^2}{98} + \frac{551x^2}{198} + \dots$$

$$\frac{0}{1} \quad \frac{x}{1} \quad \frac{6x}{6 - x^2} \quad \frac{60x + 7x^3}{60 - 3x^2} \quad \frac{5880x + 620x^3}{5880 - 360x^2 + 11x^4}$$

$$\frac{1\,164\,240x + 155\,820x^3 + 3857x^5}{1\,164\,240 - 38\,220x^2 + 525x^4}$$

$$\frac{166\,320x + 22\,260x^3 + 551x^5}{166\,320 - 5460x^2 + 75x^4}$$

3. Now applying the method of Viskovatoff to the expansion

$$\sinh x - x = \frac{x^3}{3!} + \frac{x^5}{5!} + \frac{x^7}{7!} + \frac{x^9}{9!} + \dots$$

we have:

$$\begin{array}{llll}
1 & & & \\
\frac{1}{6} & \frac{1}{120} & \frac{1}{5040} & \frac{1}{9!} \\
-\frac{1}{120} & -\frac{1}{5040} & -\frac{1}{9!} & \\
-\frac{11}{60.7!} & -\frac{13}{30.9!} & & \\
-\frac{1}{4!.9!.42} & & &
\end{array}$$

Thus,

$$\sinh x = x + \cfrac{\frac{x^3}{6}}{1 - \cfrac{\frac{x^2}{120}}{\frac{1}{6} - \cfrac{\frac{11x^2}{60.7!}}{-\frac{1}{120} - \cfrac{\frac{x^2}{4!.9!.42}}{-\frac{11}{60.7!} + \dots}}}} =$$

$$= x + \cfrac{x^3}{6 - \cfrac{\frac{x^2}{20}}{\frac{1}{6} + \cfrac{\frac{11x^2}{60}}{42 - \cfrac{300x^2}{11.72 + \dots}}}}.$$

Finally

$$\sinh x = x + \cfrac{x^3}{6 - \cfrac{3x^2}{10 + \cfrac{11x^2}{42 - \cfrac{25x^2}{66 - \dots}}}}.$$

$$\frac{x}{1} \qquad \frac{6x+x^3}{6} \qquad \frac{60x+7x^3}{60-3x^2} \qquad \frac{2520x+360x^3+11x^5}{2520-60x^2}$$

4. We have thus the following approximations for sinh x:

1) $\dfrac{6x}{6-x^2}$, 2) $\dfrac{60x+7x^3}{60-3x^2}$, 3) $\dfrac{5880x+620x^3}{5880-360x^2+11x^4}$,

4) $\dfrac{2520x+360x^3+11x^5}{2520-60x^2}$, 5) $\dfrac{166\,320x+22\,260x^3+551x^5}{166\,320-5460x^2+75x^4}$.

From these we obtain the following table:

TABLE 5

x	sinh x	1)	2)	3)	4)	5)
1	1·17520119	1·20	1·1754	1·175194	1·175203	1·17520117
2	3·62686	6·0	3·66	3·622	3·6281	3·62680
3	10·018		11·2	9·7	10·08	10·011
4	27·3					27·04
5	74					70

5. If in the expansions for sinh x given in sections 2 and 3, we replace x by ix and divide both right and left hand sides by i, then we obtain two expansions for sin x

$$\sin x = \frac{x}{1} + \frac{x^2}{6} - \frac{7x^2}{10} + \frac{11x^2}{98} - \frac{551x^2}{198} - \dots,$$

$$\sin x = x - \frac{x^3}{6} + \frac{3x^2}{10} - \frac{11x^2}{42} + \frac{25x^2}{66} + \dots.$$

Consequently for sin x we have the following approximations:

1) $\dfrac{6x}{6+x^2}$, 2) $\dfrac{60x-7x^3}{60+3x^2}$, 3) $\dfrac{5880x-620x^3}{5880+360x^2+11x^4}$,

4) $\dfrac{2520x-360x^3+11x^5}{2520+60x^2}$, 5) $\dfrac{166\,320x-22\,260x^3+551x^5}{166\,320+5460x^2+75x^4}$.

From these we obtain the following table:

TABLE 6

x	sin x	1)	2)	3)	4)	5)
1	0·84147098	0·857	0·84127	0·841465	0·841473	0·84147101
2	0·90930		0·889	0·9071	0·9102	0·90934
3	0·141			0·09	0·168	0·144
4	−0·76					−0·72
5	−0·96					−0·65

The expansions

$$\frac{x}{\sin x} = 1 + \frac{x^2}{6} - \frac{7x^2}{10} + \frac{11x^2}{98} - \frac{551x^2}{198} + \dots$$

and

$$\frac{x}{\sin x} = \frac{1}{1} - \frac{x^2}{6} + \frac{3x^2}{10} - \frac{11x^2}{42} + \frac{25x^2}{66} - \ldots$$

occur in the book by Kornoukhoff [1].

The approximation

$$\sin x \sim \frac{60x - 7x^3}{60 + 3x^2}$$

is given in a paper by Deschmann [13].

§ 9. Rational Function Approximations for cosh x and cos x

1. Applying the method of Viskovatoff to the expansion

$$\cosh x = 1 + \frac{x^2}{2!} + \frac{x^4}{4!} + \frac{x^6}{6!} + \ldots,$$

we have

$$\begin{array}{lllll}
1 & & & & \\
1 & \frac{1}{2} & \frac{1}{24} & \frac{1}{720} & \frac{1}{8!} \\
-\frac{1}{2} & -\frac{1}{24} & -\frac{1}{720} & -\frac{1}{8!} & \\
-\frac{5}{24} & -\frac{7}{360} & -\frac{27}{8!} & & \\
-\frac{1}{960} & -\frac{11}{6.8!} & & & \\
\frac{313}{720.8!} & & & &
\end{array}$$

Thus,

$$\cosh x = \frac{1}{1} - \frac{\frac{x^2}{2}}{1} - \frac{\frac{5x^2}{24}}{-\frac{1}{2}} - \frac{\frac{x^2}{960}}{-\frac{5}{24}} + \frac{\frac{313x^2}{720.8!}}{-\frac{1}{960}} + \ldots =$$

$$= \frac{1}{1} - \frac{\frac{x^2}{2}}{1} + \frac{\frac{5x^2}{6}}{1} - \frac{\frac{3x^2}{50}}{1} + \frac{\frac{313x^2}{126}}{1} - \dots$$

$$\frac{0}{1} \quad \frac{1}{1} \quad \frac{2}{2 - x^2} \quad \frac{12 + 5x^2}{12 - x^2} \quad \frac{600 + 244x^2}{600 - 56x^2 + 3x^4} \quad \frac{75\,600 + 34\,500x^2 + 5.313x^4}{75\,600 - 3300x^2 + 65x^4}$$

$$\frac{15\,120 + 6900x^2 + 313x^4}{15\,120 - 660x^2 + 13x^4}$$

2. We now apply the method of Viskovatoff to the expansion

$$\cosh x - 1 = \frac{1}{2}\, x^2 + \frac{1}{24}\, x^4 + \frac{1}{6!}\, x^6 + \frac{1}{8!}\, x^8 + \dots .$$

We have:

$$\begin{array}{llll}
1 & & & \\
\frac{1}{2} & \frac{1}{24} & \frac{1}{720} & \frac{1}{8!} \\
-\frac{1}{24} & -\frac{1}{720} & -\frac{1}{8!} & \\
-\frac{1}{960} & -\frac{11}{6.8!} & & \\
-\frac{13}{24.30.8!} & & &
\end{array}$$

Thus,

$$\cosh x \sim 1 + \cfrac{\frac{x^2}{2}}{1} - \cfrac{\frac{x^2}{24}}{\frac{1}{2}} - \cfrac{\frac{x^2}{960}}{\frac{1}{24}} - \cfrac{\frac{13x^2}{24.30.8!}}{\frac{1}{960}} + \dots =$$

$$= 1 + \frac{\frac{x^2}{2}}{1} - \frac{\frac{x^2}{6}}{1} + \frac{\frac{3x^2}{10}}{1} - \frac{\frac{13x^2}{126}}{1} - \dots .$$

$$\frac{1}{1} \quad \frac{2+x^2}{2} \quad \frac{12+5x^2}{12 - x^2} \quad \frac{120+56x^2+3x^4}{120 - 4x^2} \quad \frac{15\,120+6900x^2+313x^4}{15\,120-660x^2+13x^4}$$

3. Thus, we have the following approximations for cosh x:

$$1)\ \frac{2}{2-x^2},\quad 2)\ \frac{12+5x^2}{12-x^2},\quad 3)\ \frac{600+244x^2}{600-56x^2+3x^4},$$

$$4)\ \frac{120+56x^2+3x^4}{120-4x^2},\quad 5)\ \frac{15\,120+6900x^2+313x^4}{15\,120-660x^2+13x^4}.$$

From these we obtain the following table:

TABLE 7

x	cosh x	1)	2)	3)	4)	5)
1	1·5430806	2	1·545	1·54296	1·543103	1·5430802
2	3·7622		4·0	3·72	3·769	3·7617
3	10·07			8·2	10·3	10·02
4	27				32	26·1
5	74					57

4. Replacing x by ix in the expansions for cosh x derived above, we obtain the corresponding expansions for cos x, which lead to the following approximations:

$$1)\ \frac{2}{2+x^2},\quad 2)\ \frac{12-5x^2}{12+x^2},\quad 3)\ \frac{600-244x^2}{600+56x^2+3x^4},$$

$$4)\ \frac{120-56x^2+3x^4}{120+4x^2},\quad 5)\ \frac{15\,120-6900x^2+313x^4}{15\,120+660x^2+13x^4}.$$

We obtain the table:

TABLE 8

x	cos x	1)	2)	3)	4)	5)
1	0·5403023	0·67	0·5385	0·54021	0·540323	0·5403027
2	−0·4161		−0·50	−0·431	−0·412	−0·4159
3	−0·990				−0·90	−0·978
4	−0·65					−0·52

The expansion

$$\cos x = 1 - \frac{x^2}{2 + \frac{x^2}{6 - \frac{3x^2}{10 + \frac{13x^2}{126 - \cdots}}}}$$

occurs in the book by Kornoukhoff [1].

The approximation

$$\cos x \sim \frac{12 - 5x^2}{12 + x^2}$$

is given in the paper by Deschmann [13].

§ 10. Rational Function Approximations for the Error Function

1. Applying the method of Viskovatoff to the expansion

$$\int_0^x e^{-x^2}\,dx = \int_0^x \left(1 - \frac{x^2}{1!} + \frac{x^4}{2!} - \frac{x^6}{3!} + \ldots\right) dx =$$

$$= x - \frac{x^3}{3} + \frac{x^5}{10} - \frac{x^7}{42} + \frac{x^9}{216} - \ldots$$

we have:

$$\begin{array}{cccccc}
 & 1 & & & & \\
 & 1 & -\frac{1}{3} & \frac{1}{10} & -\frac{1}{42} & \frac{1}{216} \\
 & \frac{1}{3} & -\frac{1}{10} & \frac{1}{42} & -\frac{1}{216} & \\
 & -\frac{1}{90} & \frac{1}{105} & -\frac{5}{1512} & & \\
 & -\frac{13}{6300} & \frac{19}{22\,680} & & & \\
-\frac{739}{71\,442\,000} & & & & &
\end{array}$$

From this

$$\int_0^x e^{-x^2}\,dx = \cfrac{x}{1 + \cfrac{\frac{1}{3}x^2}{1 + \cfrac{-\frac{1}{90}x^2}{\frac{1}{3} + \cfrac{-\frac{13}{6300}x^2}{-\frac{1}{90} + \cfrac{-\frac{739}{71\,442\,000}x^2}{-\frac{13}{6300} + \ldots}}}}} =$$

$$= \frac{x}{1 +}\,\frac{x^2}{3 -}\,\frac{x^2}{10 +}\,\frac{39x^2}{7 -}\,\frac{739x^2}{18.13 -} \ldots,$$

i.e.

$$\int_0^x e^{-x^2}\,dx = \frac{x}{1+}\ \frac{x^2}{3}\ -\ \frac{x^2}{10}\ +$$

$$\frac{0}{1}\quad \frac{x}{1}\quad \frac{3x}{3+x^2}\quad \frac{30x-x^3}{30+9x^2}$$

$$+\ \frac{39x^2}{7}\ -\ \frac{739x^2}{234}\ -\ldots.$$

$$\frac{210x+110x^3}{210+180x^2+39x^4}\quad \frac{49\,140x+3570x^3+739x^5}{49\,140+19\,950x^2+2475x^4}$$

From this we obtain the following approximations for $\operatorname{erf} x \equiv$ $\equiv (2/\sqrt{\pi}) \int_0^x e^{-x^2}\,dx$:

$$1)\ \frac{2}{\sqrt{\pi}}\,\frac{30x-x^3}{30+9x^2},\qquad 2)\ \frac{2}{\sqrt{\pi}}\,\frac{210x+110x^3}{210+180x^2+39x^4},$$

$$3)\ \frac{2}{\sqrt{\pi}}\,\frac{49\,140x+3570x^3+739x^5}{49\,140+19\,950x^2+2475x^4}.$$

We have the table $(2/\sqrt{\pi} \doteq 1{,}12838)$:

TABLE 9

x	erf x	1)	2)	3)
0·5	0·52050	0·52045	0·52050	0·52050
1·0	0·84270	0·83905	0·84168	0·84274
2·0	0·99582	0·89	0·95	1·008

§ 11. The Continued Fraction Expansion of Stirling's Series

1. The following series of Stirling is known:

$$\ln \Gamma(x) = (x - \tfrac{1}{2}) \ln x - x + \tfrac{1}{2} \ln 2\pi + J(x).$$

Here

$$J(x) = \frac{B_1}{1.2x} + \frac{B_2}{3.4x^3} + \ldots + \frac{B_n}{(2n-1)2nx^{2n-1}} + \ldots$$

(B_1, B_2, ... are Bernoulli numbers).

Stieltjes [93] developed $J(x)$ as a continued fraction, not showing the general law of formation of its coefficients. We derive Stieltjes result using the method of Viskovatoff.

It is known that

$$B_1 = \frac{1}{6}, \quad B_2 = -\frac{1}{30}, \quad B_3 = \frac{1}{42}, \quad B_4 = -\frac{1}{30}, \quad B_5 = \frac{5}{66}, \quad \ldots$$

Hence

$$J(x) = \frac{1}{12x}\left(1 - \frac{1}{30x^2} + \frac{1}{105x^4} - \frac{1}{140x^6} + \frac{1}{99x^8} - \ldots\right).$$

Applying the method of Viskovatoff to this series, we obtain:

$$\begin{array}{lllll}
1 & & & & \\
1 & -\frac{1}{30} & \frac{1}{105} & -\frac{1}{140} & \frac{1}{99} \\
\frac{1}{30} & -\frac{1}{105} & \frac{1}{140} & -\frac{1}{99} & \\
\frac{53}{6300} & -\frac{43}{140.45} & \frac{1367}{99.1400} & & \\
\frac{13}{6300.14} & -\frac{391}{99.700.21} & & & \\
\frac{22\,999}{6300.99.700.42} & & & &
\end{array}$$

From this

$$J(x) = \frac{\frac{1}{12x}}{1} + \frac{\frac{1}{30x^2}}{1} + \frac{\frac{53}{6300x^2}}{\frac{1}{30}} + \frac{\frac{13}{6300.14x^2}}{\frac{53}{6300}} + \frac{\frac{22\,999}{6300.99.700.42x^2}}{\frac{13}{14.6300}} + \ldots =$$

$$= \frac{\frac{1}{12}}{x} + \frac{\frac{1}{30}}{x} + \frac{\frac{53}{210}}{x} + \frac{\frac{195}{7}}{53x} + \frac{\frac{22\,999}{11.3.13}}{x} + \ldots .$$

Consequently,

$$J(x) = \cfrac{\frac{1}{12}}{x + \cfrac{\frac{1}{30}}{x + \cfrac{\frac{53}{210}}{x + \cfrac{\frac{195}{371}}{x + \cfrac{\frac{22\,999}{22\,737}}{x + \dots}}}}}.$$

In such a form the expansion was derived by Stieltjes; he asserted that "with great advantage this continued fraction replaces the series of Stirling". One can write this continued fraction as

$$J(x) = \frac{1}{12x +} \frac{2}{5x +} \frac{53}{42x +} \frac{1170}{53x +} \frac{22\,999}{429x + \dots}.$$

Thus

$$\ln \Gamma(x) = (x - \tfrac{1}{2}) \ln x - x + \tfrac{1}{2} \ln 2\pi +$$
$$+ \frac{1}{12x +} \frac{2}{5x +} \frac{53}{42x +} \frac{1170}{53x +} \frac{22\,999}{429x + \dots}.$$

§ 12. Rational Function Approximations to $\Gamma(1 + x)$

1. It is known (Ruzhik and Gradstein [4], Nielsen [59] p. 40), that

$$\Gamma(1 + x) = \sum_{n=0}^{\infty} c_n x^n,$$

where

$$c_0 = 1, \quad c_n = \frac{1}{n} \sum_{k=1}^{n} (-1)^k c_{n-k} s_k,$$

$$s_k = \sum_{m=1}^{\infty} \frac{1}{m^k} \ (k \geqslant 2), \ s_1 = \gamma \doteqdot 0{,}57722 \text{ (Euler's constant)}.$$

In particular,

$$c_1 = -\gamma,$$

$$c_2 = \tfrac{1}{2} \sum_{k=1}^{2} (-1)^k c_{2-k} s_k = \tfrac{1}{2}\left(- c_1\gamma + \frac{\pi^2}{6}\right) \doteqdot$$
$$\doteqdot \tfrac{1}{2}(0{,}57722^2 + 1{,}64493) \doteqdot 0{\cdot}98906,$$

$$c_3 = \tfrac{1}{3} \sum_{k=1}^{3} (-1)^k c_{3-k} s_k = \tfrac{1}{3}(- c_2\gamma + c_1 . 1{\cdot}64493 + 1{\cdot}20206) \doteqdot$$
$$\doteqdot -\tfrac{1}{3} . 2{\cdot}72245 = -0{\cdot}90748,$$

$$c_4 = \tfrac{1}{4} \sum_{k=1}^{4} (-1)^k c_{4-k} s_k =$$

$$= \tfrac{1}{4}(-c_3\gamma + c_2 . 1{\cdot}64493 + \gamma . 1{\cdot}20206 + 1{\cdot}08232) \doteq$$

$$\doteq \tfrac{1}{4} . 3{\cdot}92692 = 0{\cdot}98173.$$

Thus

$$\Gamma(1+x) \sim 1 - 0{\cdot}57722x + 0{\cdot}98906x^2 -$$

$$- 0{\cdot}90748x^3 + 0{\cdot}98173x^4. \quad (12.1)$$

2. Applying the method of Viskovatoff to the approximation (12.1), we obtain:

$$\begin{array}{lllll}
1 & & & & \\
1 & -0{\cdot}57722 & 0{\cdot}98906 & -0{\cdot}90748 & 0{\cdot}98173 \\
0{\cdot}57722 & -0{\cdot}98906 & 0{\cdot}90748 & -0{\cdot}98173 & \\
0{\cdot}65588 & -0{\cdot}33708 & 0{\cdot}45791 & & \\
-0{\cdot}45413 & 0{\cdot}33088 & & & \\
-0{\cdot}063939 & & & &
\end{array}$$

Hence,

$$\Gamma(1+x) \sim \frac{1}{1+}\,\frac{0{\cdot}57722x}{1}\,+\frac{0{\cdot}65588x}{0{\cdot}57722}-\frac{0{\cdot}45413x}{0{\cdot}65588}+\frac{0{\cdot}063939x}{0{\cdot}45413} \approx$$

$$\sim \frac{1}{1+}\,\frac{0{\cdot}57722x}{1}\,+\,\frac{1{\cdot}13627x}{1}\,-\,\frac{1{\cdot}19953x}{1}\,+\,\frac{0{\cdot}21467x}{1}.$$

$$\frac{0}{1}\quad\frac{1}{1}\quad\frac{1}{1+0{\cdot}57722x}\quad\frac{1+1{,}13627x}{1+1{\cdot}71349x}\quad\frac{1-0{,}06326x}{1+0{\cdot}51396x-0{\cdot}69239x^2}\quad\frac{1+0{\cdot}15141x+0{\cdot}24392x^2}{1+0{\cdot}72863x-0{\cdot}32456x^2}$$

From this, in particular

$$\Gamma(1+x) \sim \frac{1+0{\cdot}15141x+0{\cdot}24392x^2}{1+0{\cdot}72263x-0{\cdot}32456x^2}. \quad (12.2)$$

We have the table:

TABLE 10

x	$\Gamma(1+x)$	(12.2)	x	$\Gamma(1+x)$	(12.2)
−0·5	1·7725	1·7767	0·1	0·95135	0·95135
−0·4	1·4892	1·4902	0·2	0·91817	0·91816
−0·3	1·29806	1·29823	0·3	0·89747	0·89743
−0·2	1·16423	1·16425	0·4	0·88726	0·88711
−0·1	1·06863	1·06863	0·5	0·8862	0·8858
0·0	1	1	0·6	0·8935	0·8927
			0·7	0·9086	0·9071
			1·0	1	0·994

3. From the expansion (Ruzhik and Gradstein [4], Nielsen [59] p. 38)

$$\ln \Gamma(1 + x) = - \gamma x + \sum_{n=2}^{\infty} \frac{(-1)^n x^n}{n} s_n, \tag{12.3}$$

where $s_n = \sum_{m=1}^{\infty} 1/m^n$, we have:

$$\ln \Gamma(1 + x) \sim$$

$$\sim - 0{\cdot}57722x + 0{\cdot}82247x^2 - 0{\cdot}40068x^3 + 0{\cdot}27058x^4. \tag{12.4}$$

Applying the method of Viskovatoff to expansion (12.4), we derive:

1			
−0·57722	0·82247	−0·40068	0·27058
−0·82247	0·40068	−0·27058	
−0·44518	0·17336		
−0·035791			

Hence,

$$\ln \Gamma(1 + x) \sim \frac{-0{\cdot}57722x}{1} \, \frac{0{\cdot}82247x}{- - 0{\cdot}57722 -} \, \frac{0{\cdot}44518x}{- 0{\cdot}82247 -} \, \frac{0{\cdot}035791x}{- 0{\cdot}44518} \sim$$

$$\sim \frac{-0\cdot57722x}{1} + \frac{1\cdot42488x}{1} - \frac{0\cdot93772x}{1} - \frac{0\cdot09775x}{1}.$$

$$\frac{0}{1} \quad \frac{-0\cdot57722x}{1} \quad \frac{-0\cdot57722x}{1+1\cdot42488x} \quad \frac{-057\cdot722x+0\cdot54127x^2}{1+0\cdot48716x} \quad \frac{-0\cdot57722x+0\cdot59769x^2}{1+0\cdot38941x-0\cdot13928x^2}.$$

From this, in particular

$$\ln \Gamma(1+x) \sim \frac{-0\cdot57722x+0\cdot59769x^2}{1+0\cdot38941x+0\cdot13928x^2}.$$

Consequently

$$\log \Gamma(1+x) \sim \frac{-0\cdot25068x+0\cdot25957x^2}{1+0\cdot38941x-0\cdot13928x^2}. \tag{12.5}$$

We have the table:

TABLE 11

x	$\log \Gamma(1+x)$	(12.5)	x	$\log \Gamma(1+x)$	(12.5)
$-0\cdot5$	0·2486	0·2469	0·1	$\bar{1}$·97834	$\bar{1}$·97834
$-0\cdot4$	0·1730	0·1725	0·2	$\bar{1}$·96292	$\bar{1}$·96293
$-0\cdot3$	0·11329	0·11321	0·3	$\bar{1}$·95302	$\bar{1}$·95305
$-0\cdot2$	0·066039	0·066029	0·4	$\bar{1}$·94806	$\bar{1}$·94818
$-0\cdot1$	0·0288268	0·0288266	0·5	$\bar{1}$·9475	$\bar{1}$·9479
0	0	0			

4. We consider the function $\Psi(x) = d(\ln \Gamma(1+x))/dx$. According to (12.3) it has the expansion

$$\Psi(x) = -\gamma + s_2 x - s_3 x^2 + \ldots + (-1)^{n+1} s_{n+1} x^n + \ldots,$$

whence

$$\Psi(x) \sim -0\cdot57722 + 1\cdot64493x - 1\cdot20206x^2 + 1\cdot08232x^3. \tag{12.6}$$

Applying the method of Viskovatoff to expansion (12.6), we obtain:

$$\begin{array}{llll}
1 & & & \\
-0{\cdot}57722 & 1{\cdot}64493 & -1{\cdot}20206 & 1{\cdot}08232 \\
-1{\cdot}64493 & 1{\cdot}20206 & -1{\cdot}08232 & \\
-2{\cdot}01194 & 1{\cdot}35257 & & \\
-0{\cdot}19359 & & &
\end{array}$$

Consequently,

$$\Psi(x) \sim \frac{-0{\cdot}57722}{1} \; - \; \frac{1{\cdot}64493x}{-0{\cdot}57722} \; - \; \frac{2{\cdot}01194x}{-1{\cdot}64493} \; - \; \frac{0{\cdot}19359x}{-2{\cdot}01194} \sim$$

$$\sim \frac{-0{\cdot}57722}{1} \; + \; \frac{2{\cdot}84975x}{1} \; - \; \frac{2{\cdot}11897x}{1} \; - \; \frac{0{\cdot}058495x}{1} \, .$$

$$\frac{0}{1} \quad \frac{-0{\cdot}57722}{1} \quad \frac{-0{\cdot}57722}{1 + 2{\cdot}84975x} \quad \frac{-0{\cdot}57722 + 1{\cdot}22311x}{1 + 0{\cdot}73078x} \quad \frac{-0{\cdot}57722 + 1{\cdot}25687x}{1 + 0{\cdot}67228x - 0{\cdot}16670x^2}$$

From this, in particular,

$$\Psi(x) \sim \frac{-0{\cdot}57722 + 1{\cdot}25687x}{1 + 0{\cdot}67228x - 0{\cdot}16670x^2} \, . \tag{12.7}$$

We have the table:

TABLE 12

x	$\Psi(x)$	(12.7)	x	$\Psi(x)$	(12.7)
−0·5	−1·964	−1·938	0·1	−0·4238	−0·4237
−0·4	−1·541	−1·538	0·2	−0·2889	−0·2890
−0·3	−1·220	−1·218	6·3	−0·1692	−0·1687
−0·2	−0·9650	−0·9647	0·4	−0·614	−0·0600
−0·1	−0·7549	−0·7549	0·5	0·0365	0·0396
0	−0·57722	−0·57722			

CHAPTER IV

GENERALIZED CONTINUED FRACTIONS

Among the various generalizations of continued fractions which have been suggested, that based upon the successive application of a certain matrix operator on a given vector is especially interesting. In a simple form this method was given by Euler [17], who applied it to the approximate determination of the geometric mean of two numbers whose ratio is as $1 : x$. This, incidentally, permits the approximate computation of the expression $x^{p/q}$ (p and q being arbitrary whole numbers) when x is given. If we except notes by Lorey [53] and Krafft [41] and its use in computational problems in the work of Müller [57], Euler's method appears to have been forgotten. And even in these papers the possibility of exploiting this method in practice is not shown.

In the present chapter we briefly describe those generalized continued fractions which may most easily be used for approximate calculations. We devote special attention to methods associated with matrices.

§ 1. The Computation of Square Roots with the Help of Matrices of the Second Order

1. The process of deriving rational function approximations with the help of continued fractions leads to the computation of quantities P_n and Q_n ($n = 0, 1, \ldots$) related to each other by means of the formulae

$$\left.\begin{aligned} P_n &= a_n P_{n-2} + b_n P_{n-1}, \\ Q_n &= a_n Q_{n-2} + b_n Q_{n-1} \end{aligned}\right\} \quad (n = 1, 2, \ldots). \tag{1.1}$$

In this, a_n and b_n ($n = 1, 2, \ldots$) are so chosen that $\lim\limits_{n\to\infty} P_n/Q_n$ exists and is finite. The question arises – is it not possible to employ relationships analogous to (1.1) for the determination of P_n and Q_n? In particular one can consider relationships of the form

$$\left.\begin{aligned} P_n &= \alpha_n P_{n-1} + \beta_n Q_{n-1}, \\ Q_n &= \gamma_n P_{n-1} + \delta_n Q_{n-1}, \end{aligned}\right\} \quad (n = 1, 2, \ldots). \tag{1.2}$$

With the help of a matrix this equation may be written as:

$$\begin{pmatrix} P_n \\ Q_n \end{pmatrix} = \begin{pmatrix} \alpha_n & \beta_n \\ \gamma_n & \delta_n \end{pmatrix} \begin{pmatrix} P_{n-1} \\ Q_{n-1} \end{pmatrix}. \tag{1.3}$$

2. We put $\alpha_n = a$, $\beta_n = u$, $\gamma_n = 1$, $\delta_n = a$ $(n = 1, 2, \ldots)$. Then relationships (1.2) and (1.3) become

$$\left.\begin{aligned} P_n &= aP_{n-1} + uQ_{n-1}, \\ Q_n &= P_{n-1} + aQ_{n-1} \end{aligned}\right\} \quad (n = 1, 2, \ldots) \tag{1.4}$$

and

$$\begin{pmatrix} P_n \\ Q_n \end{pmatrix} = \begin{pmatrix} a & u \\ 1 & a \end{pmatrix} \begin{pmatrix} P_{n-1} \\ Q_{n-1} \end{pmatrix} \quad (n = 1, 2, \ldots). \tag{1.5}$$

respectively.

When $a = 0$ it follows from (1.4) that $P_0/Q_0 = 0/1$, $P_1/Q_1 = u/0$, $P_2/Q_2 = 0/u = 0/1$, i.e. the process (1.4) diverges. We shall therefore assume that $a \neq 0$.

We shall use the following notation:

$$\begin{pmatrix} a & u \\ 1 & a \end{pmatrix} \qquad \frac{a}{1} \quad \frac{P_1}{Q_1} \quad \frac{P_2}{Q_2} \quad \cdots \quad \frac{P_n}{Q_n} \quad \cdots$$

We shall use an analogous notation when applying more general matrices.

3. From equation (1.4), it follows that

$$\frac{P_n}{Q_n} = \frac{aP_{n-1} + uQ_{n-1}}{P_{n-1} + aQ_{n-1}},$$

i.e.

$$\frac{P_n}{Q_n} = \frac{a\dfrac{P_{n-1}}{Q_{n-1}} + u}{\dfrac{P_{n-1}}{Q_{n-1}} + a}. \tag{1.6}$$

Let $\lim_{n\to\infty} P_n/Q_n$ exist, be finite, and be denoted by x. Then from (1.6) we obtain:

$$x = \frac{ax+u}{x+a}, \text{ i.e. } x^2 = u,\ x = \pm\sqrt{u}.$$

Thus if $\lim_{n\to\infty} P_n/Q_n$ exists, then it is equal to either $\sqrt{u}$ or $-\sqrt{u}$. Hence when $u < 0$ the process (1.4) diverges.

Denote $-\sqrt{u} = x_1$, $\sqrt{u} = x_2$.

4. From (1.6) we have

$$\frac{P_n}{Q_n} - x = \frac{a\dfrac{P_{n-1}}{Q_{n-1}} + x^2 - x\dfrac{P_{n-1}}{Q_{n-1}} - ax}{\dfrac{P_{n-1}}{Q_{n-1}} + a} =$$

$$= \frac{a\left(\dfrac{P_{n-1}}{Q_{n-1}} - x\right) - x\left(\dfrac{P_{n-1}}{Q_{n-1}} - x\right)}{\dfrac{Q_n}{Q_{n-1}}} =$$

$$= \frac{a-x}{Q_n} Q_{n-1}\left(\frac{P_{n-1}}{Q_{n-1}} - x\right) =$$

$$= \frac{(a-x)^2 Q_{n-1}Q_{n-2}}{Q_nQ_{n-1}}\left(\frac{P_{n-2}}{Q_{n-2}} - x\right) = \ldots$$

$$\ldots = \frac{(a-x)^n}{Q_n} Q_0\left(\frac{P_0}{Q_0} - x\right).$$

Finally, taking $P_0/Q_0 = a/1$,

$$\frac{P_n}{Q_n} - x = \frac{(a-x)^{n+1}}{Q_n}. \tag{1.7}$$

When $a > x_2$, we have from this $P_n/Q_n > x_2$, since when $a > 0$ it follows from (1.4) that $Q_n > 0$. Indeed in this computation $P_0 = a > 0$, $Q_0 = 1$, $P_1 = P_0 + a.Q_0 > 0$ and so on.

5. We discuss the conditions under which the quantities P_n/Q_n are monotonically decreasing with increasing n. In order to do this we first compute $(P_n/Q_n) - (P_{n-1}/Q_{n-1})$.

From (1.6) it follows that

$$\frac{P_n}{Q_n} - \frac{P_{n-1}}{Q_{n-1}} = \frac{a\dfrac{P_{n-1}}{Q_{n-1}} + u - \dfrac{P_{n-1}^2}{Q_{n-1}^2} - a\dfrac{P_{n-1}}{Q_{n-1}}}{\dfrac{Q_n}{Q_{n-1}}} = \frac{u - \dfrac{P_{n-1}^2}{Q_{n-1}^2}}{\dfrac{Q_n}{Q_{n-1}}},$$

i.e.

$$\frac{P_n}{Q_n} - \frac{P_{n-1}}{Q_{n-1}} = -\frac{\left(\dfrac{P_{n-1}}{Q_{n-1}} - x_1\right)\left(\dfrac{P_{n-1}}{Q_{n-1}} - x_2\right)}{\dfrac{Q_n}{Q_{n-1}}}. \tag{1.8}$$

From (1.8) and (1.7) it follows that when $a > x_2$, the inequality $(P_n/Q_n) < (P_{n-1}/Q_{n-1})$ obtains. Comparing this inequality with that following from (1.7), we see that when $a > x_1$

$$x_2 < \frac{P_n}{Q_n} < \frac{P_{n-1}}{Q_{n-1}}.$$

Hence, when $a > x_2$, the quantities P_n/Q_n are monotonically decreasing to a lower limit x_2. Therefore when $a > x_2$ we have $\lim\limits_{n\to\infty} (P_n/Q_n) = x_2$.

6. When $0 < a < x_2$ it follows from (1.7) that $(P_{2n}/Q_{2n}) < x_2$ and $(P_{2n+1}/Q_{2n+1}) > x_2$ since, as before, $Q_n > 0$. We discuss the behaviour of P_{2n}/Q_{2n} and P_{2n+1}/Q_{2n+1} when $0 < a < x_2$. For this we calculate $(P_n/Q_n) - (P_{n-2}/Q_{n-2})$.

In order to compute this expression we note that

$$\begin{pmatrix} a & u \\ 1 & a \end{pmatrix}\begin{pmatrix} a & u \\ 1 & a \end{pmatrix} = \begin{pmatrix} a^2 + u & 2au \\ 2a & a^2 + u \end{pmatrix}.$$

Hence there follows from (1.5) the equation

$$\begin{pmatrix} P_n \\ Q_n \end{pmatrix} = \begin{pmatrix} a^2 + u & 2au \\ 2a & a^2 + u \end{pmatrix}\begin{pmatrix} P_{n-2} \\ Q_{n-2} \end{pmatrix},$$

whence

$$\frac{P_n}{Q_n} = \frac{(a^2 + u)P_{n-2} + 2auQ_{n-2}}{2aP_{n-2} + (a^2 + u)Q_{n-2}} = \frac{(a^2 + u)\dfrac{P_{n-2}}{Q_{n-2}} + 2au}{2a\dfrac{P_{n-2}}{Q_{n-2}} + a^2 + u};$$

$$\frac{P_n}{Q_n} - \frac{P_{n-2}}{Q_{n-2}} =$$

$$= \frac{(a^2+u)\dfrac{P_{n-2}}{Q_{n-2}} + 2au - 2a\left(\dfrac{P_{n-2}}{Q_{n-2}}\right)^2 - (a^2+u)\dfrac{P_{n-2}}{Q_{n-2}}}{\dfrac{Q_n}{Q_{n-2}}} =$$

$$= 2aQ_{n-2}\,\frac{u - \left(\dfrac{P_{n-2}}{Q_{n-2}}\right)^2}{Q_n} =$$

$$= -\,2aQ_{n-2}\,\frac{\left(\dfrac{P_{n-2}}{Q_{n-2}} - x_1\right)\left(\dfrac{P_{n-2}}{Q_{n-2}} - x_2\right)}{Q_n}.$$

In particular

$$\frac{P_{2n}}{Q_{2n}} - \frac{P_{2n-2}}{Q_{2n-2}} = -\,2a\,\frac{Q_{2n-2}}{Q_{2n}}\left(\frac{P_{2n-2}}{Q_{2n-2}} - x_1\right)\left(\frac{P_{2n-2}}{Q_{2n-2}} - x_2\right) \qquad (1.9)$$

and

$$\frac{P_{2n+1}}{Q_{2n+1}} - \frac{P_{2n-1}}{Q_{2n-1}} = -\,2a\,\frac{Q_{2n-1}}{Q_{2n+1}}\left(\frac{P_{2n-1}}{Q_{2n-1}} - x_1\right)\left(\frac{P_{2n-1}}{Q_{2n-1}} - x_2\right). \qquad (1.10)$$

From (1.7) it follows that when $0 < a < x_2$ we have the inequality

$$0 < \frac{P_{2n-2}}{Q_{2n-2}} < x_2 \qquad (n = 1, 2, \ldots).$$

Therefore, when $0 < a < x_2$, it follows from (1.9) that $(P_{2n}/Q_{2n}) >$ $> (P_{2n-2}/Q_{2n-2})$. Consequently P_{2n}/Q_{2n} increases monotonically with increasing n to an upper limit x_2. Therefore when $0 < a < x_2$ we have $\lim\limits_{n\to\infty} (P_{2n}/Q_{2n}) = x_2$.

From (1.7) it follows that when $0 < a < x_2$ the inequality

$$x_2 < \frac{P_{2n-1}}{Q_{2n-1}} \qquad (n = 1, 2, \ldots)$$

obtains. It follows from (1.10), therefore, that $(P_{2n+1}/Q_{2n+1}) <$ $< (P_{2n-1}/Q_{2n-1})$. Hence P_{2n-1}/Q_{2n-1} decreases monotonically with increasing n to a lower limit x_2. In this case, therefore, when $0 < a < x_2$, then $\lim_{n\to\infty} (P_{2n-1}/Q_{2n-1}) = x_2$.

7. We replace x by $-x$ in the equation $x^2 = u$. Then x_1 goes over into $-x_2$ and x_2 goes over into $-x_1$, since $-x_1$ becomes the greater root. We also replace a by $-a$. Now the sequence of terms determined by means of relations (1.4) converges only to $-x_1$ or to $-x_2$, whence P_n/Q_n is replaced by $-(P_n/Q_n)$.

We know that when $a > x_2$, the inequality $x_2 < (P_n/Q_n) < < (P_{n-1}/Q_{n-1})$ obtains, or written in another way

$$\frac{P_{n-1}}{Q_{n-1}} > \frac{P_n}{Q_n} > x_2.$$

From this we conclude that when $-a > -x_1$, the inequality

$$-\frac{P_{n-1}}{Q_{n-1}} > -\frac{P_n}{Q_n} > -x_1$$

obtains, i.e. when $a < x_1$ we have the inequality

$$\frac{P_{n-1}}{Q_{n-1}} < \frac{P_n}{Q_n} < x_1.$$

Thus when $a < x_1$, P_n/Q_n increases monotonically with increasing n to an upper limit x_1. Hence when $a < x_1$ we have $\lim_{n\to\infty} (P_n/Q_n) = x_1$.

We know that when $0 < a < x_2$, we have the inequalities

$$\frac{P_{2n-2}}{Q_{2n-2}} < \frac{P_{2n}}{Q_{2n}} < x_2 < \frac{P_{2n+1}}{Q_{2n+1}} < \frac{P_{2n-1}}{Q_{2n-1}}.$$

From this we conclude that when $0 < -a < -x_1$ then we have the inequalities

$$-\frac{P_{2n-2}}{Q_{2n-2}} < -\frac{P_{2n}}{Q_{2n}} < -x_1 < -\frac{P_{2n+1}}{Q_{2n+1}} < -\frac{P_{2n-1}}{Q_{2n-1}},$$

i.e. when $x_1 < a < 0$, the inequalities

$$\frac{P_{2n-1}}{Q_{2n-1}} < \frac{P_{2n+1}}{Q_{2n+1}} < x_1 < \frac{P_{2n}}{Q_{2n}} < \frac{P_{2n-2}}{Q_{2n-2}}$$

obtain. Hence, when $x_1 < a < 0$, we have $\lim_{n\to\infty} (P_n/Q_n) = x_1$.

8. Examples:

1) $a > x_2$.

$$\begin{pmatrix} 5 & 22 \\ 1 & 5 \end{pmatrix} \qquad \frac{5}{1} \quad \frac{47}{10} \quad \frac{455}{97} \quad \frac{4409}{940}$$

$$5 \quad 4{\cdot}7 \quad 4{\cdot}6907 \quad 4{\cdot}69043$$

$$\sqrt{22} < 4{\cdot}69043.$$

2) $0 < a < x_2$.

$$\begin{pmatrix} 5 & 27 \\ 1 & 5 \end{pmatrix} \qquad \frac{5}{1} \quad \frac{52}{10} = \frac{26}{5} \quad \frac{265}{51} \quad \frac{2702}{520}$$

$$5 \quad 5{\cdot}2 \quad 5{\cdot}19607 \quad 5{\cdot}19616$$

$$5{\cdot}19607 < \sqrt{27} < 5{\cdot}19616.$$

3) $x_1 < a < 0$.

$$\begin{pmatrix} -1 & 2 \\ 1 & -1 \end{pmatrix} \qquad \frac{-1}{1} \quad \frac{3}{-2} \quad \frac{-7}{5} \quad \frac{17}{-12} \quad \frac{-41}{29}$$

$$-1{\cdot}5 \quad -1{\cdot}4 \quad -1{\cdot}416 \quad -1{\cdot}4137$$

$$-1{\cdot}416 < -\sqrt{2} < -1{\cdot}4138.$$

4) $a < x_1$.

$$\begin{pmatrix} -2 & 3 \\ 1 & -2 \end{pmatrix} \qquad \frac{-2}{1} \quad \frac{7}{-4} \quad \frac{-26}{15} \quad \frac{97}{-56}$$

$$-1{\cdot}75 \quad -1{\cdot}734 \quad -1{\cdot}73214$$

$$-1{\cdot}73214 < -\sqrt{3}.$$

§ 2. The Solution of Quadratic Equations with the Help of Matrices of the Second Order

1. We put in (1.3) $\alpha_n = a$, $\beta_n = -q$, $\gamma_n = 1$, $\delta_n = a + p$. Then relations (1.2) and (1.3) become

$$\left.\begin{aligned} P_n &= aP_{n-1} - qQ_{n-1}, \\ Q_n &= P_{n-1} + (a+p)Q_{n-1}, \end{aligned}\right\} \tag{2.1}$$

and

$$\begin{pmatrix} P_n \\ Q_n \end{pmatrix} = \begin{pmatrix} a & -q \\ 1 & a+p \end{pmatrix} \begin{pmatrix} P_{n-1} \\ Q_{n-1} \end{pmatrix}. \tag{2.2}$$

2. From equation (2.1) it follows that

$$\frac{P_n}{Q_n} = \frac{aP_{n-1} - qQ_{n-1}}{P_{n-1} + (a + p)Q_{n-1}},$$

i.e.

$$\frac{Q_n}{Q_n} = \frac{a\dfrac{P_{n-1}}{Q_{n-1}} - q}{\dfrac{P_{n-1}}{Q_{n-1}} + a + p}. \tag{2.3}$$

Let $\lim_{n\to\infty} (P_n/Q_n)$ exist, be finite, and be denoted by x. Then from (2.3) we obtain

$$x = \frac{ax - q}{x + a + p},$$

i.e.

$$x^2 + px + q = 0, \quad x_{1,2} = \frac{-p \pm \sqrt{p^2 - 4q}}{2}.$$

Denote:

$$x_1 = \frac{-p - \sqrt{p^2 - 4q}}{2}, \quad x_2 = \frac{-p + \sqrt{p^2 - 4q}}{2}.$$

Thus if $\lim_{n\to\infty} (P_n/Q_n)$ exists then it may be equal either to x_1 or x_2. When $p^2 - 4q < 0$ the process (2.1) diverges since in this case x_1 and x_2 are complex numbers, but a sequence of real terms cannot have a complex limit.

When $a = (x_1 + x_2)/2 = -(p/2)$ we have:

$$\begin{pmatrix} -\dfrac{p}{2} & -q \\ 1 & \dfrac{p}{2} \end{pmatrix} \quad \frac{-\dfrac{p}{2}}{1} \quad \frac{\dfrac{p^2}{4} - q}{0} \quad \frac{-\dfrac{p}{2}\left(\dfrac{p^2}{4} - q\right)}{\dfrac{p^2}{4} - q} = \frac{-\dfrac{p}{2}}{1}.$$

Hence, when $a = (x_1 + x_2)/2$, the process (2.1) diverges.

3. From (2.3) we have:

$$\frac{P_n}{Q_n} - x = \frac{a\dfrac{P_{n-1}}{Q_{n-1}} - q - x\dfrac{P_{n-1}}{Q_{n-1}} - (a+p)x}{\dfrac{Q_n}{Q_{n-1}}} =$$

$$= \frac{(a-x)\dfrac{P_{n-1}}{Q_{n-1}} + x^2 - ax}{\dfrac{Q_n}{Q_{n-1}}} = \frac{a-x}{Q_n} Q_{n-1}\left(\frac{P_{n-1}}{Q_{n-1}} - x\right) =$$

$$= \frac{(a-x)^2 Q_{n-1} Q_{n-2}}{Q_n Q_{n-1}}\left(\frac{P_{n-2}}{Q_{n-2}} - x\right) = \ldots$$

$$\ldots = \frac{(a-x)^n}{Q_n} Q_0 \left(\frac{P_0}{Q_0} - x\right).$$

Finally, taking $P_0/Q_0 = a/1$, we have:

$$\frac{P_n}{Q_n} - x = \frac{(a-x)^{n+1}}{Q_n}. \tag{2.4}$$

From this, when $a > x_2$, we have $(P_n/Q_n) > x_2$, since one can always make Q_n positive by multiplying the numerator and denominator of P_n/Q_n by -1, if the need arises.

4. We discuss the conditions under which the quantities P_n/Q_n are monotonically decreasing with increasing n. In order to do this we first compute $(P_n/Q_n) - (P_{n-1}/Q_{n-1})$. From (2.3) it follows that

$$\frac{P_n}{Q_n} - \frac{P_{n-1}}{Q_{n-1}} = \frac{a\dfrac{P_{n-1}}{Q_{n-1}} - q - \left(\dfrac{P_{n-1}}{Q_{n-1}}\right)^2 - (a+p)\dfrac{P_{n-1}}{Q_{n-1}}}{\dfrac{Q_n}{Q_{n-1}}},$$

i.e.

$$\frac{P_n}{Q_n} - \frac{P_{n-1}}{Q_{n-1}} = -\frac{Q_{n-1}}{Q_n}\left(\frac{P_{n-1}}{Q_{n-1}} - x_1\right)\left(\frac{P_{n-1}}{Q_{n-1}} - x_2\right). \tag{2.5}$$

From (2.5) and (2.4) it follows that, when $a > x_2$, the inequality $(P_n/Q_n) < (P_{n-1}/Q_{n-1})$ obtains. Comparing this inequality with that following from (2.4), we obtain the result that when $a > x_2$

$$x_2 < \frac{P_n}{Q_n} < \frac{P_{n-1}}{Q_{n-1}}.$$

Consequently when $a > x_2$ the quantities P_n/Q_n are monotonically decreasing to a lower limit x_2. Therefore when $a > x_2$ we have $\lim_{n\to\infty} (P_n/Q_n) = x_2$.

When $(x_1 + x_2)/2 < a < x_2$ it follows from (2.4) that $(P_{2n}/Q_{2n}) < x_2$ and $(P_{2n+1}/Q_{2n+1}) > x_2$, since as before one can assume $Q_n > 0$. We discuss the behaviour of P_{2n}/Q_{2n} and P_{2n+1}/Q_{2n+1} when $(x_1 + x_2)/2 < a < x_2$; for this we determine $(P_n/Q_n) - (P_{n-2}/Q_{n-2})$.

In order to compute this expression we note that

$$\begin{pmatrix} a & -q \\ 1 & a+p \end{pmatrix}\begin{pmatrix} a & -q \\ 1 & a+p \end{pmatrix} = \begin{pmatrix} a^2 - q & -2aq - pq \\ 2a + p & (a+p)^2 - q \end{pmatrix}.$$

Hence there follows from (2.2) the equation

$$\begin{pmatrix} P_n \\ Q_n \end{pmatrix} = \begin{pmatrix} a^2 - q & -2aq - pq \\ 2a + p & (a+p)^2 - q \end{pmatrix}\begin{pmatrix} P_{n-2} \\ Q_{n-2} \end{pmatrix},$$

whence

$$\frac{P_n}{Q_n} = \frac{(a^2 - q)P_{n-2} - (2a + p)qQ_{n-2}}{(2a + p)P_{n-2} + [(a + p)^2 - q]Q_{n-2}} =$$

$$= \frac{(a^2 - q)\dfrac{P_{n-2}}{Q_{n-2}} - (2a + p)q}{(2a + p)\dfrac{P_{n-2}}{Q_{n-2}} + (a + p)^2 - q};$$

hence,

$$\frac{P_n}{Q_n} - \frac{P_{n-2}}{Q_{n-2}} = \frac{Q_{n-2}}{Q_n}\left[(a^2 - q)\frac{P_{n-2}}{Q_{n-2}} - (2a + p)q - \right.$$

$$\left. - (2a + p)\frac{P_{n-2}^2}{Q_{n-2}^2} - (a^2 + 2ap + p^2 - q)\frac{P_{n-2}}{Q_{n-2}}\right] =$$

$$= \frac{Q_{n-2}}{Q_n}\left[- (2a + p)q - (2a + p)\frac{P_{n-2}^2}{Q_{n-2}^2} - p(2a + p)\frac{P_{n-2}}{Q_{n-2}}\right],$$

i.e.

$$\frac{P_n}{Q_n} - \frac{P_{n-2}}{Q_{n-2}} = -\frac{2a+p}{Q_n} Q_{n-2}\left(\frac{P_{n-2}}{Q_{n-2}} - x_1\right)\left(\frac{P_{n-2}}{Q_{n-2}} - x_2\right). \quad (2.6)$$

But $(x_1 + x_2)/2 = -(p/2)$, whence $-(p/2) < a$, $0 < 2a + p$. Consequently when $(x_1 + x_2)/2 < a < x_2$ the inequalities

$$\frac{P_{2n}}{Q_{2n}} > \frac{P_{2n-2}}{Q_{2n-2}}, \qquad \frac{P_{2n+1}}{Q_{2n+1}} < \frac{P_{2n-1}}{Q_{2n-1}},$$

obtain. Thus when $(x_1 + x_2)/2 < a < x_2$, P_{2n}/Q_{2n} increases monotonically with increasing n to an upper limit x_2; P_{2n+1}/Q_{2n+1} is monotonically decreasing with increasing n to a lower limit x_2. Hence when $(x_1 + x_2)/2 < a < x_2$

$$\lim_{n\to\infty} \frac{P_n}{Q_n} = x_2.$$

5. For the investigation of the remaining cases we replace x by $-x$ and p by $-p$ in the equation $x^2 + px + q = 0$. We also replace a by $-a$. Then the equation preserves its form, but x_2 goes over into $-x_1$ and x_1 into $-x_2$, so that now the greatest root is $-x_1$. The sequence of terms determined by means of relations (2.1) converges only to $-x_1$ or to $-x_2$, whence P_n/Q_n is replaced by $-(P_n/Q_n)$.

We know that when $a > x_2$ the inequality

$$x_2 < \frac{P_n}{Q_n} < \frac{P_{n-1}}{Q_{n-1}}.$$

obtains. From this, when $-a > -x_1$, we have the inequality

$$-x_1 < -\frac{P_n}{Q_n} < -\frac{P_{n-1}}{Q_{n-1}},$$

i.e. when $a < x_1$ the inequality

$$\frac{P_{n-1}}{Q_{n-1}} < \frac{P_n}{Q_n} < x_1.$$

obtains. Thus, when $a < x_1$, P_n/Q_n is monotonically increasing with increasing n to an upper limit x_1. Hence, when $a < x_1$, we have $\lim_{n\to\infty} (P_n/Q_n) = x_1$.

We know that when $(x_1 + x_2)/2 < a < x_2$ the inequality

$$\frac{P_{2n-2}}{Q_{2n-2}} < \frac{P_{2n}}{Q_{2n}} < x_2 < \frac{P_{2n+1}}{Q_{2n+1}} < \frac{P_{2n-1}}{Q_{2n-1}}.$$

obtains. From this, when $-(x_1 + x_2)/2 < -a < -x_1$, we have the inequality

$$-\frac{P_{2n-2}}{Q_{2n-2}} < -\frac{P_{2n}}{Q_{2n}} < -x_1 < -\frac{P_{2n+1}}{Q_{2n+1}} < -\frac{P_{2n-1}}{Q_{2n-1}}.$$

i.e. when $x_1 < a < (x_1 + x_2)/2$ the inequality

$$\frac{P_{2n-1}}{Q_{2n-1}} < \frac{P_{2n+1}}{Q_{2n+1}} < x_1 < \frac{P_{2n}}{Q_{2n}} < \frac{P_{2n-2}}{Q_{2n-2}}.$$

Hence, when $x_1 < a < (x_1 + x_2)/2$, we have $\lim_{n\to\infty} P_n/Q_n = x_1$.

6. Example. Consider the equation $x^2 + 2x - 1 = 0$, for which $x_{1,2} = -1 \pm \sqrt{2}$; $x_1 \doteqdot -2{,}414$, $x_2 \doteqdot 0{,}414$.

1) $a > x_2$.

$$\begin{pmatrix} 1 & 1 \\ 1 & 3 \end{pmatrix} \qquad \frac{1}{1} \quad \frac{2}{4} = \frac{1}{2} \quad \frac{3}{7} \quad \frac{10}{24} = \frac{5}{12}$$

0·5 0·43 0·417

2) $\dfrac{x_1 + x_2}{2} < a < x_2$.

$$\begin{pmatrix} 0 & 1 \\ 1 & 2 \end{pmatrix} \qquad \frac{0}{1} \quad \frac{1}{2} \quad \frac{2}{5} \quad \frac{5}{12}$$

0·5 0·40 0·417

3) $x_1 < a < \dfrac{x_1 + x_2}{2}$.

$$\begin{pmatrix} -2 & 1 \\ 1 & 0 \end{pmatrix} \qquad \frac{-2}{1} \quad \frac{5}{-2} \quad \frac{-12}{5} \quad \frac{29}{-12}$$

− 2·0 − 2·5 − 2·40 − 2·416

4) $a < x_1$.

$$\begin{pmatrix} -3 & 1 \\ 1 & -1 \end{pmatrix} \qquad \frac{-3}{1} \quad \frac{10}{-4} = -\frac{5}{2} \quad \frac{17}{-7} \quad \frac{-58}{24} = -\frac{29}{12}$$

− 2·5 − 2·428 − 2·416

§ 3. The Calculation of Cube Roots with the Help of Matrices

1. Up to this point we have considered two sequences $\{P_n\}$ and $\{Q_n\}$, the terms of which are connected with one another by certain relations which are used to define them. We now consider three sequences $\{P_n\}$, $\{Q_n\}$, $\{R_n\}$ the terms of which are connected to one another by means of the relations

$$\left.\begin{aligned} P_n &= aP_{n-1} + \alpha Q_{n-1} + \alpha R_{n-1}, \\ Q_n &= P_{n-1} + aQ_{n-1} + \alpha R_{n-1}, \\ R_n &= P_{n-1} + Q_{n-1} + aR_{n-1} \end{aligned}\right\} \quad (n = 1, 2, \ldots). \tag{3.1}$$

With the help of a matrix these relationships may be written as

$$\begin{pmatrix} P_n \\ Q_n \\ R_n \end{pmatrix} = \begin{pmatrix} a & \alpha & \alpha \\ 1 & a & \alpha \\ 1 & 1 & a \end{pmatrix} \begin{pmatrix} P_{n-1} \\ Q_{n-1} \\ R_{n-1} \end{pmatrix}. \tag{3.2}$$

From (3.1) we obtain:

$$\frac{P_n}{R_n} = \frac{a\dfrac{P_{n-1}}{R_{n-1}} + \alpha\dfrac{Q_{n-1}}{R_{n-1}} + \alpha}{\dfrac{P_{n-1}}{R_{n-1}} + \dfrac{Q_{n-1}}{R_{n-1}} + a}, \quad \frac{Q_n}{R_n} = \frac{\dfrac{P_{n-1}}{R_{n-1}} + a\dfrac{Q_{n-1}}{R_{n-1}} + \alpha}{\dfrac{P_{n-1}}{R_{n-1}} + \dfrac{Q_{n-1}}{R_{n-1}} + a}. \tag{3.3}$$

2. Let $\lim\limits_{n\to\infty} P_n/R_n$ and $\lim\limits_{n\to\infty} Q_n/R_n$ exist and be finite. Denote these by x and y respectively. Then from (3.3) we obtain

$$x = \frac{ax + \alpha y + \alpha}{x + y + a}, \quad y = \frac{x + ay + \alpha}{x + y + a}.$$

We transcribe this system in the form

$$\left.\begin{aligned} x^2 + xy &= \alpha(y + 1), \\ xy + y^2 - x &= \alpha, \end{aligned}\right\} \tag{3.4}$$

multiply the second of the derived equations by $y + 1$ and subtract it from the first. We have:

$$x^2 + xy = xy^2 + y^3 - xy + xy + y^2 - x,$$

i.e.

$$y(y^2 - x) + x(y^2 - x) + (y^2 - x) = 0$$

or

$$(x+y+1)(y^2-x)=0.$$

When $x+y+1=0$ the system (3.4) becomes

$$\begin{aligned} -x &= \alpha(y+1) \\ 1 &= \alpha, \end{aligned}$$

i.e. this system leads to the indeterminate equation $x+y+1=0$.

In the following we shall assume that $x+y+1 \neq 0$. Then $x=y^2$, and the system (3.4) becomes

$$\begin{aligned} y^4+y^3 &= \alpha(y+1), \\ y^3 &= \alpha, \end{aligned}$$

i.e. it leads to the equation $y^3=\alpha$, $x=y^2$, whence $y=\alpha^{\frac{1}{3}}$, $x=\alpha^{\frac{2}{3}}$.

Consequently, in the case that it converges, the algorithm (3.3) converges to $\sqrt[3]{\alpha^2}$ and $\sqrt[3]{\alpha}$.

In the work to be given we confine ourselves to writing down some first approximations derived by means of this algorithm, together with numerical examples.

Taking $P_0=a^2$, $Q_0=a$, $R_0=1$, we have:

$$\begin{pmatrix} a & \alpha & \alpha \\ 1 & a & \alpha \\ 1 & 1 & a \end{pmatrix} \qquad \begin{matrix} a^2 & a^3+(a+1)\alpha & \dots \\ a & 2a^2+\alpha & \dots \\ 1 & a^2+2a & \dots \end{matrix}$$

From this

$$\sqrt[3]{\alpha} \approx \frac{2a^2+\alpha}{a^2+2a}, \quad \sqrt[3]{\alpha^2} \approx \frac{a^3+(a+1)\alpha}{a^2+2a}, \text{ if } \sqrt[3]{\alpha} \approx a.$$

For example, when $a=1$, $\alpha=2$,

$$\begin{pmatrix} 1 & 2 & 2 \\ 1 & 1 & 2 \\ 1 & 1 & 1 \end{pmatrix} \qquad \begin{matrix} 1 & 5 & 19 & 73 & 281 & 1081 \\ 1 & 4 & 15 & 58 & 223 & 858 \\ 1 & 3 & 12 & 46 & 177 & 681 \end{matrix}$$

$\sqrt[3]{4}$ (approx.)	1·67	1·583	1·5870	1·58757	1·58737
$\sqrt[3]{2}$ (approx.)	1·33	1·250	1·2609	1·25989	1·259912

It is known that $\sqrt[3]{2} \doteqdot 1{\cdot}2599210$, $\sqrt[3]{4} \doteqdot 1{\cdot}5874011$.

Using the square, cube, or a higher power of the fundamental matrix, one can accelerate the convergence of the process at will.

§ 4. The Calculation of Fourth Roots with the Help of Matrices

1. Generalizing the system (3.1), we consider the following relationships

$$\left.\begin{aligned} P_n &= aP_{n-1} + \alpha Q_{n-1} + \alpha R_{n-1} + \alpha S_{n-1}, \\ Q_n &= P_{n-1} + aQ_{n-1} + \alpha R_{n-1} + \alpha S_{n-1}, \\ R_n &= P_{n-1} + Q_{n-1} + aR_{n-1} + \alpha S_{n-1}, \\ S_n &= P_{n-1} + Q_{n-1} + R_{n-1} + aS_{n-1}. \end{aligned}\right\} \tag{4.1}$$

With the help of a matrix, these relationships may be transcribed as:

$$\begin{pmatrix} P_n \\ Q_n \\ R_n \\ S_n \end{pmatrix} = \begin{pmatrix} a & \alpha & \alpha & \alpha \\ 1 & a & \alpha & \alpha \\ 1 & 1 & a & \alpha \\ 1 & 1 & 1 & a \end{pmatrix} \begin{pmatrix} P_{n-1} \\ Q_{n-1} \\ R_{n-1} \\ S_{n-1} \end{pmatrix}. \tag{4.2}$$

Proceeding as in the preceding section, one can prove that

$$\lim_{n\to\infty} \frac{P_n}{S_n} = \sqrt[4]{\alpha^3}, \quad \lim_{n\to\infty} \frac{Q_n}{S_n} = \sqrt[4]{\alpha^2} = \sqrt{\alpha}, \quad \lim_{n\to\infty} \frac{R_n}{S_n} = \sqrt[4]{\alpha},$$

if these limits exist and are finite. The proof of this assertion is valid only for $a = 1$. In this case, denoting the limits considered by x, y and z, we obtain from (4.1):

$$x = \frac{x + \alpha y + \alpha z + \alpha}{x + y + z + 1},$$

$$y = \frac{x + y + \alpha z + \alpha}{x + y + z + 1},$$

$$z = \frac{x + y + z + \alpha}{x + y + z + 1}.$$

From these

$$y = z + \frac{(\alpha - 1)z}{x + y + z + 1} = z\,\frac{x + y + z + \alpha}{x + y + z + 1} = z^2,$$

$$x = y + \frac{(\alpha - 1)y}{x + y + z + 1} = y\,\frac{x + y + z + \alpha}{x + y + z + 1} = z^3.$$

Finally,

$$z = \frac{z^3 + z^2 + z + \alpha}{z^3 + z^2 + z + 1}, \quad z^4 = \alpha, \quad z = \sqrt[4]{\alpha}, \quad y = \sqrt{\alpha}, \quad x = \sqrt[4]{\alpha^3}.$$

Putting $P_0 = Q_0 = R_0 = S_0 = 1$, we have:

$$\begin{pmatrix} 1 & \alpha & \alpha & \alpha \\ 1 & 1 & \alpha & \alpha \\ 1 & 1 & 1 & \alpha \\ 1 & 1 & 1 & 1 \end{pmatrix} \quad \begin{matrix} 1 & 1 + 3\alpha & 1 + 12\alpha + 3\alpha^2 & 1 + 31\alpha + 31\alpha^2 + \alpha^3 \\ 1 & 2 + 2\alpha & 3 + 12\alpha + \alpha^2 & 4 + 40\alpha + 20\alpha^2 \\ 1 & 3 + \alpha & 6 + 10\alpha & 10 + 44\alpha + 10\alpha^2 \\ 1 & 4 & 10 + 6\alpha & 20 + 40\alpha + 4\alpha^2. \end{matrix}$$

In particular, we consider an inequality which may be derived from this:

$$\sqrt{\alpha} \vee \frac{\alpha^2 + 12\alpha + 3}{6\alpha + 10}.$$

Since both sides of this are positive, then it is equivalent to the inequality

$$36\alpha^3 + 120\alpha^2 + 100\alpha \vee \alpha^4 + 24\alpha^3 + 150\alpha^2 + 72\alpha + 9,$$

i.e.

$$\alpha^4 - 12\alpha^3 + 30\alpha^2 - 28\alpha + 9 \wedge 0.$$

Observing that the left hand side of this inequality changes sign when $\alpha = 9$, one can reduce it to the form

$$(\alpha - 1)^3(\alpha - 9) \wedge 0.$$

Therefore

$$\sqrt{\alpha} \geqslant \frac{\alpha^2 + 12\alpha + 3}{6\alpha + 10} \quad \text{when} \quad 1 \leqslant \alpha \leqslant 9;$$

$$\sqrt{\alpha} \leqslant \frac{\alpha^2 + 12\alpha + 3}{6\alpha + 10} \quad \text{when} \quad \alpha \geqslant 9.$$

From this

$$\frac{\alpha^2 + 12\alpha + 3}{6\alpha + 10} \leqslant \sqrt{\alpha} \leqslant \frac{6\alpha^2 + 10\alpha}{\alpha^2 + 12\alpha + 3} \qquad (1 \leqslant \alpha \leqslant 9),$$

$$\frac{6\alpha^2 + 10\alpha}{\alpha^2 + 12\alpha + 3} \leqslant \sqrt{\alpha} \leqslant \frac{\alpha^2 + 12\alpha + 3}{6\alpha + 10} \qquad (\alpha \geqslant 9).$$

The range of application of these approximations is clear from the following table

α	$\dfrac{\alpha^2+12\alpha+3}{6\alpha+10}$	$\sqrt{\alpha}$	$\dfrac{6\alpha^2+10\alpha}{\alpha^2+12\alpha+3}$
1	1·000	1·000	1·000
2	1·409	1·414	1·419
3	1·714	1·732	1·750
4	1·971	2·000	2·030
5	2·200	2·236	2·273
6	2·413	2·449	2·486
7	2·615	2·646	2·676
8	2·810	2·828	2·847
9	3·000	3·000	3·000
10	3·186	3·162	3·139
11	3·368	3·317	3·266
12	3·549	3·464	3·381
13	3·727	3·606	3·488

§ 5. The Calculation of Roots of Arbitrary Rational order with the Help of a Matrix

1. Generalizing the method set forth in the preceding section we see that the square matrix of the nth order

$$\begin{pmatrix} a & \alpha & \alpha & \dots & \alpha \\ 1 & a & \alpha & \dots & \alpha \\ \cdot & \cdot & \cdot & \cdot & \cdot \\ 1 & 1 & 1 & \dots & a \end{pmatrix},$$

in particular

$$\begin{pmatrix} 1 & \alpha & \alpha & \dots & \alpha \\ 1 & 1 & \alpha & \dots & \alpha \\ \cdot & \cdot & \cdot & \cdot & \cdot \\ 1 & 1 & 1 & \dots & 1 \end{pmatrix},$$

leads to the determination of approximate values of

$$\sqrt[n]{\alpha},\ \sqrt[n]{\alpha^2},\ \dots,\ \sqrt[n]{\alpha^{n-1}}.$$

In the event use of this matrix leads to the system of equations

$$x = \frac{x + \alpha y + \alpha z + \dots + \alpha t + \alpha}{x + y + z + \dots + t + 1},$$

$$y = \frac{x + y + \alpha z + \dots + \alpha t + \alpha}{x + y + z + \dots + t + 1},$$

$$\dots\dots\dots\dots\dots\dots\dots\dots$$

$$t = \frac{x + y + z + \dots + t + \alpha}{x + y + z + \dots + t + 1},$$

whence

$$t = 1 + \frac{\alpha - 1}{x + y + \dots + t + 1}, \dots, y = t^{n-2}, x = t^{n-1}.$$

Putting $P_0 = Q_0 = \dots = 1$, we have

$$\begin{pmatrix} 1 & \alpha & \alpha & \dots & \alpha \\ 1 & 1 & \alpha & \dots & \alpha \\ \dots & \dots & \dots & \dots & \dots \\ 1 & 1 & 1 & \dots & 1 \end{pmatrix} \qquad \begin{matrix} 1 & 1 + (n-1)\alpha \\ 1 & 2 + (n-2)\alpha \\ \dots & \dots \\ 1 & n \end{matrix}$$

For example, in order to compute $\sqrt[7]{4}$ approximately, it is sufficient to carry out the computations:

$$\begin{Bmatrix} 1 & 2 & 2 & 2 & 2 & 2 & 2 \\ 1 & 1 & 2 & 2 & 2 & 2 & 2 \\ 1 & 1 & 1 & 2 & 2 & 2 & 2 \\ 1 & 1 & 1 & 1 & 2 & 2 & 2 \\ 1 & 1 & 1 & 1 & 1 & 2 & 2 \\ 1 & 1 & 1 & 1 & 1 & 1 & 2 \\ 1 & 1 & 1 & 1 & 1 & 1 & 1 \end{Bmatrix} \qquad \begin{matrix} 1 & 13 & 127 \\ 1 & 12 & 115 \\ 1 & 11 & 104 \\ 1 & 10 & 94 \\ 1 & 9 & 85 \\ 1 & 8 & 77 \\ 1 & 7 & 70 \end{matrix}$$

In particular $\sqrt[7]{4} \approx \frac{104}{85} = 1{,}223$ or $\sqrt[7]{4} \approx \frac{85}{70} = 1{,}214$. The exact value of this root is 1,219....

§ 6. The Solution of Cubic Equations with the Help of Matrices

1. We consider the matrix

$$\begin{pmatrix} a_{11} & a_{12} & a_{13} \\ a_{21} & a_{22} & a_{23} \\ a_{31} & a_{32} & a_{33} \end{pmatrix}. \tag{6.1}$$

It leads to the equations

$$x = \frac{a_{11}x + a_{12}y + a_{13}}{a_{31}x + a_{32}y + a_{33}},$$

$$y = \frac{a_{21}x + a_{22}y + a_{23}}{a_{31}x + a_{32}y + a_{33}}.$$

Eliminating y from these equations we arrive at an equation of the third degree in the variable x. Hence, in the case of convergence of the corresponding process, the matrix (6.1) may be used for the approximate computation of one of the roots of a certain equation of the third degree. We do not go into detail but consider alone the matrix

$$\begin{pmatrix} 1 & -p & -q \\ 1 & 1 & 0 \\ 0 & 1 & 1 \end{pmatrix}. \tag{6.2}$$

It leads to the equations

$$x = \frac{x - py - q}{y + 1}, \qquad y = \frac{x + y}{y + 1}.$$

Transforming these equations, we have

$$y^2 = x,$$

$$y^3 + y^2 = y^2 - py - q,$$

$$y^3 + py + q = 0.$$

Hence, in the case of convergence of the corresponding process, the matrix (6.1) may be used for the approximate computation of one of the roots of $y^3 + py + q = 0$.

For example, for the equation $x^3 - 3x + 1 = 0$, we have:

$$\begin{pmatrix} 1 & 3 & -1 \\ 1 & 1 & 0 \\ 0 & 1 & 1 \end{pmatrix}$$

1	3	7	(18)	6	15	38	(96)	32	81
1	2	5	(12)	4	10	25	(63)	21	53
1	2	4	(9)	3	7	17	(42)	14	35
1	1	1·25		1·33	1·43	1·47		1·50	1·51

The exact value of the root is 1.532.... For accelerating convergence one could have used the square matrix

$$\begin{pmatrix} 1 & 3 & -1 \\ 1 & 1 & 0 \\ 0 & 1 & 1 \end{pmatrix}\begin{pmatrix} 1 & 3 & -1 \\ 1 & 1 & 0 \\ 0 & 1 & 1 \end{pmatrix} = \begin{pmatrix} 4 & 5 & -2 \\ 2 & 4 & -1 \\ 1 & 2 & 1 \end{pmatrix}.$$

§ 7. The Solution of Equations of Higher Order with the Help of Matrices

1. We verify that in the case of convergence of the corresponding process, the matrix ($l \neq 0$)

$$\begin{Bmatrix} k & la_n & 0 & \dots & 0 & 0 & 0 & 0 & 0 \\ 0 & k & la_n & \dots & 0 & 0 & 0 & 0 & 0 \\ \dots & \dots & \dots & \dots & \dots & \dots & \dots & \dots & \dots \\ 0 & 0 & 0 & \dots & la_n & 0 & 0 & 0 & 0 \\ 0 & 0 & 0 & \dots & k & la_n & 0 & 0 & 0 \\ 0 & 0 & 0 & \dots & 0 & k & la_n & 0 & 0 \\ 0 & 0 & 0 & \dots & 0 & 0 & k & 0 & la_n \\ -la_0 & -la_1 & -la_2 & \dots & -la_{n-5} & -la_{n-4} & -la_{n-3} & k-la_{n-1} & -la_{n-2} \\ 0 & 0 & 0 & \dots & 0 & 0 & 0 & la_n & k \end{Bmatrix}$$

may be used for the approximate computation of one of the roots of the equation

$$a_nx^n + a_{n-1}x^{n-1} + \dots + a_1x + a_0 = 0.$$

Actually this matrix leads to the equations

$$t = \frac{kt + la_ns}{la_nx + k}, \quad \dots, \quad z = \frac{kz + la_ny}{la_nx + k}, \quad y = \frac{ky + la_n}{la_nx + k},$$

$$x = \frac{-la_0t - la_1s - \dots - la_{n-4}z - la_{n-3}y + (k - la_{n-1})x - la_{n-2}}{la_nx + k}$$

whence

$$a_nx^2 + a_{n-1}x + a_{n-2} + a_{n-3}y + a_{n-4}z + \dots + a_1s + a_0t = 0,$$

$$xy = 1, \; xz = y, \; \dots, \; xt = s;$$

hence

$$a_n x^n + a_{n-1}x^{n-1} + a_{n-2}x^{n-2} + a_{n-3}x^{n-3} + \dots + a_1 x + a_0 = 0.$$

2. In particular, for the equation

$$x^4 - 8x^3 + x^2 - x + 1 = 0$$

(putting $k = l = 1$) we have:

$$\begin{pmatrix} 1 & 1 & 0 & 0 \\ 0 & 1 & 0 & 1 \\ -1 & 1 & 9 & -1 \\ 0 & 0 & 1 & 1 \end{pmatrix} \quad \begin{array}{rrrrrrrr} 1 & (2) & 1 & 2 & 4 & 11 & 58 & 455 \\ 1 & (2) & 1 & 2 & 7 & 47 & 397 & 3500 \\ 1 & (8) & 4 & 35 & 310 & 2753 & 24463 & 217403 \\ 1 & (2) & 1 & 5 & 40 & 350 & 3103 & 27566 \\ \\ 1 & & 4 & 7 & 7{\cdot}75 & 7{\cdot}866 & 7{\cdot}8837 & 7{\cdot}8866 \end{array}$$

The exact value of this root is 7·8873....

LITERATURE

in the Russian language on the General Theory of Continued Fractions

1. ARNOLD, I. V., *The theory of Numbers*, Moscow, 1939.
2. BERTRAN, ZH. *Algebra, Part II*, St. Petersburg, 1901.
3. VINAGRADOV, I. M., *The Foundations of Number Theory*, Moscow-Leningrad State Publishing House, 1949.
4. VOROBYEFF, N. N., *Fibonacci Numbers*, Moscow State Publishing House, 1951.
5. CAUCHY, O., *Course of Algebraic Analysis*, Leipzig 1864.
6. LOBACHEVSKI, N. I., *Algebra or Finite Calculations*, Vol IV of the Complete Summarized Works of N. I. Lobachevski, Moscow-Leningrad State Publishing House, 1948.
7. MARAKUEV, N. N., *Elementary Algebra, vol I Theory*, Moscow 1903.
8. MARKOFF, A. A., *Lectures on Continued Fractions* (c.f. Selected Works on the Theory of Continued Functions and the Theory of Functions), Moscow-Leningrad State Publishing House, 1948.
9. MESHKOFF, A., *A Course of Higher Algebra*, First Section, St. Petersburg 1862.
10. OSTROGRADSKII, M. V., *Lectures on Algebraic and Transcendental Analysis, First Year*, St. Petersburg 1837.
11. ROSHCHIN, P., *Treatise on Differential and Integral Calculus, First Part*, St. Petersburg 1888.
12. SEGAL, B. I., *Continued Fractions, Mathematical Education*, 7th Impression, 1936.
13. SUSHKEVICH, A. K., *The Theory of Numbers*, Kharkov, Publications of the University of Kharkov, 1954.
14. FERBER, K., *Arithmetic*, Moscow 1914.
15. KHINCHINE, A. YA., *Continued Fractions*, Moscow-Leningrad State Publishing House, 1949.
16. KHINCHINE, A. YA., *The Elementary Theory of Numbers*, Encyclopaedia of Elementary Mathematics, First Book, Moscow-Leningrad State Publishing House 1951.
17. CHEBOTAREFF, N. G., *The Theory of Continued Fractions*, Kazan, 1938.

REFERENCES

1. Kornoukhoff, N. V., *The Strength of Stationary Systems of Struts*, Moscow 1949.
2. Markushevich, A. I., *The Theory of Analytic Functions*, Moscow-Leningrad State Publishing House, 1950.
3. Markoff, A. A., *The Application of Continued Fractions in the Calculation of Probability*, Proc. Kazansk. Phys. Math. Soc. (2) 9 (1902), 30.
4. Ruzhik, I. M. and Gradstein, I. S., *Tables of Integrals, Sums, Series and Products*, 3rd Edition, Moscow-Leningrad State Publishing House, 1951.
5. Sleshinskii, I. V., *Problems in the Convergence Theory of Continued Fractions*, Math. Coll., **14** (1888), 337–343.
6. Sleshinskii, I. V., *Supplement to a Note on the Convergence of Continued Fractions*, Math. Coll, **14** (1888), 436–438.
7. Sleshinskii, I. V., *On the Convergence of Continued Fractions, Publication of the Department of Mathematics*, Novoruss. **10** (1889), 201–255.
8. Fichtengoltz, G. M., *Course of Differential and Integral Calculus*, Moscow-Leningrad State Publishing House, 1948.
9. Beck, E., *Zwei Anwendungen der Obreschkoffschen Formel*, Zeitschr. für angew. Math. und Mechanik **30** : 3 (1950), 84–93.
10. Bernoulli, D., *Disquisitiones ulteriores de indola fractionum continuarum, Novi comm.* Acad. sci. Imper. Petropol. **20** (1775).
11. Bessel, F. W., *Untersuchung des Theils der planetarischen Störungen, welcher aus der Bewegung der Sonne entsteht*, Abhandl. der Königl. Akad. Wissensch. Berlin. Math. cl. (1824).
12. Darboux, G., *Journ. de math. pures et appl.* (1876).
13. Deschmann, A., *Auflösung von transcendenten Gleichungen und Anwendung derselben auf einige geometrische Beispiele*, Programmabhandlung Cilli, 1877.
14. Euler, E., *De fractionibus continuis*, Comm. Acad. Sci. Imper. Petropol. **9** (1737).
15. Euler, L., *De fractionibus continuis observatione*, Comm. Acad. Sci. Imper. Petropol., **11** (1739), 32–81.
16. Euler, L., *Introductio in analysis infinitorum*, 1, Lausanne, 1748; russian translation, 1936.
17. Euler, L., *De inventione quotcunque mediarum proportionalium citra radicum extractionem*, Novi Comm. Acad. Petropol. **14** : 1 (1771), 188; included in: 1) Euler, L., *Opuscula Analytica* (1785); 2) Euler, L.,

Commentationes Arithmeticae collectae, vol 1, pp. 401–403, Petropoli, 1849.

18. EULER, L., *De transformatione seriei divergentis* $1 - mx + m(m+n)x^2 - m(m+n)(m+2n)x^3 + m(m+n)(m+n)(m+2n)(m+3n)x^4 + + \cdots$ *in fractionem continuam,* Nova Acta Acad. Sci. Imper. Petropol. pro annum (1784).
19. EULER, L., *De transformatione serierum in fractiones continuas; ubi simul hac theoria non mediocriter complebatur,* Opuscula analytica, II, pp. 138–177, Petropoli (1785).
20. EULER, L., *Summatio fractionis continuare, cuius indices progressionem arithmeticam constitunt dum numeratores omnes sunt unitates, ubi simul resolutio aequationes Riccatianae per huiusmodi fractiones ducetur,* Opuscula analytica, II, pp. 217–239, Petropoli (1785).
21. EULER, L., *Commentatio in fractionem continuam qua illustris La Grange potestates binomiales expressit,* Mémoires Acad. impér. Sci. Petersb. **6** (1813–1814), 3–11.
22. EULER, *Analysis facilis aequationem Riccatianam per fractionem continuam resolvendi,* Mémoires Acad. imper. Sci. Pétersb. **6** (1813–1814), 12–29.
23. FROBENIUS, G., *Ueber Relationen zwischen der Näherungbrüchen von Potenzreihen,* Journ. für die reine und angew. Math. **90** : 1 (1881), 1–17.
24. GAUSS, C. F., *Disquisitiones generales circa seriem infinitam* $1 + \frac{\alpha\beta}{1\cdot\gamma}x + \frac{\alpha(\alpha+1)\beta(\beta+1)}{1\cdot2\cdot\gamma(\gamma+1)}xx + \frac{\alpha(\alpha+1)(\alpha+2)\beta(\beta+1)(\beta+2)}{1\cdot2\cdot3\cdot\gamma(\gamma+1)(\gamma+2)}x^3 +$ $+$*etc.*, Werke, vol. III, p. 123.
25. GRAF, J. H., *Relation entre la fonction Bessélienne de 1-re espèce et une fraction continue,* Ann. matem. pura ed. appl. (2), **23** (1895), 45–65.
26. GÜNTHER, S., *Bemerkungen über Cylinderfunktionen,* Archiv für Math. und Physik **56** (1874), 292–297.
27. HANKEL, H., *Ueber die Transformation von Reihen in Kettenbruch,* Berichte der königl. Sächs. Gesselsch. der Wissensch. Math. Phys. Class. Sitzung am **15**, III (1962).
28. HEILERMANN, J. B. H., *De transformatione serierum in fractiones continuas,* Diss. Münster (1845).
29. HEILERMANN, J. B. H., *Ueber Verwandlung der Reihen in Kettenbrüche,* Journ. für die reine und angew. Math. **33** (1846), 174–188.
30. HEILERMANN, J. B. H., *Zusammenhang unter den Koeffizienten zweier gleichen Kettenbrüche von verschiedener Form,* Zeits. für Math. und Physik **5** (1860).
31. HERMITE, CH., *Sur la formule d'interpolation de Lagrange,* Journ. für die reine und angew. Math. **84** (1878), 70.
32. HERZ, N., *Astronomische Nachrichten* **107**, 17.
33. JACOBI, C. I. J., *De fractione continua, in quam integrale* $\int_x^\infty e^{-x^2}\,dx$ *evolvere licet,* Journ. für die reine und angew. Math. **12** (1834) 346-347.

34. JENSEN, J. L. W. V., *Bijdrag til Kjaedebrökers Theori*, Festschrift till H. G. Zeuthen, 1909.
35. KAUSLER, C. F., *Die Lehre von den continuirlichen Brüchen*, Stuttgart, 1803.
36. KAUSLER, C. F., *Expositio methodi series quascunque datas in fractiones continuas convertendi*, Mémoires Acad. Impér. Sci. Pétersb. **1** (1803–1806), 156–174.
37. KOCH, HELGE VON, *Quelques théorèmes concernant la théorie générale des fractions continues*, Öfversigt of Kongl. Vetenskaps - Akad. Förhandl **52** (1895).
38. KOCH, HELGE VON, *Sur un théorème de Stieltjes et sur fonctions définies par des fractions continues*, Bull Soc.. math. de France **23** (1895), 33–49.
39. KOWALEWSKI, G., *Interpolation and genäherte Quadratur*, Leipzig, 1932.
40. KOWALEWSKI, G., *Ueber das neue theorem von Obreschkoff*, Deutsche Math. **6** (1942), 342–351.
41. KRAFFT, M., *Ueber ein Eulersches Verfahren zur Wurzelberechnung*, Monatshefte für Math. und Physik, Leipzig und Wien, Akad. Verlagsgesellschaft **49** (1941), 312–315.
42. LAGRANGE, J. L., *Complement chez Élements d'algèbre etc.* par M. L. Euler, vol. II 1774, pp. 380 et 391.
43. LAGRANGE, J. L., *Sur l'usage des fractions continues dans le calcul intégrale*, Nouv. Acad. Royale Sci. Belle-Lettres de Berlin (1776); Oeuvres, vol. IV, pp. 301–332.
44. LAGUERRE, E., *Oeuvres, vol.* I.
45. LAGUERRE, E., *Sur l'intégrale* $\int_x^\infty \frac{e^{-x}}{x} dx$, Bull. Soc. Math. de France **7** (1879); Oeuvres, vol. I.
46. LAGUERRE, E., *Sur la fonction* $\left(\frac{x+1}{x-1}\right)^\omega$, Bull. Soc. Math. de France 8 (1879); Oeuvres, vol. I.
47. LAGUERRE, E., *Sur la réduction en fractions continues d'une fonction que satisfait à une équation différentielle linéaire du premier ordre dont les coefficients sont rationelles*, Journ. math. pures et appl. (4), **1** (1885); Oeuvres, vol. II.
48. LAMBERT, J. H., *Beiträge zum Gebrauch der Mathematik und deren Anwendung*, r. II, vol. 1, 1770.
49. LAPLACE, P. S., *Traité de mecanique céleste*, Book 10; ch. 1; Oeuvres, IV.
50. LEGENDRE, A. M., *Traité des fonctions elliptiques et des intégrales Eulériennes*, vol. II, ch. 17, Paris, 1826.
51. LERCH, M., *Ueber einige Punkte der Theorie der Eulerschen Integral*, Monatshefte für Math. und Phys. **19** (1908).
52. LOMMEL, E. C. I., VON *Studien über die Bessel'schen Functionen*, Leipzig, 1868.
53. LOREY, W., *Ueber ein Eulersches Verfahren zur Wurzelberechnung*, Monatshefte für Math. und Phys. Leipzig und Wien, Akad. Verlaggesellschaft **48** (1939), 190–197.

54. Muir, Th., *On the Transformation of Gauss' hypergeometric series into a Continued Fraction*, Proc. London Math. Soc. **7** (1875–1876), 112–118.
55. Muir, Th., *New General Formulae for the Transformation of Infinite Series into Continued Fractions*, Trans. Roy. Soc. Edinburgh **27** : 4 (1875–1876), 467–471.
56. Müller, J. H. T., *Lehrbuch der Mathematik*, erster Teil die gesamte Arithmetik enthaltend, Halle, 1838.
57. Müller, M., *Verfahren zur Wurzelberechnung*, Math. Zeits. **51** : 4 (1948) 474–496.
58. Nachreiner, V., *Beziehungen zwischen Determinanten und Kettenbrüchen*, Preisschrift, München, 1872.
59. Nielsen, N., *Handbuch der Theorie der Gammafunktion*, Leipzig, 1906.
60. Nielsen, N., *Theorie des Integrallogarithmus und verwandten Transzendenten*, Leipzig, 1906.
61. Nielsen, N., *Ueber den Legendre-Bessel'schen Kettenbruch*, Münchner Sitzungsberichte **38** (1908), 85–88.
62. Obreschkoff, N., *Neue Quadratur formeln*, Abhandlungen preuß. Akad. Wiss. Math.-Naturwiss. Klasse, No. 4, **5** (1940), 1–20.
63. Oppermann, *Tijdskrift for Math.*, Zeuthen **5** (1883).
64. Padé, H., *Sur la représentation approchée d'une fonction par des fractions rationelles*, Ann. Sci., École Normale Supér. (3) **9** (1892) 1–92 (thesis)
65. Padé, H., *Sur les séries entières convergents ou divergents et les fractions continues rationelles*, Acta Math. **18** (1894), 97–112.
66. Padé, H., *Sur la généralisation des fractions continues algébriques*, Jour. Math. pures. et appl. (4), **10** (1894).
67. Padé, H., *Memoire sur les développements en fractions continues de la fonction exponentielle, pouvant servir d'introduction à la théorie des fractions continues algebriques*, Ann. Sci. École Normale Supér. (3), **16** (1899), 394–426.
68. Padé, H., *Sur la distribution des réduites anormales d'une fonction*, Compt. Rend. hébdomadaires des séances Acad. Sci. **132** (1900).
69. Padé, H., *Sur l'expression générale de la fonction rationelle approchée de* $(1 + x)^n$, Compt. Rend. hébdomadaires des séances Acad. Sci. **132** (1901).
70. Padé, H., *Recherches sur la convergence de développements en fractions continues d'une certaine catégorie de fonctions*, Ann. Sci. École Normale Supér. (3), **24** (1907).
71. Perron, O., *Ueber die Kettenbruchentwicklung des Quotienten zweier Bessel'schen Funktionen*, Sitzungsber. der math.-phys. Klasse der Kgl. Bayer. Akad. Wiss., München **37** (1907), 423–504.
72. Perron, O., *Ueber eine spezielle Klasse von Kettenbrüchen*, Rend. circ. matem. Palermo **29** (1910).
73. Perron, O., *Die Lehre von den Kettenbrüchen*, Leipzig und Berlin, Teubner, 1913, 520 (there is a second edition, published in 1924).
74. Pflans, E., *Bemerkungen über die Methode von G. Duffing zur Integration von Differentialgleichungen*, Zeits. angew. Math. und Mech. **28** : 6 (1948), 167–172.

75. POINCARÉ, H., *Notice sur Halphen,* Journ. École Polytech, **60** (1890), 137–161.

76. PRINGSHEIM, A., *Ueber die Convergenz unendlicher Kettenbrüche,* Sitzungsber. der math.-phys. Klasse der Kgl. Bayer. Akad. Wiss., München **28** (1898), 295–324.

77. PRINGSHEIM, A., *Ueber ein Convergenz-Kriterium für die Kettenbrüche mit positiven Gliedern,* Sitzungsber. der math.-phys. Klasse der Kgl. Bayer. Akad. Wiss., München **29** (1899), 261-268.

78. PRINGSHEIM, A., *Ueber einige Konvergenzkriterien für Kettenbrüche mit Komplexen Gliedern,* Sitzungsber. der math.-phys. Klasse der Kgl. Bayer. Akad. Wiss., München **35** (1905), 359–380.

79. PRINGSHEIM, A., *Ueber Konvergenz und funktionen-theoretischen Charakter gewisser limitär-periodischer Kettenbrüche,* Sitzungsber. der math.-phys. Klasse der Kgl. Bayer. Akad. Wiss., München **6** (1910), 1–52.

80. RIEMANN, B., *Sullo svolgimento del quoziente di due serie ipergeometriche in frazione continua infinita,* Gesammelte Werke (there is a Russian translation).

81. ROGERS, L. J., *On the representation of certain asymptotic series as convergent continued fractions,* Proc. London Math. Soc. (2), **4** (1907) 72–89; Supplementary note, Ibidem, pp. 393–395.

82. SANIELEVICI S., *Sur l'intégration des équations différentielles par les fractions continues,* Ann. Sci. de l'Université de Jassy **18** (1933), 197–214

83. SCHLÖMILCH, O., *Ueber die Bessel'schen Funktionen,* Zeitschr. Math. u. Phys. **2** (1857), 137–165.

84. SCHLÖMILCH, O., *Ueber den Kettenbruch für* tg x, Zeits. Math. u. Phys. **16** (1876), 259–260.

85. SCHUBERT, F. T., *De transformatione seriei in fractionem continuam,* Memoires Acad. Impér. Sci. Pétersb. **7** (1815—1816), 139–158

86. Scott, W. T. and WALL, H. S., *A convergence theorem for continued fractions,* Trans. Amer. Mat. Soc. **47** (1940), 155–172.

87. SEIDEL, *Untersuchung über die Convergenz und Divergenz Kettenbrüche,* Doktor. Diss., München, 1846.

88. SEIDEL, *Bemerkung über den Zusammenhang zwischen dem Bildungsgesetze eines Kettenbruches und der Art des Fortgangs seiner Näherungsbrüche,* cf. Abhandlungen der Kgl. Bayer. Akad. Wiss., München, zweite Klasse **7** : 3 (1855), 582.

89. SOLDNER, J., *Théorie et tables d'une nouvelle fonction transcendante,* Munich, 1809.

90. STERN, *Ueber die Kennzeichen der Convergenz eines Kettenbruches,* Journ. reine und angew. Math. **37** (1848) 1255–272.

91. STERN, *Lehrbuch der algebraischen Analysis,* Leipzig, 1860.

92. STIELTJES, T. J., *Recherches sur les fractions continues,* Ann. faculté des sci. Toulouse pour les sci. math. et les sci. phys. **8** (1894); 9 (1895).

93. STIELTJES, T. J., *Correspondance d'Hermite et Stieltjes,* vol. I–II, Paris, 1905.

94. STOLZ, O. u. GMEINER, A., *Einleitung in die Funktionentheorie*, Leipzig, 1905.

95. TANNERY, J., *Sur les intégrales eulériennes*, Compt. Rend. hebdomadaires des séances de l'Akad. Sci. **94** (1882).

96. THOMÉ, L. W., *Ueber die Kettenbruchentwicklung der Gauß'schen Funktion* $F(\alpha, 1, \gamma; u)$, Journ. reine und angew. Math. **66** (1866).

97. THOME, L. W., *Ueber die Kettenbruchentwicklung des Gauß'schen Quotienten* $\frac{F(\alpha, \beta + 1, \gamma + 1; x)}{F(\alpha, \beta, \gamma; x)}$, Journ. reine und angew. Math. **67** (1867).

98. TREMBLEY, J., *Recherches sur les fractions continues*, Memoires Acad. Royale des sciences et belles-lettres en Berlin (1794–1795), 109–142.

99. TSCHAKALOFF, L., *Eine Integraldarstellung des Newton'schen Differenzquotienten und ihre Anwendung*, Ann. Univ. Sofia. Tac. Phys.-Math. **34** (1938), 353–394.

100. TSCHEBYSCHEFF, P., *Sur le développement des fonctions à une seule variable*, Bull. Acad. Imper. Sci. Petersb. **1** (1860).

101. VAN VLECK, E. B., *On the convergence of continued fractions with complex elements*, Trans. Amer. Math. Soc. 2 (1901), 215–233.

102. VAN VLECK, E. B., *On the convergence and character of the continued fraction* $\frac{a_1 z|}{|1} + \frac{a_2 z|}{|1} + \frac{a_3 z|}{|1} + \dots$, Trans. Amer. Math. Soc. 2 (1901),

103. VISCOVATOFF, B., *De la méthode générale pour réduir toutes séries des quantités en fractions continues*, Mémoires Acad. Impér. Sci. Petersb. **1** (1803–1806), 226–247.

104. WALLIS, J., *Arithmetica infinitorum*, 1655.

105. WALLIS, J., Tractatus de algebra, 1685.

106. WÖLFFING, E., *Wer hat über Kettenbrüche gearbeitet?* Math.-naturwiss. Mitteil., begründet von Dr. O. Böklin (2), **10** (1908).

107. WORPITZKY, J., *Untersuchungen über die Entwicklung der monodromen und monogenen Funktionen durch Kettenbrüche*, Jahresber. Friedrichgymnasium und Realschule, Berlin, 1865, 3–39.

108. TITCHMARSH, E. C., *The Theory of Functions*, Oxford 1932.

109. WHITTAKER, E. T. and WATSON, E. N., *A Course of Modern Analysis*, Cambridge 1946.

SUPPLEMENTARY REFERENCES

1. BAUER, F. L., *The g-Algorithm*, J. Soc. Indust. Appl. Math., vol. 8, 1960, pp. 1–17.
2. DANILOVA, V. L., IVANOVA, A. N., ISAKOVA, E. K., LIUSTERNIK, L. A., SALEKHOV, G. S., KHOVANSKII, A. N., TSLAFF, L. YA. and YANPOLSKII, A. R., *Mathematical Analysis (Functions, Limits, Series and Continued Fractions)*, State Publishing House of Physico-Mathematical Literature, Moscow 1961.
3. FRANK, E., *Corresponding Type Continued Fractions*, Amer. Jour. of Math., vol. 68, 1946, pp. 89–108.
4. PERRON, O., *Die Lehre von den Kettenbrüchen*, vols I and II, Teubner, Stuttgart, 1957.
5. RUTISHAUSER, H., *Der Quotienten-Differenzen-Algorithmus*, Birkhäuser, Basel, 1957.
6. RUTISHAUSER, H., *Über eine Verallgemeinerung der Kettenbrüche*, Z. angew. Math. Mech., vol. 39, 1958, pp. 278–279.
7. WALL, H., *Analytic Theory of Continued Fractions*, van Nostrand, New York, 1950.
8. WYNN, P., *Converging Factors for Continued Fractions*, Num. Math., vol. 1, 1959, pp. 272–307.
9. WYNN, P., *The Numerical Efficiency of Certain Fraction Expansions*, Proc. Kon. Akad. Wet. – Amsterdam, Ser. A, vol. 65, pp. 127–148.
10. WYNN, P., *The Rational Approximation of Functions which are Formally Defined by a Power Series Expansion*, Maths. of Comp., vol. 14, pp. 147–186.

INDEX